22

Edition No. 10317

CHORAL
PRAISE

COMPREHENSIVE ■ EDITION

OCP Publications

CHORAL PRAISE: COMPREHENSIVE EDITION

© 1996, OCP Publications
5536 NE Hassalo
Portland, OR 97213
Phone: (503) 281-1191
E-mail address: liturgy@ocp.org
WWW:http://www.ocp.org

Publisher: John J. Limb
Editorial Director: Paulette McCoy
Executive Editor: Randall DeBruyn
Project Editor: Lori Modlin Rux
Editorial Assistance: Barbara Bridge, Maggie Daane, Robert Hawthorne, Denise Healey, William C. Robbins, David Simmons, Rob Stoltz, James A. Wilde
Music Engraving: Sharon Norton, Director; Brian Healey, Jon Jonsson, Laura C. Kantor, Didi King, Rolf Wulfsberg
Cover Design: Jean Germano, Director; Le Vu

Fourth Printing: September 1999

PUBLISHED WITH ECCLESIASTICAL APPROBATION

PREFACE

In the last several years, *Choral Praise* has been meeting the needs of many parish choirs by offering full score versions of songs within the OCP Publications music program.

Choral Praise: Comprehensive Edition departs from this philosophy by offering settings that meet the particular needs of small parish choirs with limited resources. Rather than a repackaging of octavos for a few select songs, *Choral Praise: Comprehensive Edition* is a compilation of over 400 titles in one volume of the most used, most popular hymns and songs with simple arrangements that a small choir will find easily accessible. These songs have been edited to match and be used with the accompaniments in the *Keyboard* and *Guitar Accompaniment Books*. The full score versions, with introductions, modulations and alternate harmonizations are still available in the octavos, collections and, for some songs, previous *Choral Praise* volumes from OCP.

The broad liturgical usefulness of the songs and indices in *Choral Praise: Comprehensive Edition*, along with the quality of its content and beautiful hardbound cover, should last and please your parish choir for many years to come.

TABLE OF CONTENTS

A Child Is Born

REFRAIN: *Lively*

A child is born for us to - day, al - le -
al - le - lu -

lu - ia.
ia, al - le - lu - ia. He is our sav - ior

and our God, al - le - lu - ia.
al - le - lu - ia, al - le - lu - ia.

1-8 to Verses

Final

ia, al - le - lu - ia, al -
le - lu - ia, al - le - lu - ia, al - le - lu - ia, al -

le - lu - ia.
le - lu - ia, al - le - lu - ia.

Fine

Text: Weston Priory, Gregory Norbet, OSB, b. 1940.
Music: Weston Priory, Gregory Norbet, OSB; choral arr. by Craig S. Kingsbury, b. 1952.
Text and music ©1973, 1986, from the recording *Locusts and Wild Honey*, The Benedictine Foundation of the State of Vermont, Inc., Weston, VT.

VERSES:

1. Let our hearts re - sound with joy and sing ___ a
2. Tell the world of our good news: ___ Je - sus the
3. Christ is born, the Christ has come! ___ Sing ev - 'ry-
4. Glo - ry to God, ___ born to - day ___ of ___ the
5. His name ___ shall be E - man - u - el: ___ God ___ who
6. The Ma - gi went and wor - shipped him with gifts ___ so
7. The Lord ___ will make in - teg - ri - ty and peace ___ to
8. A - rise, ___ shine out, Je - ru - sa - lem! The glo - ry of

1. song ___ of glad - ness, ___ for the Lord ___ our broth -
2. Christ is a - mong ___ us, ___ and his pres-ence we cel - e -
3. one: Al - le - lu - ia! ___ Caught in won - der at this
4. Vir - gin Ma - ry, ___ in a cave ___ at Beth - le -
5. lives ___ a - mong ___ us. ___ An - gels sing ___ and shep-herds
6. pre - cious and cost - ly. ___ In the fer - vor of their
7. grow in our times. ___ A cov - e - nant ___ he of - fers
8. Yah-weh has come to you. Lift up ___ your eyes ___ and look a -

D.C.

1. er is come ___ and we are re-deemed. ___
2. brate ___ of - fer-ing peace and our joy ___ to all. ___
3. birth we wor - ship God be-come one ___ with us. ___
4. hem: ___ is there room in our lives ___ for him? ___
5. cry: ___ born is the Sav - ior our Lord. ___
6. faith they sought ___ the child who is Lord ___ and King. ___
7. us. ___ Last-ing joy will be ours ___ to share. ___
8. round! ___ Ra - di - ant is your sal - va - tion. ___

5

A Mighty Fortress
(Original Text)

1. A might-y for-tress is   our God, A bul-wark nev-er fail - ing; Our
2. Did we in our own strength con-fide, Our striv-ing would be los - ing; Were

1. help-er he   a - mid   the flood Of mor-tal ills pre - vail - ing: For
2. not the Sav - ior   on   our side, The man of God's own choos - ing; Dost

1. still our an - cient   foe Doth seek to work us woe; His craft   and pow'r are
2. ask who that may   be? Christ Je-sus, it   is   he; Lord Sab - a - oth, his

1. great, And armed with cru - el   hate, On earth is   not   his   e - qual.
2. name, From age   to age the same, And   he must win   the bat - tle.

Text: 87 87 66 66 7; Based on Psalm 46; Martin Luther, 1483–1546; tr. by Frederick H. Hedge, 1805–1890.
Music: EIN' FESTE BURG; Martin Luther; harm. by Johann S. Bach, 1685–1750.

A Mighty Fortress
(Schuller Text)

1. A might-y for-tress is our God, Our strong-hold and pro-tec - tion; He
2. Great and e-ter-nal is our God, The God of all cre-a - tion; He

1. is our hope, our friend, our guide, The giv-er of sal-va - tion.
2. made the sun to shine through cloud, He formed earth's deep foun-da - tion.

1. Our Lord is God a-lone, He made the world his own; He speaks and
2. Re-joice and praise his name, His good-ness will re-main; With strong and

1. winds o-bey, He rules till end-less day; His truth a-bides for-ev - er.
2. guid-ing hand, Firm shall his jus-tice stand; His prom-ise is e-ter - nal.

Text: 87 87 66 66 7; Based on Psalm 46; Martin Luther, 1483–1546; alt. by Arvella Schuller ©Arvella Schuller.
Music EIN' FESTE BURG; Martin Luther; harm. by Johann S. Bach, 1685–1750.

7

A Voice Cries Out

VERSE 1: *With strength (♩ = 168)*

Cantor:

1. Con - sole my peo-ple, the ones dear to me; speak to the
1. heart of Je - ru-sa-lem: the time of your mourn-ing is
1. end - ed now, the Lord of life will come.

REFRAIN: All

Soprano
Alto (Melody)
Tenor
Bass

A voice cries out in the wil - der - ness: "Pre - pare a
way for the Lord!" A voice cries out in the
wil - der - ness: "Make straight a high-way for God!"

Fine

Text: Isaiah 40:1-11; Michael Joncas, b. 1951.
Music: Michael Joncas.
Text and music ©1981, 1982, 1995, Michael Joncas. Published by Cooperative Ministries, Inc. Exclusive agent: OCP Publications.

VERSES 2, 4:

2. Ev - 'ry val - ley is made a plain, ev - 'ry
4. Zi - on, shout from the moun - tain top, lift up your

2. moun-tain is lev - eled; the glo - ry of God __ shall
4. voice, O Je - ru-sa-lem, and say to the peo - ple of

D.S.

2. then be re - vealed, and the na - tions will sing in praise.
4. God's __ own land, "Be - hold, be - hold your God!"

VERSES 3, 5:

3. A voice _ shouts: "Cry!" O what shall I cry? All flesh is like
5. The Lord will ap - pear as a shep - herd, _____ keep-ing his

3. grass and its flow-ers: _____ the grass __ may with - er, the
5. lambs in his arms, _____ keep-ing his flock so

D.S.

3. flow - ers may fade, but the Word of the Lord is for - ev - er.
5. close to his heart, lead - ing them all, old and young.

9

Abba! Father!

Slowly, reverently

REFRAIN: *Ab - ba,* *Ab - ba,*
VERSES: 1. Mold us, mold us and
2. Fa - ther, may we be
3. Glo - ry, glo - ry and

Fa - ther. *You are the pot - ter;*
1. fash - ion us in - to the im - age
2. one in you. May we be one in you
3. praise to you. Glo - ry and praise to you

we are the clay, *the*
1. of Je - sus, your Son, of
2. as he is in you, and
3. for - ev - er, a - men, for -

2 *D.C.* Final

work of your hands.
1. Je - sus, your Son.
2. you are in him.
3. ev - er, a - men. *Ab - ba!*

Text: Refrain based on Jeremiah 18:6, Romans 8:15; verses based on Romans 8:29, John 17:21; Carey Landry, b. 1944.
Music: Carey Landry; choral arr. by Louise Anderson, alt.
Text and music ©1977, 1978, North American Liturgy Resources (N.A.L.R.).

All Glory, Laud, and Honor

1-5. All glo-ry, laud, and hon - or To you, Re-deem-er, King!

1-5. To whom the lips of chil - dren Made sweet ho-san-nas ring.

1. You are the King of Is - ra - el, And Da - vid's roy - al Son,
2. The com-pa - ny of an - gels Are prais - ing you on high;
3. The peo-ple of the He - brews With palms be - fore you went:
4. To you be - fore your pas - sion They sang their hymns of praise:
5. Their prais-es you ac - cept - ed, Ac - cept the prayers we bring,

1. Now in the Lord's Name com - ing, Our King and Bless - ed One.
2. And mor-tals, joined with all things Cre - a - ted, make re - ply.
3. Our praise and prayers and an - thems Be - fore you we pre - sent.
4. To you, now high ex - alt - ed, Our mel - o - dy we raise.
5. Great source of love and good - ness, Our Sav - ior and our King.

Text: 76 76 D; Theodulph of Orleans, ca. 760–821; tr. by John M. Neale, 1818–1866, alt.
Music: ST. THEODULPH; Melchior Teschner, 1584–1635.

All Creatures of Our God and King

1. All crea-tures of our God and King, Lift up your voic-
2. Great rush-ing winds who are so strong, You clouds a - bove
3. Swift flow-ing wa - ter, pure and clear, Make mu - sic for
4. Dear moth-er earth, who day by day Un - fold your bless-
5. Let all things their cre - a - tor bless, And wor-ship him

1. es, let us sing: Al - le - lu - ia! Al - le -
2. that sail a - long, O____ praise him! Al - le -
3. your Lord to hear, Al - le - lu - ia! Al - le -
4. ings on our way, O____ praise him! Al - le -
5. in hum - ble - ness, O____ praise him! Al - le -

1. lu - ia! Bright burn-ing sun with gold - en beams, Soft
2. lu - ia! Fair ris - ing morn with praise re - joice, Stars
3. lu - ia! Fire so in - tense and fierce - ly bright, Who
4. lu - ia! All flow'rs and fruits that in you grow, Let
5. lu - ia! Praise God the Fa - ther, praise the Son, And

1. sil - ver moon that gent - ly gleams, 1-5. O
2. night - ly shin - ing, find a voice,
3. gives to us both warmth and light, (Melody)
4. them his glo - ry al - so show: 1-5. O
5. praise the Spir - it Three in One:

Text: LM with additions; St. Francis of Assisi, 1182–1226; tr. by William H. Draper, 1855–1933; adapt. by Anthony G. Petti, 1932–1985 ©1923 (Renewed) by J. Curwen & Sons, Ltd. All rights for the U.S. and Canada controlled by G. Schirmer, Inc. International copyright secured. All rights reserved. Reprinted by permission.
Music: LASST UNS ERFREUEN; melody fr. *Auserlesene, Catholische, Geistliche Kirchengesäng*, Cologne, 1623; choral arr. by Randall DeBruyn, b. 1947 ©1994, OCP Publications.

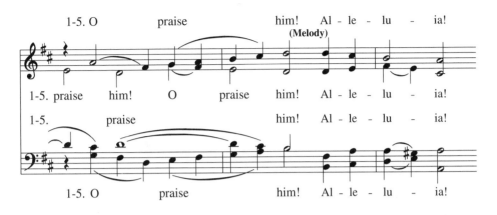

All Good Gifts

VERSES: *Vigorously* (♩ = 65 – 70)

1. We plow the fields and scat - ter the good seed on the land,
2. You on - ly are the mak - er of all things near and far,
3. We thank you, then, Cre - a - tor, for all things bright and good,

1. but it is fed and wa - tered by God's al - might - y hand.
2. you paint the way - side flow - er, you light the eve - ning star.
3. the seed-time and the har - vest, our life, our health, our food.

1. God sends the snow in win - ter, the warmth to swell the grain,
2. The winds and waves o - bey you, by you the birds are fed;
3. And all that we can of - fer, your bound-less love im - parts;

1. the breez - es and the sun - shine, and soft, re - fresh-ing rain.
2. much more, to us, your chil - dren, you give our dai - ly bread.
3. the gifts to you most pleas - ing are hum - ble, thank-ful hearts.

Text: 76 76 D with refrain; Matthias Claudius, 1740–1815; tr. by Jane M. Campbell, 1817–1878, alt.
Music: HEISLMAN; Kevin Keil, b. 1956 ©1993, Kevin Keil. Published by OCP Publications.

REFRAIN: Harmony

All good gifts a-round us are sent from heav-en a-bove;

thank you, Lord, O thank you for all your love.

All Hail, Adored Trinity

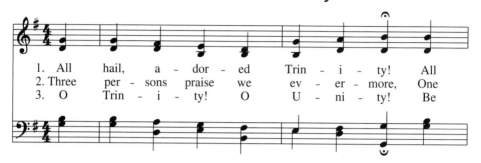

1. All hail, a - dor - ed Trin - i - ty! All
2. Three per - sons praise we ev - er - more, One
3. O Trin - i - ty! O U - ni - ty! Be

1. hail, e - ter - nal U - ni - ty! O God the Fa - ther,
2. on - ly God our hearts a - dore: In thy sure mer - cy,
3. pres - ent as we wor - ship thee; And with the songs that

1. God the Son, And God the Spir - it, ev - er One.
2. ev - er kind, May we your strong pro - tec - tion find.
3. an - gels sing U - nite the hymns of praise we bring.

Text: LM; *Ave, colenda Trinitas*; ca. 11th cent.; tr. by John D. Chambers, 1805–1893, alt.
Music: OLD HUNDREDTH; melody fr. *Pseaumes octante trois de David,* 1551; harm. attr. to Louis Bourgeois, ca. 1510–1561, alt.

All Hail the Power of Jesus' Name

Text: 86 86 86; Edward Perronet, 1726–1792, alt. by John Rippon, 1751–1836.
Music: CORONATION; Oliver Holden, 1765–1844.

All My Days

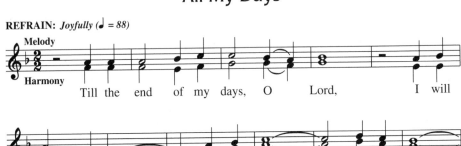

REFRAIN: *Joyfully (♩ = 88)*

Till the end of my days, O Lord, I will

bless your name, sing your praise, give you thanks,

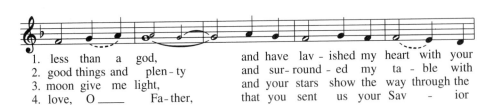

Fine VERSES:

all my days.

1. You have made me lit - tle
2. You have blessed ___ me with
3. ⸨ Your sun ___ and your
4. ⸨ How great ___ is your

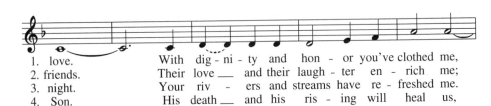

1. less than a god, and have lav - ished my heart with your
2. good things and plen - ty and sur - round - ed my ta - ble with
3. moon give me light, and your stars show the way through the
4. love, O ___ Fa - ther, that you sent us your Sav - ior

1. love. ___ With dig - ni - ty and hon - or you've clothed me,
2. friends. Their love ___ and their laugh - ter en - rich me;
3. night. Your riv - ers and streams have re - freshed me.
4. Son. His death ___ and his ris - ing will heal us,

D.C.

1. ⸨ giv - en me rule o - ver all.
2. to - geth - er we sing your ___ praise.
3. ⸨ I ___ will sing your ___ praise.
4. and draw us ___ all un - to you.

Text: Based on Psalm 8; adapt. by J. Glenn Murray, SJ.
Music: Dan Schutte, b.1947.
Text and music ©1971, 1979, Daniel L. Schutte and James G. Murray, SJ. Administered by New Dawn Music.

All People That on Earth Do Dwell

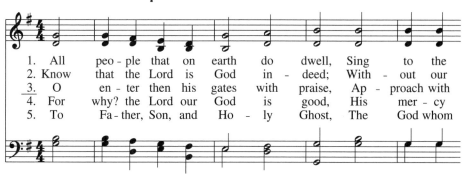

1. All peo - ple that on earth do dwell, Sing to the
2. Know that the Lord is God in - deed; With - out our
3. O en - ter then his gates with praise, Ap - proach with
4. For why? the Lord our God is good, His mer - cy
5. To Fa - ther, Son, and Ho - ly Ghost, The God whom

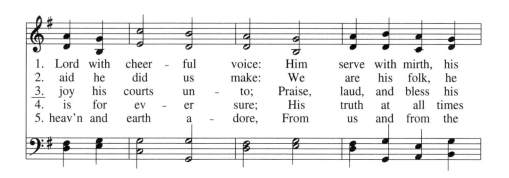

1. Lord with cheer - ful voice: Him serve with mirth, his
2. aid he did us make: We are his folk, he
3. joy his courts un - to; Praise, laud, and bless his
4. is for ev - er sure; His truth at all times
5. heav'n and earth a - dore, From us and from the

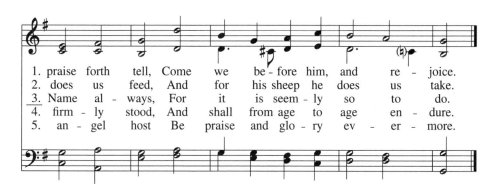

1. praise forth tell, Come we be - fore him, and re - joice.
2. does us feed, And for his sheep he does us take.
3. Name al - ways, For it is seem - ly so to do.
4. firm - ly stood, And shall from age to age en - dure.
5. an - gel host Be praise and glo - ry ev - er - more.

Text: LM; Psalm 100; William Kethe, d. ca. 1608, alt.
Music: OLD HUNDREDTH; melody fr. *Pseaumes octante trois de David,* 1551; harm. attr. to Louis Bourgeois, ca. 1510–1561, alt.

All That Is Hidden

VERSES: (♩ = 72-80)

1. If you would fol-low me, fol - low where life will lead: ___
2. If you would hon-or me, hon - or the least of these: ___
3. If you would speak of me, live all your life in me: ___
4. If you would rise with me, rise through your des - ti - ny: ___

1. ___ do not look for me a - mong the dead, for I am
2. ___ you will not find me dressed in fin - er - y. My Word cries
3. ___ my ways are not the ways that you would choose; my thoughts are
4. ___ do not re-fuse the death which brings you life, for as the

1. hid - den in pain, _____ ris - en in love;
2. out to be heard; _____ breaks through the world:
3. far be - yond yours, _____ as heav - en from earth:
4. grain in the earth _____ must die for re - birth,

1. there is no har - vest with - out sow - ing of grain.
2. my Word is on your lips and lives in your heart.
3. if you be - lieve in me my voice will be heard.
4. so I have plant - ed your life deep with - in mine.

REFRAIN: *More vigorously*

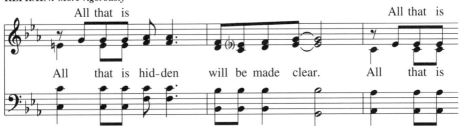

All that is

All that is hid-den will be made clear. All that is

All that is

Text: Refrain based on Luke 12:2−3; Bernadette Farrell, b. 1957.
Music: Bernadette Farrell; choral arr. by Paul Inwood, b. 1947.
Text and music ©1986, 1988, 1989, Bernadette Farrell. Published by OCP Publications.

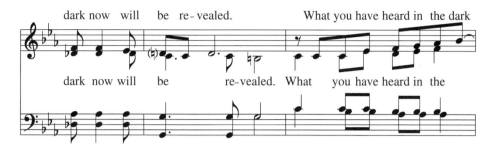

dark now will be re-vealed. What you have heard in the dark

dark now will be re-vealed. What you have heard in the

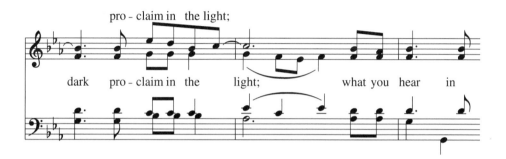

pro - claim in the light;

dark pro - claim in the light; what you hear in

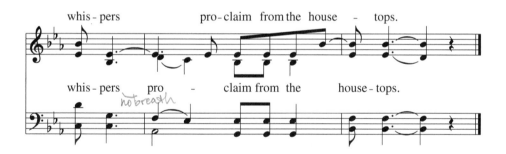

whis - pers pro-claim from the house - tops.

whis - pers pro - claim from the house - tops.

no breath

21

All the Ends of the Earth

Text: Based on Psalm 98; David Haas, b. 1957 and Marty Haugen, b. 1950.
Music: David Haas and Marty Haugen.
Text and music ©1983, G.I.A. Publications, Inc.

VERSE 2: *(more lyrically)*

2. The Lord has made his sal - va - tion known, his jus - tice re -

2. vealed to all. Re - mem-bered his kind-ness and faith - ful -

2. ness to Is - ra - el.

VERSE 3: *(more lyrically)*

3. All of the ends of earth have seen sal - va - tion by our God.

3. Joy-ful-ly sing out all you lands, break forth in song.

VERSE 4: *(more lyrically)*

4. Sing to the Lord with harp and song, with trum - pet and with horn.

4. Sing in your joy be-fore the king, the king, our Lord.

All the Ends of the Earth

REFRAIN: *Briskly in 1 (♩. = 63)*

Text: Based on Psalm 98:1, 3–6; Bob Hurd, b. 1950.
Music: Bob Hurd; choral arr. by Craig S. Kingsbury, b. 1952.
Text and music ©1988, Bob Hurd. Published by OCP Publications.

VERSES:

1. Let us sing a new song for the won - drous
2. All the ends of the earth have seen the
3. Sing the prais - es of God; with the harp and

1. deeds of our God, whose ho - ly
2. pow - er of God. Ring out your
3. song give praise. O trum - pets

1. arm has pre - vailed, bring - ing sal -
2. joy. Break in - to song; all you
3. sound! Joy - ful - ly sing; sing to the

(Melody)

1. va - tion and vic - t'ry.
2. lands sing praise.
3. rul - er of all!

25

All Praise and Glad Thanksgiving

1. All praise and glad thanks-giv - ing To God the Fa - ther be: The
2. Christ Je - sus, we a - dore you, The Son of God most high; With
3. O Ho - ly Spir - it, bless - ing To you who reign a - bove! Your

1. Font of all things liv - ing, Who reigns e - ter - nal - ly.
2. thanks we sing be - fore you, Who came for us to die.
3. won-drous gifts con - fess - ing, The Church sings forth your love!

1-3. Praise to God for - ev - er be, One in life, in Per - sons three:

1-3. Might-y God, Sav - ing God, God e - ter - nal Trin - i - ty!

Text: 76 76 with refrain; Melvin Farrell, SS, 1930–1986 ©1976, OCP Publications.
Music: GOTT VATER SEI GEPRIESEN; *Limburg Gesangbuch,* 1838; choral arr. by Randall DeBruyn, b. 1947 ©1982, OCP Publications.

Alleluia! Alleluia!

1. Al - le - lu - ia! Al - le - lu - ia! Hearts to heav'n and voic - es raise;
2. Now the i - ron bars are bro - ken, Christ from death to life is born,
3. Al - le - lu - ia! Al - le - lu - ia! Glo - ry be to God on high;

1. Sing to God a hymn of glad - ness, Sing to God a hymn of praise.
2. Glo - rious life, and life im - mor - tal, On this res - ur - rec - tion morn;
3. Al - le - lu - ia to the Sav - ior, Who has won the vic - to - ry;

1. He who on the cross as Sav - ior For the world's sal - va - tion bled,
2. Christ has tri - umphed, and we con - quer By his might - y en - ter - prise,
3. Al - le - lu - ia to the Spir - it, Font of love and sanc - ti - ty;

1. Je - sus Christ, the King of Glo - ry, Now is ris - en from the dead.
2. We with him to life e - ter - nal By his res - ur - rec - tion rise.
3. Al - le - lu - ia! Al - le - lu - ia! To the Tri - une Maj - es - ty.

Text: 87 87 D; Christopher Wordsworth, 1807–1885, alt.
Music: HYMN TO JOY; Ludwig van Beethoven, 1770–1827; adapt. by Edward Hodges, 1796–1867.

Alleluia! Alleluia!
Let the Holy Anthem Rise

1. Al-le - lu - ia! Al - le - lu - ia! Let the ho - ly an-them rise, And the
2. Al-le - lu - ia! Al - le - lu - ia! Like the sun from out the wave, He has
3. Al-le - lu - ia! Al - le - lu - ia! Bless-ed Je - sus, make us rise From the

1. choirs of heav-en chant it In the tem - ple of the skies; Let the
2. ris - en up in tri-umph From the dark-ness of the grave. He's the
3. life of this cor - rup - tion To the life that nev-er dies. May your

1. moun - tains skip with glad-ness, And the joy - ful val-leys ring With ho -
2. splen - dor of the na - tions, He's the lamp of end-less day; He's the
3. glo - ry be our por - tion When the days of time are past And the

1. san - nas in the high - est To our Sav - ior and our King.
2. ver - y Lord of glo - ry Who is ris - en up to - day.
3. dead shall be a - wak - ened By the trum - pet's might-y blast.

Text: 87 87 D; Anon., probably American, ca. 1887.
Music: LET THE HOLY ANTHEM RISE; St. Basil's Hymnal, 1889.

Alleluia No. 1

REFRAIN:

Descant / Melody:
Al-le-lu-ia, Al-le-lu-ia, give thanks to the ris-en Lord.

Al-le-lu-ia, Al-le-lu-ia, give praise to his name. *Fine*

Soprano / Alto:
1. Je-sus is Lord of all the earth,
2. Spread the good news o'er all the earth,
3. We have been cru-ci-fied with Christ.
4. Come let us praise the liv-ing God;

Tenor / Bass:
1. He is the king of cre-a-tion.
2. Je-sus has died and has ris-en.
3. Now we shall live for-ev-er.
4. Joy-ful-ly sing to our Sav-ior. *D.C.*

Text: Donald Fishel, b.1950.
Music: Donald Fishel; choral arr. by Randall DeBruyn, b. 1947.

29

Alleluia! Give the Glory
(Gathering or Gospel Acclamation)

Text: Adapt. by Ken Canedo and Bob Hurd, b. 1950.
Music: *Mass of Glory*; Ken Canedo; choral arr. by Craig S. Kingsbury, b. 1952.
Text and music ©1991, 1992, Ken Canedo and Bob Hurd. Published by OCP Publications.

Final *freely*

Give the glo - ry and the hon - or

Final

glo - ry and the hon - or

to the... to the Lord! *Fine*

to the Lord! *Fine*

*GATHERING VERSES 1,2:

Cantor or All:

1. Where two or three are gath - ered _____ in my
2. I am the vine and you _____ are the

1. name, _____ there I am in the
2. branch-es. _____ A - bide in _____

D.C.

1. midst of them; _____ there I'll be. _____
2. me _____ and _____ bear much fruit. _____

*Verse 1: Matthew 18:20; Verse 2: John 15:5

32

*GOSPEL VERSES 3-6:

Cantor:

(Ord.) 3. I ___ am the ___ Light ___ of the World; ___
(Ord.) 4. Speak, O Lord, your ___ ser - vant ___ is ___ lis-t'ning; ___
(Advent) 5. Pre - pare the ___ way ___ of the Lord; ___
(Easter) 6. I ___ am the good shep-herd, ___ says the Lord; ___

3. ___ ev - 'ry-one who fol - lows me ___
4. ___ you ___ have the words ___
5. ___ ev - 'ry-one shall see ___
6. ___ I ___ know my sheep ___

D.C.

3. ___ will have the light ___ of life.
4. ___ of ev - er - last - ing life.
5. ___ the sav - ing pow'r ___ of God.
6. ___ and mine ___ know ___ me.

**GOSPEL VERSES 7, 8:

Cantor:

(Easter) 7. Make your word plain to us, Lord Je - sus; ___
(Pentecost) 8. Come to us, Spir - it of God; ___

7. ___ may our hearts burn with love
8. ___ come and fill our ___ hearts

D.C.

7. as we hear your ___ voice.
8. with the fire of your love.

*Verse 3: John 8:12; Verse 4: 1 Samuel 9:3, John 6:69; Verse 5: Luke 3:4, 6; Verse 6: John 10:14
**Verse 7: Luke 24:32

Alleluia! Sing to Jesus

1. Al - le - lu - ia! Sing to Je - sus! His the
2. Al - le - lu - ia! King e - ter - nal, Thee the
3. Al - le - lu - ia! Al - le - lu - ia! Glo - ry

1. scep - ter, his the throne. Al - le - lu - ia! His the
2. Lord of lords we own. Al - le - lu - ia! Born of
3. be to God on high; Al - le - lu - ia to the

1. tri - umph, His the vic - to - ry a - lone; Hark! The
2. Ma - ry, Earth thy foot - stool, heav'n thy throne: Thou with-
3. Sav - ior Who has won the vic - to - ry; Al - le -

1. songs of peace - ful Si - on Thun - der like a
2. in the veil has en - tered, Robed in flesh our
3. lu - ia to the Spir - it, Font of love and

Text: 87 87 D; Revelation 5:9–14; William C. Dix, 1837–1898, and others.
Music: HYFRYDOL; Rowland H. Prichard, 1811–1887.

34

1. might - y flood; Je - sus out of ev - 'ry
2. great High Priest; Thou on earth both priest and
3. sanc - ti - ty; Al - le - lu - ia! Al - le -

1. na - tion Hath re - deem'd us by his blood.
2. vic - tim In the Eu - cha - ris - tic feast.
3. lu - ia To the tri - une maj - es - ty.

Amazing Grace

1. A - maz - ing grace! How sweet the sound That saved *a
2. 'Twas grace that taught my heart to fear, And grace my
3. Thru' man - y dan - gers, toils, and snares I have al -
4. The Lord has prom - ised good to me, His word my
5. When we've been there ten thou - sand years, Bright shin - ing

1. wretch like me! I once was lost, but
2. fears re - lieved; How pre - cious did that
3. read - y come; 'Tis grace has brought me
4. hope se - cures; He will my shield and
5. as the sun, We've no less days to

1. now am found, Was blind but now I see.
2. grace ap - pear The hour I first be - lieved!
3. safe thus far, And grace will lead me home.
4. por - tion be As long as life en - dures.
5. sing God's praise Than when we first be - gun.

*Alternate text: "and set me free!"

Text: CM; Verses 1–4: John Newton, 1725–1807; verse 5: anon., from *A Collection of Sacred Ballads,* 1790.
Music: NEW BRITAIN; *Columbia Harmony,* 1829; arr. by Edwin O. Excell, 1851–1921; adapt. by Randall DeBruyn, b.1947 ©1995, OCP
Publications.

America

1. My coun - try, 'tis of thee, sweet land of
2. My na - tive coun - try, thee, land of the
3. Let mu - sic swell the breeze, and ring from
4. Our fa - thers' God, to thee, au - thor of

1. lib - er - ty, of thee I sing; Land where my
2. no - ble free, thy name I love; I love thy
3. all the trees sweet free - dom's song; Let mor - tal
4. lib - er - ty, to thee we sing; Long may our

1. fa - thers died, land of the pil - grim's pride,
2. rocks and rills, thy woods and tem - pled hills;
3. tongues a - wake; let all that breathe par - take;
4. land be bright with free - dom's ho - ly light,

1. From ev - 'ry moun - tain - side let free - dom ring.
2. My heart with rap - ture thrills like that a - bove.
3. Let rocks their si - lence break, the sound pro - long.
4. Pro - tect us by thy might, great God, our King.

Text: 66 4 666 4; Samuel F. Smith, 1808–1895.
Music: AMERICA; *Thesaurus Musicus*, 1745.

America, the Beautiful

1. O beau-ti-ful for spa-cious skies, For amber waves of grain, For
2. O beau-ti-ful for pil-grim feet, Whose stern, im-pas-sioned stress A
3. O beau-ti-ful for he-roes proved In lib-er-a-ting strife, Who
4. O beau-ti-ful for pa-triot dream That sees be-yond the years Thine

1. pur-ple moun-tain maj-es-ties A-bove the fruit-ed plain!
2. thor-ough-fare for free-dom beat A-cross the wil-der-ness!
3. more than self their coun-try loved, And mer-cy more than life!
4. al-a-bas-ter cit-ies gleam, Un-dimmed by hu-man tears!

1. A-mer-i-ca! A-mer-i-ca! God shed his grace on thee, And
2. A-mer-i-ca! A-mer-i-ca! God mend thine ev-'ry flaw, Con-
3. A-mer-i-ca! A-mer-i-ca! May God thy gold re-fine, Till
4. A-mer-i-ca! A-mer-i-ca! God shed his grace on thee, And

1. crown thy good with broth-er-hood From sea to shin-ing sea.
2. firm thy soul in self-con-trol, Thy lib-er-ty in law.
3. all suc-cess be no-ble-ness, And ev-'ry gain di-vine.
4. crown thy good with broth-er-hood From sea to shin-ing sea.

Text: CMD; Katherine L. Bates, 1859–1929, alt.
Music: MATERNA; Samuel A. Ward, 1848–1903.

Angels, from the Realms of Glory

1. An - gels, from the realms of glo - ry, Wing your flight o'er
2. Shep - herds, in the fields a - bid - ing, Watch - ing o'er your
3. Sa - ges, leave your con - tem - pla - tions, Bright - er vi - sions
4. Though an in - fant now we view him, He shall fill his
5. All cre - a - tion, join in prais - ing God, the Fa - ther,

1. all the earth; Ye who sang cre - a - tion's sto - ry,
2. flocks by night, God on earth is now re - sid - ing,
3. beam a - far; Seek the great De - sire of na - tions,
4. Fa - ther's throne, Gath - er all the na - tions to him;
5. Spir - it, Son, Ev - er - more your voic - es rais - ing,

1. Now pro - claim Mes - si - ah's birth:
2. Yon - der shines the in - fant light:
3. Ye have seen his na - tal star: } Come and wor - ship,
4. Ev - 'ry knee shall then bow down:
5. To the e - ter - nal Three in One:

1-5. come and wor - ship, Wor - ship Christ, the new - born King.

Text: 87 87 87; James Montgomery, 1771–1854.
Music: REGENT SQUARE; Henry T. Smart, 1813–1879.

39

Angels We Have Heard on High

1. An - gels we have heard on high Sweet - ly sing - ing
2. Shep - herds, why this ju - bi - lee? Why your joy - ous
3. Come to Beth - le - hem and see Him whose birth the

1. o'er the plains, And the moun - tains in re - ply
2. strains pro - long? Say what may the tid - ings be
3. an - gels sing; Come, a - dore on bend - ed knee

1. Ech - o - ing their joy - ous strains.
2. Which in - spire your heav'n - ly song. } Glo -
3. Christ, the Lord, the new - born King.

ri - a

Text: 77 77 with refrain; French, ca. 18th cent.; tr. fr. *Crown of Jesus Music, II*, London 1862; tr. by James Chadwick, 1813–1882.
Music: GLORIA; Trad. French Carol.

40

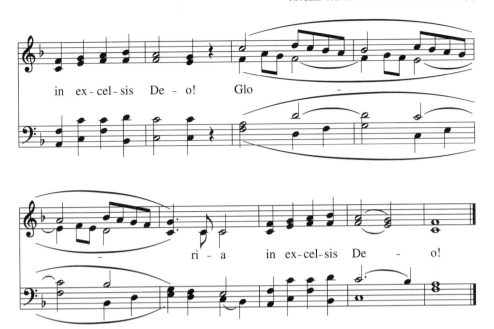

in ex - cel - sis De - o!   Glo

ri - a   in ex - cel - sis De - o!

Anthem

REFRAIN: *Strict tempo*

Descant

Melody

We are called, we are cho-sen. We are Christ for one an-oth-er. We are

prom-ised to to-mor-row, while we are for him to-day. We are

sign, we are won-der. We are sow-er, we are seed. We are

Fine

har-vest, we are hun-ger. We are ques-tion, we are creed.

VERSES:

1. Then where can we stand jus-ti-fied? __ In what can we be-
2. Then how are we to stand at all, __ this world of bend-ed
3. Then shall we not stand emp-ty __ at the al-tar of our

1. lieve? In no one else but he who suf-fered, noth-ing
2. knee? In noth-ing more than bar-ren shad-ows. No one
3. dreams: __ When he prom-ised us our-selves. __ Who mark

Text: Tom Conry, b.1951.
Music: Tom Conry.
Text and music ©1978, 1979, New Dawn Music.

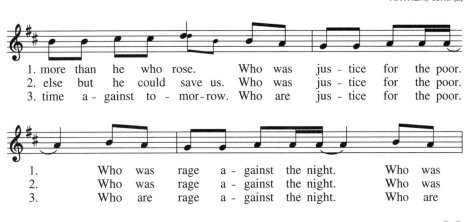

1. more than he who rose. Who was jus - tice for the poor.
2. else but he could save us. Who was jus - tice for the poor.
3. time a - gainst to - mor-row. Who are jus - tice for the poor.

1. Who was rage a - gainst the night. Who was
2. Who was rage a - gainst the night. Who was
3. Who are rage a - gainst the night. Who are

D.C.

1. hope for peace - ful peo - ple. Who was light.
2. hope for peace - ful peo - ple. Who was light.
3. hope for peace - ful peo - ple. Who are light.

As We Celebrate

*Refrain may be sung with 2 parts (Descant and Soprano/Melody), 3 parts (Soprano/Melody, Alto, Tenor) or 4 parts (Soprano/Melody, Alto, Tenor, Bass).

Text: Carey Landry, b. 1944.
Music: Carey Landry; choral arr. by Jeffrey Honoré.
Text and music ©1993, Carey Landry and North American Liturgy Resources (N.A.L.R.).

VERSES 1, 2: unison

1. You are the Christ; in you we find our un - i -
2. You are the Christ; you are for us the Bread of

D.C.

1. ty, com - mun - i - ty, our joy and our peace.
2. Life, the Bread of Hope, true Bread for the world.

VERSES 3, 4:

3. You are the Christ; through faith you dwell with - in our hearts, your
4. You are the Christ; you walk with us, you speak with us, you

D.C.

3. ris - en life brings light to our lives.
4. strength - en us, you com - fort our hearts.

As with Gladness Men of Old

1. As with glad-ness men of old Did the guid-ing star be-hold,
2. As with joy-ful steps they sped To that low-ly man-ger bed,
3. As they of-fered gifts most rare At that man-ger rude and bare,

1. As with joy they hailed its light, Lead-ing on-ward, beam-ing bright,
2. There to bend the knee be-fore Him whom heav'n and earth a-dore,
3. So may we with ho-ly joy, Pure, and free from sin's al-loy,

1. So, most gra-cious God, may we Ev-er-more be led to thee.
2. So may we with will-ing feet Ev-er seek thy mer-cy seat.
3. All our cost-liest trea-sures bring, Christ, to thee, our heav'n-ly King.

Text: 77 77 77; William C. Dix, 1837–1898.
Music: DIX; Conrad Kocher, 1786–1872; choral arr. by William H. Monk, 1823–1889.

46

At the Cross Her Station Keeping

1. At the cross her sta-tion keep-ing, Stood the mourn-ful
2. Through her heart, his sor-row shar-ing, All his bit-ter
3. O how sad and sore dis-tress-ed, Was that moth-er
4. Christ a-bove in tor-ment hangs, ___ She be-neath be-

1. moth-er weep-ing, Close to Je-sus to the last.
2. an-guish bear-ing, Now at length the sword has passed!
3. high-ly bless-ed Of the sole be-got-ten Son.
4. holds the pangs___ Of her dy-ing, glo-rious Son.

5. Is there one who would not weep,
Whelmed in miseries so deep,
Christ's dear Mother to behold?

6. Can the human heart refrain
From partaking in her pain,
In that Mother's pain untold?

7. Bruised, derided, cursed, defiled,
She beheld her tender Child,
All with bloody scourges rent.

8. For the sins of his own nation
Saw him hang in desolation
Till his spirit forth he sent.

9. O thou Mother! Font of love,
Touch my spirit from above,
Make my heart with thine accord.

10. Make me feel as thou hast felt;
Make my soul to glow and melt
With the love of Christ my Lord.

11. Holy Mother, pierce me through,
In my heart each wound renew
Of my Savior crucified.

12. Let me share with thee his pain,
Who for all my sins was slain,
Who for me in torment died.

13. Let me mingle tears with thee,
Mourning him who mourned for me,
All the days that I may live.

14. By the cross with thee to stay;
There with thee to weep and pray,
All I ask of thee to give.

15. Virgin of all Virgins best!
Listen to my fond request:
Let me share thy grief divine.

Text: 88 7; *Stabat Mater dolorosa*; Jacopone Da Todi, 1230–1306; tr. by Edward Caswall, 1814–1878.
Music: STABAT MATER; *Maintzisch Gesangbuch*, 1661; choral arr. by Randall DeBruyn, b. 1947 ©1990, OCP Publications.

At the Lamb's High Feast

1. At the Lamb's high feast we sing, Praise to our vic-
2. Where the Pas-chal blood is poured, Death's dark an-gel
3. Eas-ter tri-umph, Eas-ter joy, Sin a-lone can

1. to-rious King, He has washed us in the tide
2. sheathes his sword; Is-rael's hosts tri-um-phant go
3. this de-stroy; From sin's pow'r do thou set free

1. Flow-ing from his o-pen side; Praise we him, whose
2. Thru' the wave that drowns the foe. Praise we Christ, whose
3. Souls new-born, O Lord, in thee. Hymns of glo-ry,

1. love di-vine Gives his sa-cred Blood for wine,
2. blood was shed, Pas-chal vic-tim, Pas-chal bread;
3. songs of praise, Fa-ther, un-to thee we raise:

Text: 77 77 D; Latin, *Ad regias agni dapes;* 1632; tr. by Robert Campbell, 1814–1868, alt.
Music: SALZBURG; melody by Jakob Hintze, 1622–1702; harm. by Johann S. Bach, 1685–1750.

1. Gives his Bod - y   for   the feast, Christ the   vic - tim, Christ the priest.
2. With sin - cer - i - ty   and love   Eat   we   man - na   from   a - bove.
3. Ris - en Lord, all praise to   thee With the   Spir - it   ev - er   be.

At the Name of Jesus

Text: Refrain by Caroline M. Noel, 1817–1877; verses adapt. fr. Philippians 2 by Christopher Walker, b. 1947 ©1995, Christopher Walker. Published by OCP Publications.
Music: Christopher Walker ©1995, Christopher Walker. Published by OCP Publications.

VERSES:

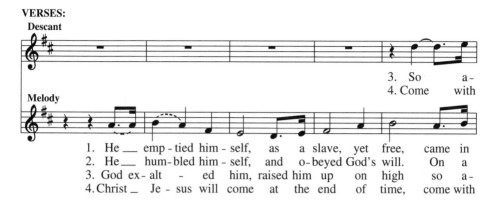

Descant

3. So a-
4. Come with

Melody

1. He __ emp - tied him - self, as a slave, yet free, came in
2. He __ hum - bled him - self, and o - beyed God's will. On a
3. God ex - alt - ed him, raised him up on high so a-
4. Christ __ Je - sus will come at the end of time, come with

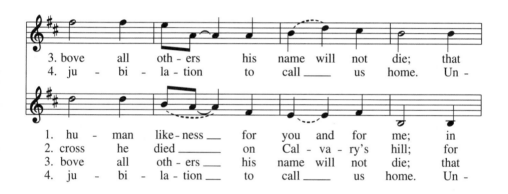

3. bove all oth - ers his name will not die; that
4. ju - bi - la - tion to call __ us home. Un -

1. hu - man like - ness __ for you and for me; in
2. cross he died __ on Cal - va - ry's hill; for
3. bove all oth - ers __ his name will not die; that
4. ju - bi - la - tion __ to call __ us home. Un -

D.C.

3. name we hon - or and glo - ri - fy.
4. til that day you and I __ will pro - claim:

D.C.

1. hu - man like - ness, __ for you and for me.
2. you and me he o - beyed __ God's will.
3. name we hon - or __ and glo - ri - fy.
4. til that day you and I will pro - claim:

51

Away in a Manger

1. A - way in a man - ger, no crib for a bed,
2. The cat - tle are low - ing, the Ba - by a - wakes,
3. Be near me, Lord Je - sus, I ask thee to stay

1. The lit - tle Lord Je - sus laid down his sweet head;
2. But lit - tle Lord Je - sus, no cry - ing he makes;
3. Close by me for ev - er, and love me, I pray;

1. The stars in the sky ___ looked down where he lay,
2. I love thee, Lord Je - sus! Look down from the sky,
3. Bless all the dear chil - dren in thy ten - der care,

1. The lit - tle Lord Je - sus, a - sleep on the hay.
2. And stay by my cra - dle till morn - ing is nigh.
3. And fit us for heav - en to live with thee there.

Text: 11 11 D; Verses 1–2, *Little Children's Book for Schools and Families*, ca. 1885; verse 3, Gabriel's *Vineyard Songs*, 1892.
Music: MUELLER; attr. to James R. Murray, 1841–1905; choral arr. by Randall DeBruyn, b. 1947 ©1990, OCP Publications.

Be Joyful, Mary

1. Be joy-ful, Ma-ry, heav'n-ly queen,
2. The Son you bore by heav-en's grace, Gau-de, Ma-ri -
3. The Lord has ris-en from the dead,

1. a: Your Son who died was liv-ing seen, Al -
2. a: Did all our guilt and sin ef-face, Al -
3. a: He rose with might as he had said, Al -

1-3. le-lu-ia, lae-ta-re, O Ma-ri-a!

Text: 85 84 7; *Regina Caeli, jubila;* Latin, 17th Cent.; tr. anon. in *Psallite,* 1901.
Music: REGINA CAELI; Leisentritt's *Catholicum Hymnologium Germanicum,* 1584.

Be Not Afraid

VERSE 1: *Slow, andante (♩ = 80)*

1. You shall cross the bar-ren des-ert, but you shall not die of
1. thirst. You shall wan-der far in safe-ty though you
1. do not know the way. You shall speak your words in
1. for-eign lands and all will un - der - stand.
1. You shall see the face of God and live.

rit. **to Antiphon**

𝄋 ANTIPHON:

Melody *a tempo*

Be not a-fraid. I go be-fore you al-ways.

Harmony

Be not a-fraid. I go be-fore you al-ways.

Text: Based on Isaiah 43:2–3, Luke 6:20ff; Bob Dufford, SJ, b. 1943.
Music: Bob Dufford, SJ.
Text and music ©1975, 1979, Robert J. Dufford, SJ and New Dawn Music.

Come fol-low me, and I will give you rest.

Come fol - low me, I will give you rest.

1,2 to Verses 2, 3 | Final 2 Fine

1,2 to Verses 2, 3 | Final 2 Fine

VERSE 2:

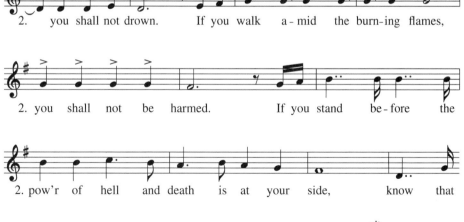

2. If you pass through rag-ing wa-ters in the sea,

2. you shall not drown. If you walk a-mid the burn-ing flames,

2. you shall not be harmed. If you stand be-fore the

2. pow'r of hell and death is at your side, know that

2. I am with you through it all.

VERSE 3:

Descant

3. Ooo _____ king-dom shall be theirs.

Melody

3. Bless-ed are your poor, for the king-dom shall be theirs.

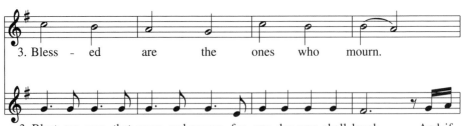

3. Bless - ed are the ones who mourn.

3. Blest are you that weep and mourn, for one day you shall laugh. And if

3. If they hate you all be-cause of me,

3. wick-ed tongues in - sult and hate you all be-cause of me,

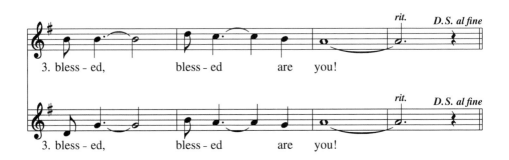

rit. ***D.S. al fine***

3. bless - ed, bless - ed are you!

rit. ***D.S. al fine***

3. bless - ed, bless - ed are you!

Beautiful Savior

1. Beau - ti - ful Sav - ior, King of Cre - a - tion,
2. Fair are the mead - ows, Fair are the wood - lands,
3. Fair is the sun - shine, Fair is the moon - light,
4. Beau - ti - ful Sav - ior, Lord of the na - tions,

1. Son of God and Son of Man!
2. Robed in flow'rs of bloom - ing spring;
3. Bright the spar - kling stars on high;
4. Son of God and Son of Man!

1. Tru - ly I'd love thee, Tru - ly I'd
2. Je - sus is fair - er, Je - sus is
3. Je - sus shines bright - er, Je - sus shines
4. Glo - ry and hon - or, Praise, ad - o -

1. serve thee, Light of my soul, my joy, my crown.
2. pur - er; He makes our sor-r'wing spir - it sing.
3. pur - er, Than all the an - gels in the sky.
4. ra - tion, Now and for - ev - er - more be thine!

Text: 55 7 55 8; *Schönster Herr Jesu*; *Münster Gesangbuch*, 1677; based on Psalm 45:3; tr. by Joseph A. Seiss, 1823–1904.
Music: ST. ELIZABETH; Silesian Melody; *Schlesische Volkslieder*, Leipzig, 1842; choral arr. by Randall DeBruyn, b. 1947 ©1983, OCP Publications.

Be with Me, Lord

REFRAIN: *Lyrical (♩ = ca. 108)* **1st time: Cantor, All repeat; Thereafter: All**

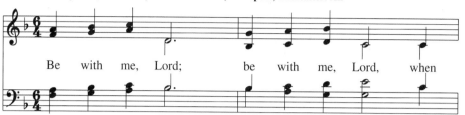

Be with me, Lord; be with me, Lord, when

I am in trou - ble and need.

VERSE 1:

1. You who dwell in the shel - ter of God most high, who a -

1. bide in Al - might - ty's shade, say to the Lord: "My

1. re - fuge, my strong - hold, my God, in whom I trust."

VERSE 2:

2. E - vil shall nev - er be - fall you, nor af - flic - tion come

*Repeat Refrain first time only.

Text: Based on Psalm 91; Michael Joncas, b. 1951.
Music: Michael Joncas.
Text and music ©1981, 1982, Michael Joncas. Published by Cooperative Ministries, Inc. Exclusive agent: OCP Publications.

2. near to your tent. Un - to his an - gels he's

D.C.

2. giv - en com - mand to guard you in all your ways.

VERSE 3:

Alto (Harmony)

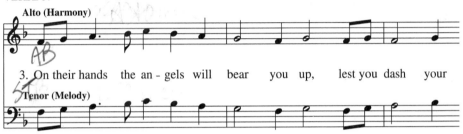

3. On their hands the an - gels will bear you up, lest you dash your

Tenor (Melody)

3. foot 'gainst a stone. Li - on or vi - per might

D.C.

3. strike at your life, but you will not come to harm.

VERSE 4:

S/A

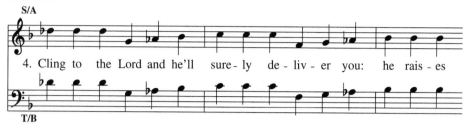

4. Cling to the Lord and he'll sure - ly de - liv - er you: he rais - es

T/B

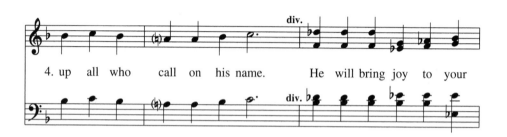

4. up all who call on his name. He will bring joy to your

4. hearts and bless you with peace in all your days.

Blessed by Your Sacrifice

1. Blessed by your sac - ri - fice, Strong in your
2. O Splen - dor, Glo - ry bright, Brought forth as
3. Come, raise the an - them high! Let prais - es

1. love, O Christ, Our grate - ful voic - es to you we
2. Light from Light! O Day, all days en - light - en -
3. fill the sky! Sing out a new song un - to the

1. raise. True ad - o - ra - tion Through - out cre -
2. ing! An - gels with one ac - cord Cry "Ho - ly,
3. Lord! Let all, with heart and voice, Be - fore the

1. a - tion Rings out in joy - ful songs of praise.
2. Ho - ly Lord!" To you our ev - er - last - ing King.
3. throne re - joice Of him whom heav'n and earth a - dore.

Text: 66 9 55 8; Owen Alstott, b. 1947 and Jeanne Frolick ©1979, 1982, OCP Publications.
Music: ST. ELIZABETH; Silesian Melody; *Schlesische Volkslieder*, Leipzig, 1842; choral arr. by Randall DeBruyn, b. 1947 ©1983, OCP Publications.

Beatitudes

VERSES:

(Harmony Vss 3, 4)

Melody

1. Blest are you, the poor who trust the Fa - ther
2. Blest are you, the low - ly ones, who know your
3. Blest are those whose mer - cy shows the Fa - ther's
4. Blest are you who work for peace a - mong the

1. with your lives,
2. need to share,
3. love to all,
4. Fa - ther's own,

For with - in your heart

1-4. is born the King-dom of the Lord.

1. Blest are you, the sor - row-ing, _____ who know your Fa-ther wise,
2. Blest are you whose search-ing souls _____ will draw you to God's care,
3. Blest are you, the pure in heart, _____ who live the Fa-ther's call,
4. Blest are you who suf - fer hate _ to pre-pare the day to come,

1-4. For with-in your heart is born the

1,3

D.C.

2,4

to Refrain

1-4. King-dom of the Lord. 2,4.

Text: Based on Matthew 5; Mike Balhoff, b. 1946.
Music: Darryl Ducote, b. 1945.
Text and music ©1973, Damean Music.

REFRAIN:

Let your light shine for all the world to see: the

bright-ness of your life with-in, the peace that set you free.

Let your light shine to fill your nights and days;

all will see the deeds you do and

give your Fa - ther praise.

Because the Lord Is My Shepherd

VERSES: (♩. = ca. 46)

1. Be - cause the Lord is my shep-herd, I have
2. And when the road leads to dark - ness, I shall
3. In love you make me a ban - quet for my
4. Your good-ness al - ways is with me and your

1. ev' - ry - thing _____ I need. He lets me
2. walk there _____ un - a - fraid. E - ven when
3. en - e - mies _____ to see. You make me
4. mer - cy _____ I know. Your lov - ing

1. rest in the mead - ow and leads me to the
2. death is close ___ I have cour - age for your
3. wel - come, ___ pour - ing down hon - or from your
4. kind - ness ___ strength-ens me al - ways as I

1. qui - et streams. He re - stores ___ my soul and he
2. help is there. You are close ___ be - side me with
3. might - y hand; and this joy _____ fills me with
4. go through life. I shall dwell in your pres - ence for -

Text: Psalm 23; Christopher Walker, b. 1947.
Music: Christopher Walker.
Text and music ©1985, Christopher Walker. Published by OCP Publications.

REFRAIN:

1. leads me in the paths that are right:
2. com-fort, you are guid-ing my way:
3. glad-ness, it is too much to bear;
4. -ev-er, giv-ing praise to your name:

Lord,

you are my shep-herd, you are my friend. I want to

fol-low you al - ways, just to fol-low my

1-3

D.C. **Final** *rall.* *a tempo* **4**

friend. fol - low my friend.

Behold the Lamb

Text: Based on John 1:29; Martin Willett, b. 1960.
Music: Martin Willett; choral arr. by Randall DeBruyn, b. 1947.
Text and music ©1984, OCP Publications.

REFRAIN:

Behold the Lamb of God

Text: Based on John 1:29, Isaiah 53:4–5, Luke 23–24, Revelation 11:15; Bob Dufford, SJ, b. 1943.
Music: Bob Dufford, SJ.
Text and music ©1985, Robert J. Dufford, SJ and New Dawn Music.

rit. D.S.

2. -ject-ed and scorned, and by his wounds we are healed.

VERSE 3: (♩. = 56 - 60)

Women 3. Fa - ther, for-give them, they do not un - der - stand, they

poco rit. D.S.

3. do not un - der - stand what they do.

VERSE 4: (♩. = 56 - 60) *parts*

4. The king - dom of this world has be - come the

4. king-dom of Christ, and he shall reign for

D.S. al fine
rit.

4. end - less days. Worth - y is the Lamb.

div.

rit.

69

Behold the Wood

REFRAIN: *With feeling (♩ = 76)*
(a tempo)

Be - hold, be - hold the wood of the cross, on which is hung our sal - va - tion. O come, let us a - dore.

Fine

VERSES:
Melody

1. Un - less a grain of wheat shall fall up -
2. And when my hour of glo - ry comes as
3. For there can be no great - er love
4. My Fa - ther, if it be your plan, this
5. For sure - ly he has borne our tears, is
6. My bod - y now is torn with pain, my

Harmony

1. Let _____ wheat _____
2. When _____ glo - ry
3. Care no great - er
4. Fa - ther be our
5. He has borne tears
6. Bod - y torn pain

Text: Based on Good Friday Liturgy and John 12,15; Dan Schutte, b. 1947.
Music: Dan Schutte.
Text and music ©1976, Daniel L. Schutte and New Dawn Music.

70

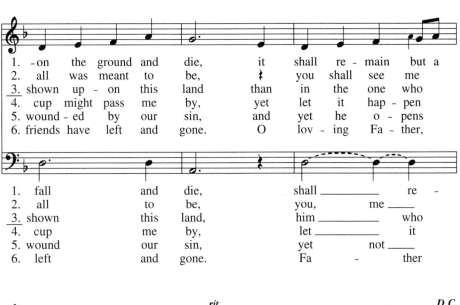

1. -on the ground and die, it shall re - main but a
2. all was meant to be, ₹ you shall see me
3. shown up - on this land than in the one who
4. cup might pass me by, yet let it hap - pen
5. wound - ed by our sin, and yet he o - pens
6. friends have left and gone. O lov - ing Fa - ther,

1. fall and die, shall _____ re -
2. all to be, you, me _____
3. shown this land, him _____ who
4. cup me by, let _____ it
5. wound our sin, yet not _____
6. left and gone. Fa - ther

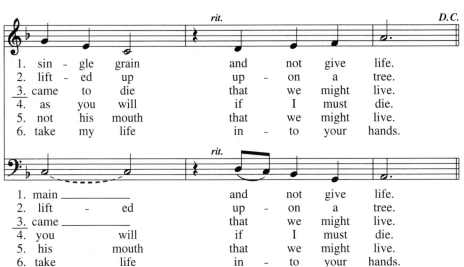

rit. D.C.

1. sin - gle grain and not give life.
2. lift - ed up up - on a tree.
3. came to die that we might live.
4. as you will if I must die.
5. not his mouth that we might live.
6. take my life in - to your hands.

rit.

1. main _____ and not give life.
2. lift - ed up - on a tree.
3. came _____ that we might live.
4. you will if I must die.
5. his mouth that we might live.
6. take life in - to your hands.

Blest Are They

VERSES 1, 2, 4, 5: *Tenderly, prayerfully (♩ = 112-120)*

1. Blest are they, the poor in spir - it, theirs is the
2. Blest are they, the low - ly ones, they shall in -
4. Blest are they who seek peace; they are the
5. Blest are you who suf - fer hate, all be -

1. king - dom of God. _____ Blest ___ are they, _____
2. her - it the earth. _____ Blest ___ are they who
4. chil - dren of God. _____ Blest ___ are they who
5. cause of me. _____ Re - joice and be glad, _____

1. full ___ of sor - row, they shall be con - soled.
2. hun - ger and thirst, _____ they shall have their fill.
4. suf - fer in faith, the glo - ry of God is theirs.
5. yours is the king - dom; shine for all to see.

REFRAIN: (Descant begins after Vs 5)

Descant

Melody

Re - joice and be glad! Bless - ed are

Harmony

Re - joice and be glad!

you, ho - ly are you! Re - joice and be

Bless - ed, ho - ly are you! Re - joice and be

Text: Based on Matthew 5:3–12, Luke 6:20–23; David Haas, b. 1957.
Music: David Haas; choral arr. by Michael Joncas, b. 1951.
Text and music ©1985, G.I.A. Publications.

72

glad!   Yours   is   the   king - dom   of   God!

glad!   Yours   is   the   king - dom   of   God!

1-4   to Verses 2-5   **Final**   *Fine*

VERSE 3:

Melody

Harmony

3. Blest   are   they   who   show   mer - cy,   mer - cy

3. shall   be   theirs.   Blest   are   they,   the

D.S.

3. pure   of   heart,   they   shall   see   God!

Blest Be the Lord

Text: Based on Psalm 91; Dan Schutte, b. 1947.
Music: Dan Schutte.
Text and music ©1976, 1979, Daniel L. Schutte and New Dawn Music.

VERSES:

1. He will re - lease ____ me ____ from the
2. I need not ____ shrink be - fore ____ the
3. Al - though a thou - sand strong ____ have

1. nets of all my foes. He will pro -
2. ter - rors of the night, nor stand a -
3. fall - en at my side, I'll not be

1. tect me from their wick - ed hands.
2. lone be - fore the light of day.
3. shak - en with the Lord at hand.

1. Be - neath ____ the shad - ow
2. No harm shall ____ come to me,
3. His faith - ful ____ love is all

1. of his wings I will re - joice
2. no ar - row strike me down,
3. the ar - mor that I need

D.C.

1. to find a dwell - ing place se - cure.
2. no e - vil set - tle in my soul.
3. to wage my bat - tle with the foe.

75

Bread of Life

REFRAIN: (♩ = 80)

Soprano

Alto

I my-self am the bread of life.

Tenor/Bass

You and I are the bread of life,

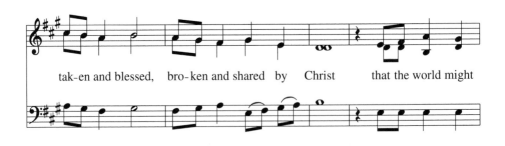

tak-en and blessed, bro-ken and shared by Christ that the world might

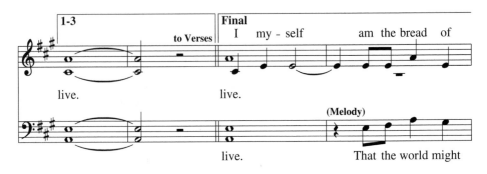

1-3 | to Verses | Final | I my-self am the bread of

live. | live. | I my-self am the bread of

(Melody)

live. | That the world might

Text: Rory Cooney, b. 1952.
Music: Rory Cooney.
Text and music ©1987, North American Liturgy Resources (N.A.L.R.).

I my - self am the bread of life.

live. That the world might live.

VERSES:

S/A

1. This bread is spir - it, gift of the Mak - er's love, and
2. Here is God's king-dom giv - en to us as food. This
3. Lives bro - ken o - pen, sto - ries __ shared a - loud, be -

T/B

1. we who share it _____ know that we can be one:
2. is our bod - y, _____ this _____ is our blood: a
3. come a ban-quet, a shel - ter __ for the world:

D.C.

1-3. liv - ing sign of God in Christ.

Bread of Life

VERSES:

1. As we pro-claim your death,   as we re-call your life,   we re-
2. The bread we break and share   was scat-tered once as grain: just as
3. We eat this liv-ing bread,   we drink this sav-ing cup: sign of
4. Hold us in u-ni-ty,   in love for all to see;   that the
5. You are the bread of peace,   you are the wine of joy,   bro-ken

1. mem-ber your prom - ise   to re-turn a-gain.
2. now it is gath - ered,   make your peo - ple one.
3. hope in our bro-ken world,   source of last - ing love.
4. world may be-lieve in you,   God of all who live.
5. now for your peo - ple,   poured in end - less love.

Text: Bernadette Farrell, b. 1957.
Music: Bernadette Farrell.
Text and music ©1982, 1987, Bernadette Farrell. Published by OCP Publications.

ALTERNATE VERSES: for Advent/Christmas

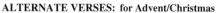

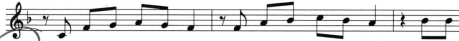

Adv. 1. Be with your peo-ple, Lord,   send us your sav-ing Word: Je - sus
Adv. 2. Bring to our world of fear   the truth we long to hear: Je - sus
Chr. 1. A child is born for us,   a son is given to us,   In our
Chr. 2. With our own eyes we see,   with our own ears we hear   The sal-
Chr. 3. You are the hope of all,   our prom-ise and our call,   Ra-diant

D.C.

Adv. 1. Christ, light of glad - ness,   come a-mong us now.
Adv. 2. Christ, hope of a - ges,   come to save us now.
Chr. 1. midst, Christ our Lord and God   comes as one who serves.
Chr. 2. va - tion of all the world,   God's in - car - nate Word.
Chr. 3. light in our dark - ness,   truth to set us free.

Bread That Was Sown

REFRAIN: *Reverently, with feeling*

Bread that was sown in our hills and val - leys

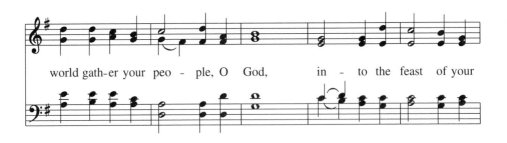

now har-vest-ed be-comes one; from all the

world gath-er your peo - ple, O God, in - to the feast of your

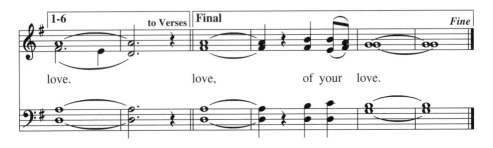

love. love, of your love.

Text: Based on *Didache* 9; Weston Priory, Gregory Norbet, OSB, b. 1940.
Music: Weston Priory, Gregory Norbet, OSB; choral arr. by Craig S. Kingsbury, b. 1952.
Text and music ©1973, 1986, from the recording *Spirit Alive*, The Benedictine Foundation of the State of Vermont, Inc., Weston, VT.

VERSES:

Unison

1. With grate-ful hearts, we sing our joy _____ for know -
2. Leav - en and wheat: so let us be _____ for oth -
3. Plant - ed, your name be - comes our thirst ___ for more be -
4. Feast _____ of jus - tice to which ___ all are wel -
5. Har - vest of peace where love can be _____ the song
6. Sign of the near - ness of one whose life sus - tains

Unison

1. ing ___ Spir - it with - in, a - mong us all;
2. ers, ___ nur - tur - ing good with ear - nest care,
3. ing, ___ hope to be bread for oth - ers' lives,
4. come to share _____ the full - ness of our God;
5. that ___ heals bro - ken - ness with lis - ten - ing;
6. us, ___ heart of our heart, cre - a - tor, friend,

div.

1. life and ___ know - ledge re - vealed _ through your word:
2. bring - ing to birth new life where hope ___ has gone stale,
3. vi - sion of what it means to give all that we are:
4. in Je - sus' ris - ing be - yond _ death we've found
5. touch - ing, per - ceiv - ing in bread of Je - sus' life,
6. call - ing us all ___ to be spir - it a - live:

D.C.

1. Je - sus, the Christ, Em - man - u - el.
2. faith - giv - ing mo - ments to share.
3. this is the seed ___ you have sown.
4. new springs of hope ___ in our lives.
5. gift to be - come our flesh as well.
6. you God, our fu - ture, last - ing life.

Bless the Feast

(♩. = ca. 76)

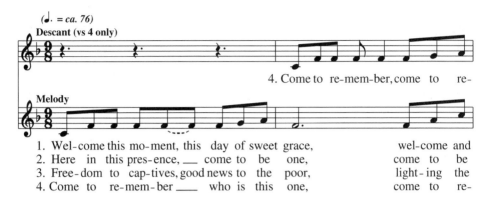

1. Wel-come this mo-ment, this day of sweet grace, wel-come and
2. Here in this pres-ence, __ come to be one, come to be
3. Free-dom to cap-tives, good news to the poor, light-ing the
4. Come to re-mem-ber __ who is this one, come to re-

Descant (vs 4 only)
4. Come to re-mem-ber, come to re-

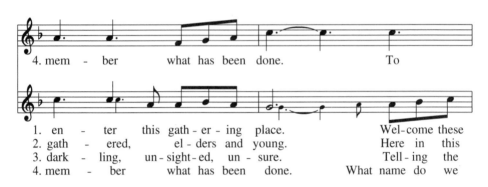

4. mem - ber what has been done. To

1. en - ter this gath - er - ing place. Wel-come these
2. gath - ered, el - ders and young. Here in this
3. dark - ling, un - sight-ed, un - sure. Tell - ing the
4. mem - ber what has been done. What name do we

4. call you, our breath, re -

1. sym - bols, _____ feast-ing and tell - ing; signs of thanks-
2. pres - ence, _____ gath - er - ing force, pres - ent on
3. sto - ry: _____ love with - out end, breath of cre -
4. call you? From where is our breath? Come to re -

4.-mem - ber our death.

1. - giv - ing, signs of in - dwell - ing. _____
2. pur - pose, life - giv - ing source. _____
3. - a - tion, all life to de - fend. _____
4.-mem - ber life wrest - ed from death. _____

4. Come to re - mem - ber,

1. Wel-come a priv - i - lege, sis - ter and broth - er, _____
2. Now is this peo - ple, now to the last, _____
3. Tell - ing the cov - e - nant sto - ry a - gain; _____
4. Come to re - mem-ber in Eu - cha - rist faith, _____

T/B (Vs 4)
4. Come to re - mem - ber,

4. come to pro - claim, weav - ing the

1. shar-ing this in-break-ing light with each oth - er. Wel-come the
2. fus - ing the fu - ture with pres-ent and past. _____ Now is this
3. ex - o - dus jour-ney for wom-en and men. _____ Tell - ing once
4. this is the ban-quet, the cup we pro-claim: _____ weav - ing the

4. come to pro - claim, the

4. gar - ment,   jus - tice on earth, come,   come to cre - ate,

1. strang - er   be - yond and a - bove;   here on - ly friends,
2. peo - ple   here to re - veal,   pres - ence in Word,
3. more and   hear - ing the Word   whose shin - ing con - clu - sion,
4. gar - ment of jus - tice on earth,   come to cre - ate,

4. gar - ment   jus - tice on earth,   come to cre - ate,

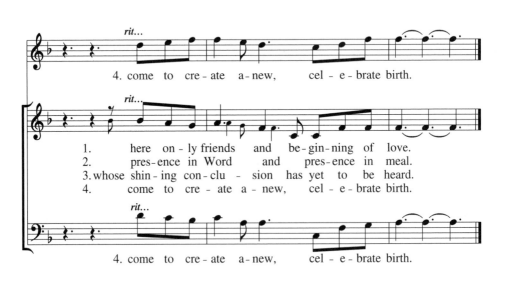

4. come to cre - ate a - new,   cel - e - brate birth.

1.   here on - ly friends   and be - gin - ning of love.
2.   pres - ence in Word   and   pres - ence in meal.
3. whose shin - ing con - clu - sion has yet to be heard.
4.   come to cre - ate a - new,   cel - e - brate birth.

4. come to cre - ate a - new,   cel - e - brate birth.

Christ Be beside Me

Peacefully

1. Christ be be - side me, Christ be be - fore me,
2. Christ on my right hand, Christ on my left hand,
3. Christ be in all hearts think - ing a - bout me;

poco rit.

1. Christ be be - hind me, King of my heart.
2. Christ all a - round me, shield in the strife.
3. Christ be on all tongues tell - ing of me.

a tempo

1. Christ be with - in me, Christ be be - low me,
2. Christ in my sleep - ing, Christ in my sit - ting,
3. Christ be the vi - sion in eyes that see me;

1. Christ be a - bove me, nev - er to part.
2. Christ in my ris - ing, light of my life.
3. In ears that hear me, Christ ev - er be.

Text: 55 54 D; *New Hymns for All Seasons*; James D. Quinn, SJ, b. 1919. Translation ©1969, James D. Quinn, SJ. Used with permission of Geoffrey Chapman Publishers (an imprint of Cassell, PLC), London. Exclusive agent for North America: Selah Publishing Co., Kingston, N.Y.
Music: ST. ROSE; Laura Wasson, b. 1952; choral arr. by Craig S. Kingsbury, b. 1952 ©1993, OCP Publications.

Canticle of the Sun

REFRAIN: *Light and dancing (♩. = 60)*

The heav-ens are tell-ing the glo-ry of God, and all cre-a-tion is shout-ing for joy. Come, dance in the for-est, come, play in the field, and sing, sing to the sing the glo-ry of the Lord.

Lord. Sing, sing to the glo-ry

Text: Marty Haugen, b. 1950.
Music: Marty Haugen.
Text and music ©1980, G.I.A. Publications, Inc.

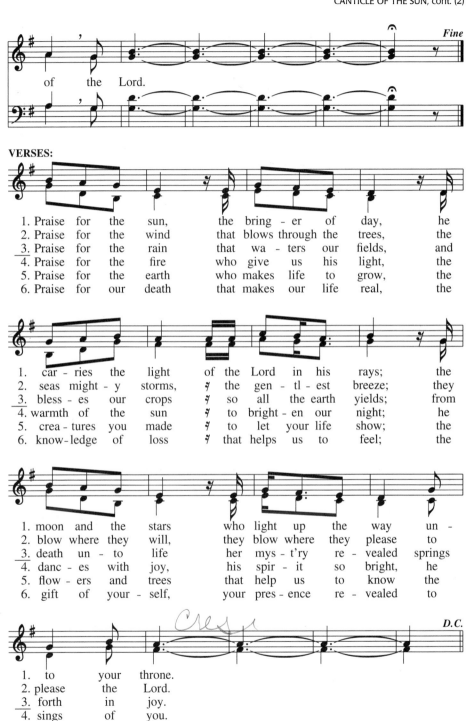

of the Lord.

VERSES:

1. Praise for the sun, the bring - er of day, he
2. Praise for the wind that blows through the trees, the
3. Praise for the rain that wa - ters our fields, and
4. Praise for the fire who give us his light, the
5. Praise for the earth who makes life to grow, the
6. Praise for our death that makes our life real, the

1. car - ries the light of the Lord in his rays; the
2. seas might - y storms, the gen - tl - est breeze; they
3. bless - es our crops so all the earth yields; from
4. warmth of the sun to bright - en our night; he
5. crea - tures you made to let your life show; the
6. know - ledge of loss that helps us to feel; the

1. moon and the stars who light up the way un -
2. blow where they will, they blow where they please to
3. death un - to life her mys - t'ry re - vealed springs
4. danc - es with joy, his spir - it so bright, he
5. flow - ers and trees that help us to know the
6. gift of your - self, your pres - ence re - vealed to

Cresc.

D.C.

1. to your throne.
2. please the Lord.
3. forth in joy.
4. sings of you.
5. heart of love.
6. lead us home.

Canticle of Zachary

VERSES 1, 3, 5: *Strong and March-like (♩ = ca. 112)*

1. Blest be the God of Is - ra - el, The ev - er - liv - ing
3. Of old he gave his sol - emn oath To Fa - ther A - bra -
5. The ris - ing sun shall shine on us To bring the light of

1. Lord, Who comes in pow'r to save his own, His peo - ple
3. ham; His seed a might - y race should be And blest for -
5. day To all who dwell in dark - est night And shad - ow

1. Is - ra - el. For Is - ra - el he rai - ses up, Sal -
3. ev - er - more. He vowed to set his peo - ple free From
5. of the grave. Our foot-steps God shall safe - ly guide To

1. va - tion's tow'r on high In Da - vid's house who
3. fear of ev - 'ry foe, That we might serve him
5. walk the ways of peace; His name for - ev - er -

Text: Adapt. fr. Luke 1:68–79; James D. Quinn, SJ, b. 1919 ©1969, 1985, James D. Quinn, SJ. Reprinted by permission of Selah
   Publishing Co., Kingston, NY.
Music: Michael Joncas, b.1951 ©1981, 1982, Michael Joncas. Published by Cooperative Ministries, Inc. Exclusive agent: OCP
   Publications.

(Fine)

1. reigned as king And ser - vant of the Lord.
3. all our days In good - ness, love, and peace.
5. -more be blest, Who lives and loves and saves.

VERSES 2, 4:

2. Through ho - ly proph - ets did he speak His Word in days of
4. O tin - y child, your name shall be The proph - et of the

2. old, That he would save us from our foes And
4. Lord; The way of God you shall pre - pare To

2. all who bear us ill. To our an - ces - tors did he give His
4. make his com-ing known. You shall pro - claim to Is - ra - el Sal-

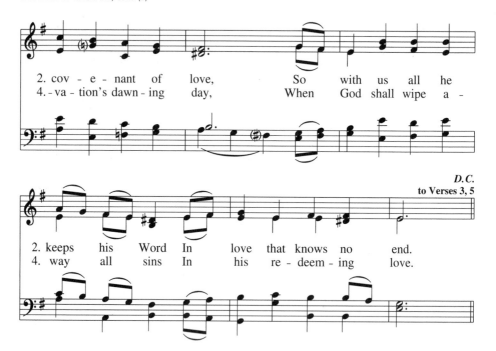

2. cov - e - nant of love, So with us all he
4. -va - tion's dawn - ing day, When God shall wipe a -

D.C.
to Verses 3, 5

2. keeps his Word In love that knows no end.
4. way all sins In his re - deem - ing love.

Christ, Be Our Light

VERSES: (♩ = ca. 132)

1. Long-ing for light,___ we wait in dark-ness. Long-ing for
2. Long-ing for peace,___ our world is trou-bled. Long-ing for
3. Long-ing for food,___ man-y are hun-gry. Long-ing for
4. Long-ing for shel-ter, man-y are home-less. Long-ing for
5. Man-y the gifts,___ man-y the peo-ple, man-y the

1. truth,_____ we turn to you. Make us your own,_____
2. hope,_____ man-y de-spair. Your word a-lone_____
3. wa-ter, man-y still thirst. Make us your bread,_____
4. warmth,_____ man-y are cold. Make us your build-ing,
5. hearts that yearn to be-long. Let us be ser-vants

1. your ho-ly peo-ple, light for the world to see.
2. has pow'r to save us. Make us your liv-ing voice.
3. bro-ken for oth-ers, shared un-til all are fed.
4. shel-ter-ing oth-ers, walls made of liv-ing stone.
5. to one an-oth-er, mak-ing your king-dom come.

REFRAIN:

Christ, be our light! Shine out
Descant
Melody
Christ, be our light! Shine in our hearts.

through the dark, shine!

Shine through the dark-ness. Christ, be our light!

(⌢)

Shine in your church gath-ered to-day.

Text: Bernadette Farrell, b. 1957.
Music: Bernadette Farrell.
Text and music ©1993, Bernadette Farrell. Published by OCP Publications.

91

Center of My Life

REFRAIN: (♩ = ca. 80)

O Lord, you are the cen-ter of my life:

I will al-ways praise you, I will al-ways serve you,

1 · 2-5, Final · to Vss
(Fine)

I will al-ways keep you in my sight. sight.

VERSES 1-3:

1. Keep me safe, O God ___ I take ref-uge in you. ___ I
2. I will bless the Lord who gives me coun - sel, _____ who
3. And so my heart re-joic - es, my soul is glad; _____

1. say to the Lord, "You are my God. My
2. e - ven at night di - rects my heart. I
3. e - ven in safe - ty shall my bod-y rest. For

Text: Psalm 16:1−2, 7−11; verses text ©1963, The Grail (England). Used with permission of G.I.A. Publications, Inc.;
refrain, Paul Inwood, b. 1947 ©1985, Paul Inwood. Published by OCP Publications.
Music: Paul Inwood ©1985, Paul Inwood. Published by OCP Publications.

1. hap - pi - ness _____ lies in you a - lone; my
2. keep _____ the Lord _____ ev - er in my sight: since
3. you will not leave _____ my soul a - mong the dead, nor

D.C.

1. hap - pi - ness _____ lies in you a - lone." _____
2. he is at my right _____ hand, _____ I shall stand firm.
3. let _____ your be - lov - ed know de - cay. _____

VERSE 4:

4. You will show me the path of life, the full - ness of

4. joy in your pres - ence, at your right hand,

D.C. al fine

4. at your right hand hap - pi - ness for - ev - er.

Children, Run Joyfully

REFRAIN: Children's Chorus *Lightly, not too fast* (♩ = 96)
Descant (Final Refrain only: Adult soloist)

(a tempo)

Je - sus, Sav - ior, hear us

Melody *(a tempo)*

Harmony

Chil - dren, run joy - ful - ly, Je - sus is born. Tell all the

sing, hear us pray. Bless us,

moun - tains to sing. Pray to our Fa - ther in

Fine

Lord God. Come to us, be born.

Fine

heav - en this day: Thank you, for Je - sus is born.

VERSE 1: Adult Solo *Slightly faster* (♩ = 108)

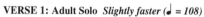

1. Shep - herds stood watch - ing, keep - ing their sheep, and sud - den - ly

1. an - gels ap - peared. "Don't be a - fraid. We

1. bring you great joy: Your Sav-ior is born this night."

VERSE 2: Adult Solo *Slightly faster (♩ = 108)*

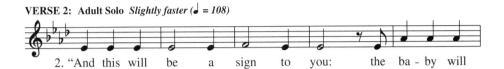

2. "And this will be a sign to you: the ba - by will

2. lie in a man-ger, in the cit-y of Da-vid, in

2. Beth - le - hem. Go now, vis - it your Lord."

Christ, the Lord, Is Risen Again

1. Christ, the Lord is ris'n a-gain, Christ has con-quered death and sin.
2. He who gave for us his life, Who for us en-dured the strife,
3. He who bore all pain and loss, Com-fort-less up - on the cross,

1. Hark! the an - gel choirs__ raise Songs of ev - er - last-ing praise:
2. Is our Pas - chal Lamb to-day; We, too, sing for joy, and say:
3. Lives in glo - ry now on high, Pleads for us, and hears our cry:

1-3. Al - le - lu - ia! Al - le - lu - ia! Al -

1-3. le - lu - ia! Al - le - lu - ia!

Text: 77 77 with alleluias; Michael Weisse, 1480–1534; tr. by Catherine Winkworth, 1827–1878, alt. ©1979, OCP Publications.
Music: SURGIT IN HAEC DIES; 12th cent. Plainsong; choral arr. by Randall DeBruyn, b. 1947 ©1990, OCP Publications.

Christ, the Lord, Is Risen Today (I)

1. Christ, the Lord, is ris'n to-day; Chris-tians, haste your vows to pay;
2. Christ, the vic-tim un-de-filed, God and sin-ners rec-on-ciled;
3. Christ, who once for sin-ners bled, Now the first-born from the dead,

1. Of-fer ye your prais-es meet At the pas-chal vic-tim's feet.
2. When in strange and aw-ful strife Met to-geth-er death and life;
3. Thron'd in end-less might and pow'r, Lives and reigns for-ev-er-more.

1. For the sheep the Lamb has bled, Sin-less in the sin-ner's stead.
2. Chris-tians, on this hap-py day, Haste with joy your vows to pay.
3. Hail, e-ter-nal hope on high! Hail, thou King of Vic-to-ry!

1. Christ, the Lord, is ris'n on high; Now he lives, no more to die!
2. Christ, the Lord, is ris'n on high; Now he lives, no more to die!
3. Hail, thou Prince of Life a-dored! Help and save us, gra-cious Lord!

Text: 77 77 D; *Victimae paschali laudes*; ascr. to Wipo of Burgundy, ca. 1000–1050; tr. by Jane E. Leeson, 1807–1881.
Music: VICTIMAE PASCHALI; Würth's *Katholisches Gesangbuch*, 1859; choral arr. by Randall DeBruyn, b. 1947 ©1990, OCP Publications.

Christ, the Lord, Is Risen Today (II)

1. Christ, the Lord, is ris'n to-day,
2. Lives a-gain our glo-rious King;
3. Love's re-deem-ing work is done,
4. Soar we now where Christ has led,
Al - le - lu - ia!

1. All on earth with an-gels say.
2. Where, O death, is now thy sting?
3. Fought the fight, the bat-tle won.
4. Fol-lowing our ex-alt-ed head;
Al - le - lu - ia!

1. Raise your joys and tri-umphs high,
2. Once he died our souls to save,
3. Death in vain for-bids him rise;
4. Made like him, like him we rise,
Al - le - lu - ia!

1. Sing ye heav'ns and earth re-ply,
2. Where thy vic-to-ry, O grave?
3. Christ has o-pen'd par-a-dise.
4. Ours the cross, the grave, the skies.
Al - le - lu - ia!

Text: 77 77 with alleluias; Charles Wesley, 1707–1788.
Music: LLANFAIR; Robert Williams, 1781–1821; choral harm. by Randall DeBruyn, b. 1947 ©1990, OCP Publications.

Christians, Let Us Love One Another

1. Chris-tians, let us love one an-oth-er, As we share the true liv-ing bread. Je-sus is our God and our broth-er; With his flesh and blood we are fed.
2. We who break this bread are one bod-y, We who share this cup are all one. Chil-dren of our Fa-ther in heav-en, We are heirs with God's on-ly Son.
3. We who eat and drink at this ta-ble Die and rise a-gain with our Lord. Draw-ing from our Rock liv-ing wa-ter, Giv'n to all who thirst for ac-cord.
4. On the path of life we may fal-ter, Earth-ly food a-lone leaves us weak; Al-ways you in-vite from the al-tar: "Hun-gry souls their food here must seek."
5. Wheat and grape in-car-nate a mys-t'ry: Je-sus is the true liv-ing bread. Let us eat with joy and thanks-giv-ing, Trust-ing in the word he has said.
6. Je-sus is the vine, we the branch-es; We are grains of wheat, Christ the bread. Those who eat this bread live for-ev-er, One with Christ, our Lord and our Head.

Ev-'ry-one who loves is

1-6. born of God. Je-sus is our life. God is love.

Text: 98 98 98; Sr. Claudia Foltz, SNJM and Armand Nigro, SJ ©1973, Claudia Foltz, SNJM and Armand Nigro, SJ. Published by OCP Publications.
Music: PICARDY; French, 17th cent.; melody fr. *Chansons populaires des Provinces de France*, 1860; choral arr. by Randall DeBruyn, b. 1947 ©1990, OCP Publications.

City of God

Text: Based on Isaiah 9:60, 1 John 1; Dan Schutte, b. 1947.
Music: Dan Schutte.
Text and music ©1981, Daniel L. Schutte and New Dawn Music.

VERSE 3: Choir

Soprano / Alto

3. God is light; in him there is no

Tenor / Bass

3. God is light; in him there is no

3. dark-ness. Let us walk in his light, his

(dark - ness.)

3. dark-ness. Let us walk in his light, his

Come, Christians, Join to Sing

1. Come, Chris-tians, join to sing
2. Come, lift your hearts on high;
3. Praise yet our Christ a-gain;

Al - le - lu - ia! A - men!

1. Loud praise to Christ our King;
2. Let prais-es fill the sky;
3. Life shall not end the strain;

Al - le - lu - ia! A - men!

1. Let all, with heart and voice, Be - fore his throne re-joice;
2. He is our guide and friend; Our cry he will at-tend;
3. On heav-en's joy-ful shore His good-ness we'll a-dore,

1. Praise is his gra-cious choice:
2. His love shall nev-er end:
3. Sing - ing for - ev - er - more:

Al - le - lu - ia! A - men!

Text: 66 66 D; Christian H. Bateman; 1813−1889, alt.
Music: MADRID; Anon. melody, Philadelphia, 1826; choral arr. by Randall DeBruyn, b. 1947 ©1990, OCP Publications.

Come, Holy Ghost

1. Come, Ho - ly Ghost, Cre - a - tor blest, And in our
2. O Com - fort - er, to thee we cry, Thou heav'n - ly
3. Praise be to thee, Fa - ther and Son, And Ho - ly

1. hearts take up thy rest; Come with thy grace
2. gift of God most high; Thou font of life
3. Spir - it, with them one; And may the Son

1. and heav'n - ly aid To fill the hearts which thou hast
2. and fire of love, And sweet a - noint - ing from a -
3. on us be - stow The gifts that from the Spir - it

1. made; To fill the hearts which thou hast made.
2. bove; And sweet a - noint - ing from a - bove.
3. flow; The gifts that from the Spir - it flow.

Text: LM with repeat; *Veni, Creator Spiritus*; attr. to Rabunus Maurus, 776–856; tr. by Edward Caswall, 1814–1878, alt.
Music: LAMBILLOTTE; Louis Lambillotte, SJ, 1796–1855; choral arr. by Randall DeBruyn, b. 1947 ©1990, OCP Publications.

Come Now, Almighty King

1. Come now, Al - might - y King, Help us your
2. Come now, In - car - nate Word, Who for us
3. Come, Ho - ly Com - fort - er, Your sa - cred
4. To you, O Trin - i - ty, E - ter - nal

1. name to sing, Help us to praise:
2. death en - dured; Our prayer at - tend:
3. wit - ness bear In this glad hour:
4. prais - es be For - ev - er - more!

1. Fa - ther, all glo - ri - ous, O'er all vic - to - ri - ous,
2. Come, and your peo - ple bless, And give your word suc - cess;
3. To us your grace im - part, And rule in ev - 'ry heart!
4. Your sov - 'reign maj - es - ty May we in glo - ry see,

1. Come, and reign o - ver us, An - cient of Days.
2. Fill us with righ - teous - ness, Sav - ior and friend.
3. Nev - er from us de - part, Spir - it of pow'r.
4. And to e - ter - ni - ty Love and a - dore.

Text: 66 4 666 4; Anon., ca. 1757, alt.
Music: ITALIAN HYMN; Felice de Giardini, 1716–1796, alt.

Come, Thou Long-Expected Jesus

1. Come, thou long-ex-pect-ed Je-sus,
2. Is-rael's strength and con-so-la-tion,
3. Born thy peo-ple to de-liv-er,
4. By thine own e-ter-nal Spir-it

1. Born to set thy peo-ple free; From our fears and
2. Hope of all the earth thou art: Dear de-sire of
3. Born a child, and yet a king, Born to reign in
4. Rule in all our hearts a-lone; By thine all-suf-

1. sins re-lease us, Let us find our rest in thee.
2. ev-'ry na-tion, Joy of ev-'ry long-ing heart.
3. us for ev-er, Now thy gra-cious king-dom bring.
4. fi-cient mer-it Raise us to thy glo-rious throne.

Text: 87 87; Charles Wesley, 1707–1788.
Music: STUTTGART; melody fr. C.F. Witt's *Psalmodia Sacra*, 1715; adapt. and harm. by Henry J. Gauntlett, 1805–1876.

Come, Ye Thankful People, Come

1. Come, ye thank-ful peo-ple, come, Raise the song of har-vest-home:
2. All the world is God's own field, Fruit un-to his praise to yield;
3. For the Lord our God shall come, And shall take his har-vest home;
4. E-ven so, Lord, quick-ly come To your fi-nal har-vest-home;

1. All is safe-ly gath-ered in, Ere the win-ter storms be-gin;
2. Wheat and tares to-geth-er sown, Un-to joy or sor-row grown:
3. From his field shall in that day All of-fens-es purge a-way;
4. Gath-er all your peo-ple in, Free from sor-row, free from sin;

1. God, our Mak-er, does pro-vide For our wants to be sup-plied;
2. First the blade, and then the ear, Then the full corn shall ap-pear:
3. Give his an-gels charge at last In the fire the tares to cast,
4. There, for ev-er pu-ri-fied, In your pres-ence to a-bide;

1. Come to God's own tem-ple, come, Raise the song of har-vest-home.
2. Grant, O har-vest Lord, that we Whole-some grain and pure may be.
3. But the fruit-ful ears to store In his gar-ner ev-er-more.
4. Come, with all your an-gels, come, Raise the glo-rious har-vest-home.

Text: 77 77 D; Henry Alford, 1810–1871, alt.
Music: ST. GEORGE'S WINDSOR; George J. Elvey, 1816–1893.

Come to Me

REFRAIN: *Moderately*

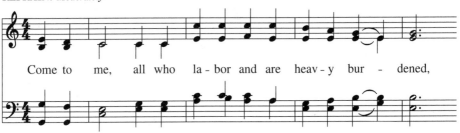

Come to me, all who la-bor and are heav-y bur - dened,

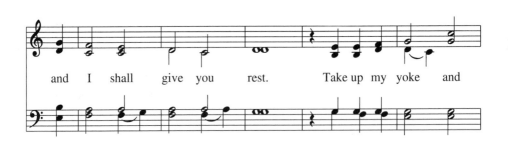

and I shall give you rest. Take up my yoke and

learn from me, for I am meek and hum - ble of

heart, and you'll find rest for your souls.

Text: Based on Matthew 11:28 – 30, Psalm 23; Weston Priory, Gregory Norbet, OSB, b. 1940.
Music: Weston Priory, Gregory Norbet, OSB; choral arr. by Craig S. Kingsbury, b. 1952.
Text and music ©1971, 1988, 1994, from the recording *Locusts and Wild Honey*, The Benedictine Foundation of the State of Vermont,
Inc., Weston, VT.

Yes, my yoke is eas - y and my bur -
den is light.

1-5 to Verses | Final | Fine

VERSES:

1. You, God, are my shep-herd. I shall nev-er be in need.
2. Be - side peace-ful wa - ters you re - store ___ my true self;
3. Should I be sur - round - ed by the shad - ows of death,
4. Be - fore my deep hun - ger you spread out ___ your ___ feast.
5. Pur - sue me, O God, ___ with your fa - thom-less love.

D.C.

1. Fresh and green are the mead-ows where you give me ___ rest.
2. There you lead me to walk ___ in the path of new life.
3. I will not fear, for you are stead - fast in your ___ love.
4. My ___ skin you a - noint ___ with the rich - est of oil.
5. In your tent let me dwell ___ all the days of my life.

Come to the Water

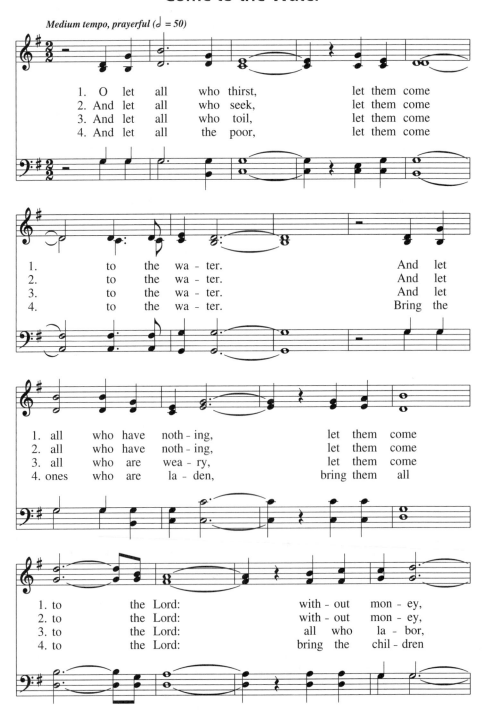

Text: Suggested by Isaiah 55:1–2, Matthew 11:28–30; John Foley, SJ, b. 1939.
Music: John Foley, SJ.
Text and music ©1978, John B. Foley, SJ and New Dawn Music.

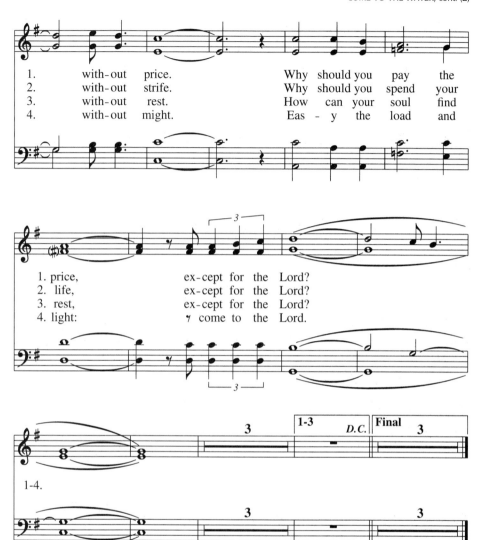

1. with-out price.   Why should you pay the
2. with-out strife.   Why should you spend your
3. with-out rest.   How can your soul find
4. with-out might.   Eas - y the load and

1. price,   ex-cept for the Lord?
2. life,   ex-cept for the Lord?
3. rest,   ex-cept for the Lord?
4. light: ♪ come to the Lord.

1-4.

1-3   D.C.   Final

Come, Worship the Lord

*First Refrain: Cantor or Unison Choir.

Text: Based on Psalm 95; John Michael Talbot, b. 1954.
Music: John Michael Talbot; choral arr. by Rick Modlin, b. 1966.
Text and music ©1980, 1995, Birdwing Music/Cherry Lane Music Publishing Co., Inc. Administered by EMI Christian Music Publishing.

VERSES 1,2:

1. Come, let us sing to the Lord, and shout with joy ___ to the
2. Come, let us bow down and wor-ship, bend-ing the knee be-fore the

1. rock who saves us, Let us come with thanks-giv - ing,
2. Lord our ma - ker. ⁷ For we are his peo - ple,

2 D.C.

1. and sing joy - ful songs to the Lord.
2. ⁷ ⁏ we are the flock that he shep-herds.

VERSE 3:

Descant
3. The Lord is God; great

Melody
3. The Lord is God, the might - y God, the great king o'er

3. God. He holds the
3. all oth-er gods. He holds in his hands the

3. earth and moun - tains as well.
3. depths of the earth and the high - est moun-tains as well.

3. He made the sea, the
3. He made the sea, it be-longs now to him; the dry land,

3. land by his hand. **D.C. al fine**
2
3. too, was formed by his hand.

113

Companions on the Journey

REFRAIN: *With energy* (♩ = ca. 104-108)

Descant (begin after Vs 1)

Melody: We are com-pan-ions on the jour-ney, break-ing

Harmony (begin after Vs 2)

We are com-pan-ions;

bread and shar-ing life; and in the love we bear is the

break-ing bread, shar-ing life; in our love is the

hope we share for we be-lieve in the love of our

hope we share; we be-

God, we be-lieve in the love of our God. *Fine*

lieve in God, we be-lieve in the love of our God. *Fine*

Text: Based on Micah 6:8 and Matthew 7:7; Carey Landry, b. 1944.
Music: Carey Landry.
Text and music ©1985, Carey Landry and North American Liturgy Resources (N.A.L.R.).

VERSE 1:

1. No long-er stran-gers to each oth - er; no long-er

1. stran-gers in God's house; we are fed and we are

1. nour-ished by the strength of those who care,

1. by the strength of those who care.

VERSE 2:

2. We have been gift-ed with each oth - er, and we are

2. called by the Word of the Lord: to act with jus-tice, to love

2. ten - der - ly, and to walk hum-bly with our

2. God, to walk hum-bly with our God.

VERSE 3:

3. We will seek and we shall find; we will

3. knock and the door will be o-pened; we will ask and it

3. shall be giv-en, for we be - lieve in the love of our

D.C.

3. God, we be - lieve in the love of our God.

VERSE 4: *slowly – ad lib.*

4. We are made for the glo - ry of our God, for

4. ser-vice in the name of Je - sus; to walk side by side with

a tempo

4. hope in our hearts, for we be - lieve in the love of our

D.C.

4. God, we be - lieve in the love of our God.

Create in Me

Text: Based on Psalm 51:3–4, 9, 12, 14; Bob Hurd, b. 1950.
Music: Bob Hurd; choral arr. by Craig S. Kingsbury, b. 1952.
Text and music ©1986, Bob Hurd. Published by OCP Publications.

Creator Spirit, by Whose Aid

1. Cre - a - tor Spir - it, by whose aid The world's foun - da -
2. O Source of un - cre - a - ted light, The Fa - ther's prom -
3. All ad - o - ra - tion ev - er be, E - ter - nal Par -

1. tions first were laid! Al - le - lu - ia! Al - le - lu - ia! Give
2. ised Par - a - clete; Al - le - lu - ia! Al - le - lu - ia! Thrice
3. a - clete to thee. Al - le - lu - ia! Al - le - lu - ia! From

1. us thy - self that we may see The Fa - ther and
2. ho - ly Font, thrice ho - ly Fire, Our hearts with heav'n -
3. sin and sor - row set us free That we may live

1. the Son by thee.
2. ly love in - spire.
3. e - ter - nal - ly.

(Melody)

1-3. Al - le - lu - ia! Al - le -

1-3. Al - le - lu - ia! Al - le - lu -

1-3. Al - le - lu -

Text: LM with additions; composite, based on tr. of *Veni Creator Spiritus* by John Dryden, 1631–1700.
Music: LASST UNS ERFREUEN; melody fr. *Auserlesene, Catholische, Geistliche Kirchengesäng*, Cologne, 1623; choral arr. by Randall
DeBruyn, b. 1947 ©1994, OCP Publications.

118

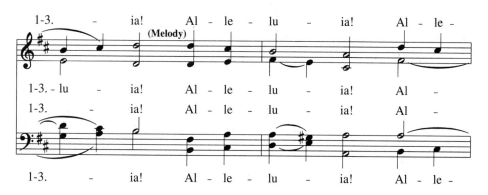

Crown Him with Many Crowns

1. Crown him with man-y crowns, The Lamb up-on his throne; All
2. Crown him the Lord of life, Who tri-umphed o'er the grave, Who
3. Crown him the Lord of heav'n, Where an-gels sing a-bove, Crown

1. king-doms of the earth re-sound In praise of him a-lone. A-
2. on the third day did a-rise And hope to sin-ners gave. His
3. him the King, to whom is giv'n The won-drous name of Love. Crown

1. wake, my soul, and sing Of him who died for thee, And
2. glo-ry now we sing, Who died and rose on high, Who
3. him with man-y crowns, As thrones be-fore him fall. Through-

1. hail him as thy ri-sen King For all e-ter-ni-ty.
2. came e-ter-nal life to bring, Who lives, no more to die.
3. out the earth his praise re-sounds For he is Lord of all.

Text: SMD; Matthew Bridges, 1800–1894, alt.; Compilers, 1978 ©1978, OCP Publications.
Music: DIADEMATA; George J. Elvey, 1816–1893.

Day Is Done

1. Day is done, but love un-fail-ing Dwells ev - er here;
2. Dark de-scends, but light un-end-ing Shines through our night;
3. Eyes will close, but you un-sleep-ing Watch by our side;

1. Shad-ows fall, but hope pre-vail-ing, Calms ev - ery fear.
2. You are with us, ev - er lend-ing New strength to sight.
3. Death may come, in love's safe-keep-ing Still we a - bide.

1. God, our Mak - er, none for-sak-ing, Take our hearts, of love's own mak-ing;
2. One in love, your truth con-fess-ing, One in hope of heav-en's bless-ing,
3. God of love, all e - vil quell-ing, Sin for - giv-ing, fear dis - pel-ling:

1. Watch our sleep-ing, guard our wak-ing, Be al - ways near.
2. May we see, in love's pos-sess-ing, Love's end-less light!
3. Stay with us, our hearts in-dwell-ing, This e - ven - tide.

Text: 84 84 88 84; James D. Quinn, SJ, b. 1919 ©1969, James D. Quinn, SJ. Reprinted by permission of Selah Publishing Co.,
Kingston, N.Y.
Music: AR HYD Y NOS; Trad. Welsh Melody; choral arr. by Randall DeBruyn, b. 1947 ©1991, OCP Publications.

Earthen Vessels

ANTIPHON: *Broad and rhythmical, Andante (♩ = 84)*

We hold a treas-ure not made of gold,

in earth-en ves-sels, wealth un-told; one treas-ure

on - ly: the Lord, the Christ, in earth - en

ves - sels.

VERSES: *Lightly, slightly faster (♩ = 96)*

1. Light has shone in our dark-ness: God has shone in our heart
2. God has cho-sen the low - ly who are small in this world;

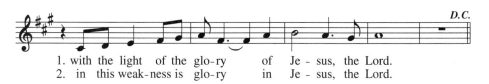

1. with the light of the glo-ry of Je - sus, the Lord.
2. in this weak-ness is glo-ry in Je - sus, the Lord.

Text: Based on 2 Corinthians 4, 1 Corinthians 1; John Foley, SJ, b. 1939.
Music: John Foley, SJ.
Text and music ©1975, 1978, John B. Foley, SJ and New Dawn Music.

Eat This Bread

OSTINATO RESPONSE: *Meditative (♩ = 80)*

Eat this bread, drink this cup, come to me and nev-er be hun-gry.

Eat this bread, drink this cup, trust in me and you will not thirst. 2. Your

Fine

VERSE 1: Cantor

1. I am the bread of life, the true bread sent from the Fa-ther.

D.C.

VERSE 2: Cantor

2. an - ces - tors ate man - na in the des - ert, but

2. this is the bread come down from heav - en.

D.C.

VERSE 3: Cantor

3. Eat my flesh and drink my blood, and

3. I will raise you up on the last day.

D.C.

Text: John 6:25−59; adapt. by Robert J. Batastini, b. 1942 and the Taizé Community.
Music: Jacques Berthier, 1923−1994 ©1982, 1983, 1984, *Les Presses de Taizé,* (France). Used by permission of G.I.A. Publications, Inc.

VERSE 4: Cantor

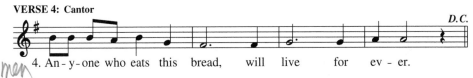

4. An-y-one who eats this bread, will live for ev - er.

VERSE 5: Cantor

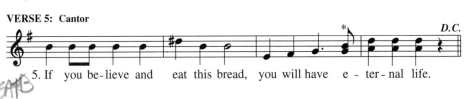

5. If you be-lieve and eat this bread, you will have e - ter - nal life.

* **Choose either part.**

Every Valley

REFRAIN: (♩ = 106 - 110)

Melody *(a tempo)*

Ev - 'ry val - ley shall be ex - alt - ed and ev - 'ry hill made

Harmony

(a tempo)

low.   And   all   God's   peo - ple   shall   see   to -

1-3 to Verses | **Final** *Fine*

geth - er   the   glo - ry   of   the   Lord.   Lord.

VERSES 1, 3:

1. A   voice   cries   out   in the   wil - der - ness, "Pre - pare   the   way
3. 𝄾 Stand   up - on   the ___   moun - tain - top.   O   lift   your   voice

1. of   the   Lord.   Make straight   in   the   des - ert   a
3. to   the   world.   Sing   joy - ful - ly,   Je -

rit.   *D.C.*

1. high - way,   a   high - way ___   for   our   God."
3. ru - sa - lem,   "Be - hold, ___   be - hold   your   God."

Text: Based on Isaiah 40:1, 3, 4, 9; Bob Dufford, SJ, b. 1943.
Music: Bob Dufford, SJ.
Text and music ©1970, Robert J. Dufford, SJ. Administered by New Dawn Music.

VERSE 2:

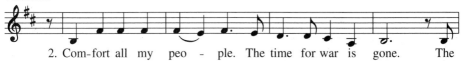

2. Com-fort all my peo - ple. The time for war is gone. The

2. blind shall see, the deaf shall hear, the lame shall leap for joy.

Eye Has Not Seen

Text: 1 Corinthians 2:9–10; Marty Haugen, b. 1950.
Music: Marty Haugen.
Text and music ©1982, 1983, G.I.A. Publications, Inc.

VERSES 1-3:

Melody

Harmony

1. When pain and sor - row weigh us down, be near to us, O
2. Our lives are but a sin - gle breath, we flow - er and we
3. To those who see with eyes of faith, the Lord is ev - er

1. Lord, for - give the weak-ness of our faith, and bear us up with-
2. fade, yet all our days are in your hands, so we re-turn in
3. near, re - flect-ed in the fac - es, of all the poor and

D.C.

1. in your peace - ful word.
2. love what love has made.
3. low - ly of the world.

VERSE 4:

4. We sing a mys-t'ry from the past in halls where saints have trod,

4. yet ev - er new the mu-sic rings to Je - sus, Liv - ing

D.C. al fine

4. Song of God.

Faith of Our Fathers

VERSES:

1. Faith of our fa - thers! liv - ing still In spite of dun - geon,
2. Faith of our fa - thers! we will strive To win all na - tions
3. Faith of our fa - thers! we will love Both friend and foe in

1. fire, and sword. O how our hearts beat high with joy
2. un - to thee. And through the truth that comes from God
3. all our strife, And preach thee, too, as love knows how

REFRAIN:

1. When-e'er we hear that glo - rious word!
2. We all shall then be tru - ly free:
3. By kind-ly words and vir - tuous life:

Faith of our fa - thers,

ho - ly faith! We will be true to thee till death.

Text: LM with refrain; Frederick W. Faber, 1814–1863, alt.
Music: ST. CATHERINE; Henri F. Hemy, 1818–1888; adapt. by James G. Walton, 1821–1905.

For All the Saints

1. For all the saints, who from their la - bors rest, Who
2. O blest com - mun - ion, fel - low - ship di - vine! ____
3. The gold - en eve - ning bright - ens in the west; ____
4. But lo! there breaks a yet more glo - rious day; The
5. From earth's wide bounds, from o - cean's far - thest coast, Through

1. you ____ by faith be - fore the world con - fessed, Your
2. We fee - bly strug - gle, they in glo - ry shine; Yet
3. Soon to the loy - al faith - ful comes their rest; ____
4. saints ____ tri - um - phant rise in bright ar - ray; The
5. gates ____ of heav'n streams in the count - less host, ____

1. Name, O ____ Je - sus, be for ev - er blest.
2. all are ____ one with - in your great de - sign.
3. Sweet is the calm of Par - a - dise so blest. } Al -
4. King of ____ Glo - ry pass - es on his way.
5. Sing - ing to Fa - ther, Son, and Ho - ly Ghost,

1-5. le - lu - ia, al - le - lu - ia!

Al - le - lu - ia!

Text: 10 10 10 with alleluias; William W. How, 1823–1897, alt.
Music: SINE NOMINE; Ralph Vaughan Williams, 1872–1958 © Oxford University Press, London.

131

Father, I Put My Life in Your Hands

ANTIPHON: (♩ = ca. 80)

Descant / Soprano / Alto
Fa - ther, I put my life in your hands.

Tenor / Bass

VERSES 1,3:

Descant (Vs 3 only)
3. I trust you, Lord; you

S/A
1. In __ you, O Lord, I take ref - uge; let me nev - er be
3. But my trust is in you, O Lord; ____ I __ say, __ "You

T/B

3. are God. In - to your hands, my

1. put to shame. In - to your hands I com - mend my
3. are my God." In - to your hands I __ place my

Text: Based on Psalm 31; John Michael Talbot, b.1954.
Music: John Michael Talbot; choral arr. by Phil Perkins, b. 1948 and Rick Modlin, b. 1966.

VERSES 2, 4:

2. For ___ all my foes re-proach me, neigh-bors laugh ___ and
4. Let your face ___ shine on your ser - vant; O ___ save me ___

2. friends stand off. I am for-got-ten like dead un-re -
4. in your love. Be stout - heart-ed and come, ___ take

2. mem-bered; I ___ am like a dish ___ cast down.
4. cour-age, all you ___ who now hope in the Lord.

133

Festival Canticle: Worthy Is Christ

REFRAIN:

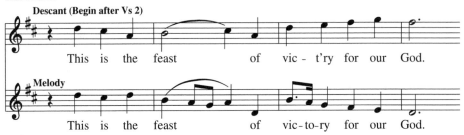

Descant (Begin after Vs 2)

This is the feast of vic- t'ry for our God.

Melody

This is the feast of vic-to-ry for our God.

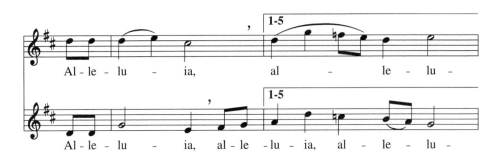

Al - le - lu - ia, al - le - lu -

Al - le - lu - ia, al - le -lu - ia, al - le - lu -

1-5

1-5

to Verses after repeat | Final

ia. al - le - lu - ia.

Fine

to Verses after repeat | Final

ia. lu - ia, al - le - lu - ia.

Fine

Text: Irregular; Based on Revelation 5; Richard Hillert, b. 1923 ©1978, *Lutheran Book of Worship*. Reprinted by permission of Augsburg Fortress.
Music: FESTIVAL CANTICLE; Richard Hillert ©1975, 1988, Richard Hillert. All rights reserved. Used with permission.

VERSES:

Descant (Vs 4)

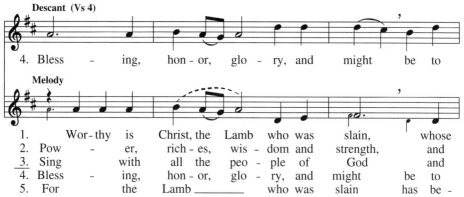

4. Bless - ing, hon - or, glo - ry, and might be to

Melody

1.   Wor-thy is Christ, the Lamb who was slain,   whose
2. Pow - er, rich - es, wis - dom and strength,   and
3. Sing with all the peo - ple of God   and
4. Bless - ing, hon - or, glo - ry, and might be to
5. For the Lamb _____ who was slain has be -

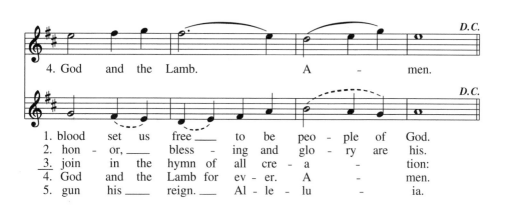

D.C.

4. God and the Lamb.   A - men.

D.C.

1. blood set us free ___ to be peo - ple of God.
2. hon - or, ___ bless - ing and glo - ry are his.
3. join in the hymn of all cre - a - tion:
4. God and the Lamb for ev - er. A - men.
5. gun his ___ reign. ___ Al - le - lu - ia.

135

Fill My Cup, Lord

VERSES:

1. Like the wom-an at the well, I was seek-ing for
2. There are mil-lions in this world who are crav-ing the
3. So, my friend, __ if the things this world gave you leave

1. things that could not sat-is-fy. And then I heard my Sav-ior
2. plea-sure earth-ly things af-ford. But none can match the won-drous
3. hun-gers that won't pass a-way, My bless-ed Lord will come and

1. speak-ing: ___ "Draw from my well that nev-er shall run dry."
2. trea-sure ___ that I find in Je-sus Christ, my Lord.
3. save you ___ if you kneel to him and hum-bly pray:

REFRAIN:

Fill my cup, Lord, I lift it up, Lord. Come and quench this

Text: Richard Blanchard, b. 1925.
Music: Richard Blanchard; choral arr. by Eugene Clark, b. 1938.
Text and music ©1959, Richard Blanchard. Assigned to Sacred Songs. ©1964, 1971, Sacred Songs (a div. of WORD, Inc.)/ASCAP.
   All rights reserved. Used by permission.

thirst-ing of my soul. Bread of heav - en, feed me till I

rit.

want no more. Fill my cup, fill it up and make me whole.

rit.

Flow River Flow

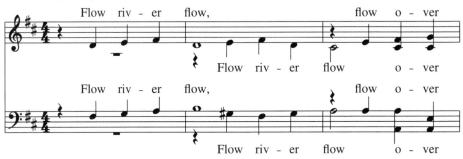

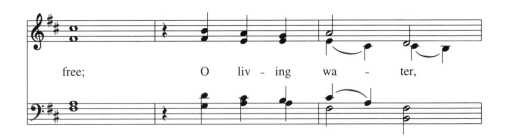

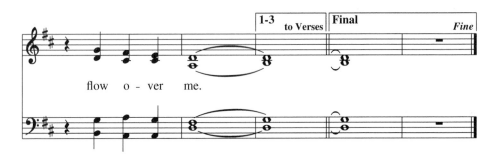

Text: Based on Ezekiel 11, Isaiah 35, John 4; Bob Hurd, b. 1950.
Music: Bob Hurd; choral arr. by Craig S. Kingsbury, b. 1952.
Text and music ©1986, 1987, Bob Hurd. Published by OCP Publications.

VERSES:

Solo (or unison voices):

1. You will be mine and I will be your
2. The blind shall see, the mute shall find a
3. Who - ev - er drinks the wa - ter I will

1. God, for I will wash you
2. voice, the lame shall leap for
3. give will nev - er thirst a -

1. clean. And a new heart, a ___
2. joy. Riv - ers will flow in - to
3. gain. The drink I give is an

1. heart of flesh and feel - ing, I will place with -
2. dry and bar - ren des - ert; Flow - ers bloom in
3. ev - er-flow - ing riv - er, well - ing up with -

D.C.

1. in you ___ for your heart of stone.
2. splen - dor, ___ glo - ry fill the land.
3. in you to give e - ter - nal life.

For the Beauty of the Earth

1. For the beau - ty of the earth, For the glo - ry
2. For the beau - ty of each hour Of the day and
3. For the joy of hu - man love, Broth - er, sis - ter,
4. For your Church, that ev - er - more Lifts its ho - ly
5. For Your - self, O Gift Di - vine! To our world so

1. of the skies, For the love which from our birth
2. of the night, Hill and vale and tree and flower,
3. par - ent, child, Friends on earth and friends a - bove,
4. hands a - bove, Of - f'ring up on ev - 'ry shore
5. free - ly giv'n; For that love from which will shine,

1. O - ver and a - round us lies:
2. Sun and moon, and stars of light:
3. For all gen - tle thoughts and mild: Lord of all to
4. A pure sac - ri - fice of love:
5. Peace on earth and joy in heav'n:

1-5. you we raise This our gift of grate - ful praise.

Text: 77 77 77; Folliot S. Pierpoint, 1835–1917.
Music: DIX; Conrad Kocher, 1786–1872; arr. by William H. Monk, 1823–1889.

For the Fruits of This Creation

1. For the fruits of this cre-a-tion, Thanks be to God;
2. In the just re-ward of la-bor, God's will be done;
3. For the har-vests of the Spir-it, Thanks be to God;

1. For the gifts of ev-'ry na-tion, Thanks be to God;
2. In the help we give our neigh-bor, God's will be done;
3. For the good we all in-her-it, Thanks be to God;

1. For the plow-ing, sow-ing, reap-ing, Si-lent growth while we are sleep-ing,
2. In the world-wide task of car-ing For the hun-gry and de-spair-ing,
3. For the won-ders that as-tound us, For the truths that will con-found us,

1. Fu-ture needs in earth's safe-keep-ing, Thanks be to God.
2. In the har-vests we are shar-ing, God's will be done.
3. Most of all, that love has found us, Thanks be to God.

Text: 84 84 88 84; Fred Pratt Green, b. 1903 ©1970, Hope Publishing Co. All rights reserved. Used by permission.
Music: AR HYD Y NOS; Trad. Welsh Melody; choral arr. by Randall DeBruyn, b. 1947 ©1991, OCP Publications.

For You Are My God

Text: Based on Psalm 16; John Foley, SJ, b. 1939.
Music: John Foley, SJ.

142

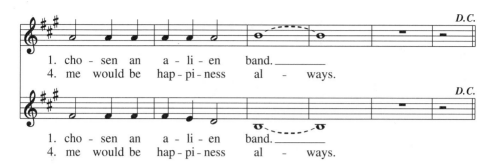

1. cho - sen an a - li - en band. _____
4. me would be hap - pi - ness al - ways.

1. cho - sen an a - li - en band. _____
4. me would be hap - pi - ness al - ways.

VERSES 2, 3:

Descant

2. You are my por - tion __ and cup; it is you that I
3. Glad are my heart __ and my soul; se - cure - ly my

Melody

2. You are my por - tion __ and cup; it is you that I
3. Glad are my heart __ and my soul; se - cure - ly my

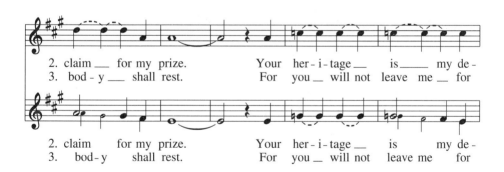

2. claim __ for my prize. Your her - i - tage __ is __ my de -
3. bod - y __ shall rest. For you __ will not leave me __ for

2. claim for my prize. Your her - i - tage __ is my de -
3. bod - y shall rest. For you __ will not leave me for

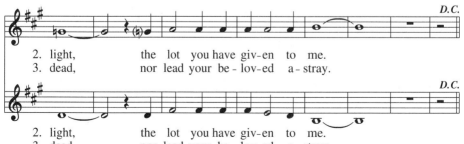

2. light, the lot you have giv - en to me.
3. dead, nor lead your be - lov - ed a - stray.

2. light, the lot you have giv - en to me.
3. dead, nor lead your be - lov - ed a - stray.

Forty Days and Forty Nights

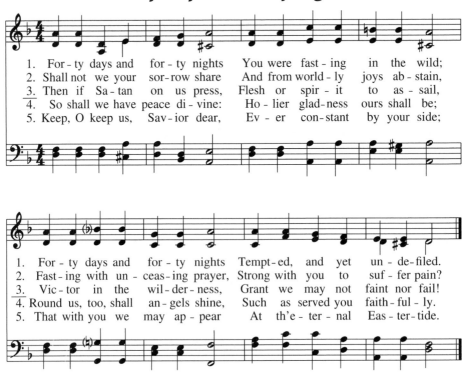

1. For - ty days and for - ty nights You were fast - ing in the wild;
2. Shall not we your sor-row share And from world - ly joys ab - stain,
3. Then if Sa - tan on us press, Flesh or spir - it to as - sail,
4. So shall we have peace di - vine: Ho - lier glad-ness ours shall be;
5. Keep, O keep us, Sav-ior dear, Ev - er con-stant by your side;

1. For - ty days and for - ty nights Tempt-ed, and yet un - de-filed.
2. Fast-ing with un - ceas-ing prayer, Strong with you to suf - fer pain?
3. Vic - tor in the wil-der-ness, Grant we may not faint nor fail!
4. Round us, too, shall an-gels shine, Such as served you faith-ful - ly.
5. That with you we may ap - pear At th'e - ter - nal Eas - ter-tide.

Text: 77 77; George H. Smyttan, 1822–1870, alt.
Music: HEINLEIN; *Aus der Tiefe rufe ich*; melody attr. to Martin Herbst, 1654–1681, alt.; harm. by William H. Monk, 1823–1889.

From All That Dwell below the Skies

1. From all that dwell be - low the skies,
2. E - ter - nal are thy mer - cies, Lord;
3. Your loft - y themes, ye mor - tals, bring;
4. In ev - 'ry land be - gin the song;

1. Let the Cre - a - tor's praise a - rise;
2. E - ter - nal truth at - tends thy word:
3. In songs of praise di - vine - ly sing;
4. To ev - 'ry land the strains be - long;

1. Let the Re - deem - er's name be sung
2. Thy praise shall sound from shore to shore
3. The great sal - va - tion loud pro - claim
4. In cheer - ful sounds all voic - es raise

1. Through ev - 'ry land, by ev - 'ry tongue!
2. Till suns shall rise and set no more.
3. And shout for joy the Sav - ior's name.
4. And fill the world with loud - est praise.

Text: LM; Para. of Psalm 117; verses 1–2, Isaac Watts, 1674–1748, alt.; verses 3–4, Anon., ca. 1781.
Music: DUKE STREET; John Hatton, ca. 1710–1793.

From East and West

*Descant and harmony are not to be sung together.

Text: Bob Dufford, SJ, b. 1943.
Music: Bob Dufford, SJ.
Text and music ©1990, Robert J. Dufford, SJ. Published by OCP Publications.

(Descant)

all. Bring them home a - gain. *Fine*

(Melody)

peo - ple be whole a - gain. *Fine*

VERSES 1, 2, 3, 5:

1. Come _____ raise up a joy - ful noise. _____ Fill the
2. Greet each oth - er with glad em - brace, with tears of
3. Call the cap - tives from ev - 'ry land: _____ "Hear the
5. Then the eyes of the blind shall see, the lame will

1. street with your dance. Bright - en your fac - es for
2. wel - come and joy. Tell _____ the tales of the
3. word of the Lord: Come out of the dark - ness and
5. leap like the deer, and fin - gers that trem - ble and

D.C.

1. you are be - lov - ed of God!
2. jour - ney be - hind you, and sing:
3. o - pen your pris - on. Be free!"
5. voic - es that fal - ter be strong!

VERSES 4, 6:

4. At ev - 'ry house in ev - 'ry land, sound the trum - pets of
6. For those who sow in tears and pain reap a har - vest of

4. day. What God has gath - ered God will send that
6. joy. For God has come to dance with us and

1 *D.C.* **2** *D.C.*

4. ev - 'ry heart may hear:
6. joins a hap - py 6. voice to our song, sing - ing:

From the Depths We Cry to Thee

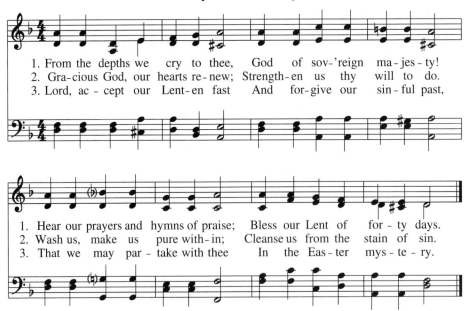

1. From the depths we cry to thee, God of sov-'reign ma-jes-ty!
2. Gra-cious God, our hearts re-new; Strength-en us thy will to do.
3. Lord, ac-cept our Lent-en fast And for-give our sin-ful past,

1. Hear our prayers and hymns of praise; Bless our Lent of for-ty days.
2. Wash us, make us pure with-in; Cleanse us from the stain of sin.
3. That we may par-take with thee In the Eas-ter mys-te-ry.

Text: 77 77; Verses 1 and 3, Alan G. McDougall, 1895–1964, alt; verse 2, Owen Alstott, b. 1947 ©1977, OCP Publications.
Music: HEINLEIN; *Aus der Tiefe rufe ich*; melody attr. to Martin Herbst, 1654–1681, alt.; harm. by William H. Monk, 1823–1889.

Gather Us Together

REFRAIN: (♩ = 110)

Lord, Je - sus Christ, gath - er us to - geth - er.

Fine

Make us one bread, one bod - y in your love.

VERSES:

Melody

1. Gath - er your peo - ple, who long to be
2. We do pro - claim you the Sav - ior of
3. For - give our fail - ings, cre - ate us a -
4. In - to your hands, Lord, we place all our
5. With - in your tem - ple your prais - es we

Harmony

D.C.

1. one, one with you, O Lord, in truth and love.
2. all, lord of all the earth and sea and sky.
3. new. Speak your words of peace in - to our hearts.
4. cares, trust - ing in your love which nev - er fails.
5. sing. Glo - rious is your name o'er all the earth.

Text: Owen Alstott, b. 1947.
Music: Owen Alstott.
Text and music ©1980, OCP Publications.

Gather Us In

VERSES: *Strongly* (♩. = 56-58)

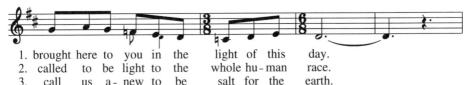

1. Here in this place new light is stream-ing, now is the dark - ness
2. We are the young— our lives are a mys - t'ry, we are the old—who
3. Here we will take the wine and the wa - ter, here we will take the
4. Not in the dark of build-ings con - fin - ing, not in some heav - en,

1. van-ished a - way, See in this space our fears and our dream-ings,
2. yearn for your face, We have been sung through-out all of his - t'ry,
3. bread of new birth, Here you shall call your sons and your daugh-ters,
4. light years a-way, but here in this place the new light is shin - ing,

1. brought here to you in the light of this day.
2. called to be light to the whole hu - man race.
3. call us a- new to be salt for the earth.
4. now is the King - dom, now is the day.

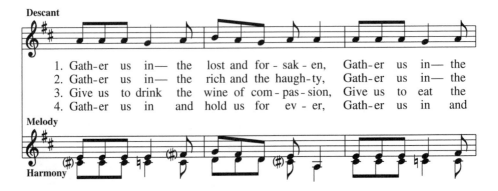

Descant

1. Gath-er us in— the lost and for - sak - en, Gath-er us in— the
2. Gath-er us in— the rich and the haugh-ty, Gath-er us in— the
3. Give us to drink the wine of com - pas - sion, Give us to eat the
4. Gath-er us in and hold us for ev - er, Gath-er us in and

Melody

Harmony

Text: Marty Haugen, b. 1950.
Music: Marty Haugen.
Text and music ©1982, G.I.A. Publications, Inc.

1. blind and the lame;   Call to us now, and   we shall a - wak - en,
2. proud and the strong;   Give us a heart so   meek and so low - ly,
3. bread that is you;   Nour-ish us well, and   teach us to fash - ion
4. make us your own;   Gath - er us in— all   peo-ples to - geth - er,

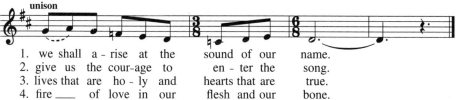

unison

1. we shall a - rise at the   sound of our   name.
2. give us the cour-age to   en - ter the   song.
3. lives that are ho - ly and   hearts that are   true.
4. fire ____ of love in our   flesh and our   bone.

Gather Your People

VERSES: *unison*

1. Draw us forth to the ta - ble of life:
2. We are parts of the bod - y of Christ,
3. No more harm on the moun - tain of God;
4. Wash us, Lord, in the wa - ters of life;

1. broth - ers and sis - ters, each of us called to
2. need - ing each oth - er, each of the gifts the
3. swords in - to plow-shares. Free us, O Lord, from
4. wa - ters of mer - cy, wa - ters of hope that

D.C.

1. walk in your light.
2. Spir - it pro - vides.
3. hard - ness of heart.
4. flow from your side.

Gentle Shepherd/Jesús, Pastor Tan Dulce

REFRAIN/ESTRIBILLO: (♩ = 82)

Melody/Melodía

O Je-sus, gen-tle shep-herd and liv — ing bread;
Je-sús, pas-tor tan dul-ce y pan ce-les-tial;

Harmony/Harmonía

Fine/Fin

feed ___ us, guide ___ us to the land of ev-er-last-ing life.
guí-a-nos, llé-va-nos a la tie-rra de tu Pa-dre Dios.

VERSES/ESTROFAS:

1. The Lord ___ is my shep-herd; there is
2. You have pre-pared ___ me a ban-quet in the
3. Sure-ly good-ness and kind-ness shall fol-low

1. El Se-ñor es mi pas-tor ___ na-
2. Me has pre-pa-ra-do un ban-que-te fren-te a
3. Me a-com-pa-ñan tu bon-dad ___ y tu fa-

Text: Based on Psalm 23; Tobias Colgan, OSB, b. 1950; Spanish tr. by Amador Garza. English text ©1979, Spanish text ©1988, St. Meinrad Archabbey. Administered by New Dawn Music.
Music: Tobias Colgan, OSB; choral arr. by Randall DeBruyn, b.1947 ©1979, 1983 St. Meinrad Archabbey. Administered by New Dawn Music.

1. noth-ing I shall want. _____ Fresh _____ and __
2. sight __ of my foes. _____ My head _____ you have a -
3. me __ all my days. _____ In the Lord's _____ own __
1. -da me fal - ta - rá _____ en ver - des y
2. mis __ e - ne - mi - gos. Con a - cei -
3. -vor to - dos mis dí - as. Mi man - sión _____ se -

1. green are the pas - tures _____ where he
2. noint - ed with pre - cious oil, _____ and my
3. house shall I dwell _____ for -
1. fres - cos _____ pa - stos _____ me __
2. te me per - fu - mas la ca - be - za y re
3. rá _____ la ca - sa de Dios _____ por __

D.C.

1. gives _____ me re - pose. _____
2. cup is o - ver - flow - ing.
3. ev - er and ev - er.
1. ha - ce re - po - sar. _____
2. lle - nas mi co - pa.
3. lar - go, lar - go tiem - po.

Gift of Finest Wheat

REFRAIN: *Legato*

Parts

You sat-is-fy the hun-gry heart With gift of fin-est wheat;

Come give to us, O sav-ing Lord, The bread of life to eat.

Fine

VERSES:

Soprano vnison

Alto

Tenor

1. As when the shep - herd calls his sheep, They
2. With joy - ful lips we sing to you Our
3. Is not the cup we bless and share The
4. The mys-t'ry of your pres-ence, Lord, No
5. You give your-self to us, O Lord; Then

Bass

1. As when the shep - herd calls his sheep, They
2. With joy - ful lips we sing to you Our
3. Is not the cup we bless and share The
4. The mys-t'ry of your pres-ence, Lord, No
5. You give your-self to us, O Lord; Then

Text: CM with refrain; Omer Westendorf, b. 1916.
Music: BICENTENNIAL; Robert Kreutz, 1922–1996.
Text and music ©1977, Archdiocese of Philadelphia.

156

1. know and heed his voice; So when you call your
2. praise and grat - i - tude, That you should count us
3. blood of Christ out-poured? Do not one cup, one
4. mor - tal tongue can tell: Whom all the world can -
5. self - less let us be, To serve each oth - er

(when you call your)

1. know and heed his voice; So when you call your
2. praise and grat - i - tude, That you should count us
3. blood of Christ out-poured? Do not one cup, one
4. mor - tal tongue can tell: Whom all the world can -
5. self - less let us be, To serve each oth - er

(when you call your)

1. fam-'ly, Lord, We fol - low and re - joice.
2. wor-thy, Lord, To share this heav'n-ly food.
3. loaf de - clare Our one - ness in the Lord?
4. not con - tain Comes in our hearts to dwell.
5. in your name In truth and char - i - ty.

1. fam-'ly, Lord, We fol - low and re - joice.
2. wor-thy, Lord, To share this heav'n-ly food.
3. loaf de - clare Our one - ness in the Lord?
4. not con - tain Comes in our hearts to dwell.
5. in your name In truth and char - i - ty.

Give Thanks to the Lord

Text: Dan Schutte, b. 1947.
Music: Dan Schutte.
Text and music ©1992, Daniel L. Schutte. Published by OCP Publications.

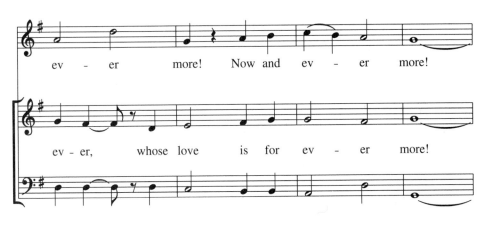

ev - er   more!   Now and   ev - er   more!

ev - er,   whose love   is   for   ev - er   more!

VERSES 3, 6, 9:

3. O   bless the Lord   for   ev - 'ry gift that comes to grace our   way.   And
6. O   bless the Lord   with   mu - sic, ev - 'ry   crea-ture great and small.   And
9. O   bless the Lord   all   peo-ple, for the   mu - sic   of   the skies.   And

D.C. to Vss 4, 7, 10

3. praise the God   of   faith-ful-ness, who comes to light our   day.
6. sing through all   the   a - ges of God's fa - vor to   us   all.
9. tell   the   won - drous sto - ry   of   a   love that nev - er   dies.

Glory and Praise to Our God

REFRAIN: *Spirited, very deliberate (♩ = ca. 162)*

Glo - ry and praise to our God, who a - lone gives light to our days. Man - y are the

bless-ings he bears to those who trust in his ways.

VERSES 1-3:
Descant

Melody

1. We, the daugh - ters and sons of him who
2. In his wis - dom he strength - ens us, like
3. Ev - 'ry mo - ment of ev - 'ry day our

Text: Based on Psalms 65, 66; Dan Schutte, b. 1947.
Music: Dan Schutte.
Text and music ©1976, 1979, Daniel L. Schutte and New Dawn Music.

1. built the val - leys and plains, praise the
2. gold that's test - ed in fire. Though the
3. God is wait - ing to save, al - ways

1. won - ders our God has done in ev - 'ry
2. pow - er of sin pre - vails, our God is
3. read - y to seek the lost, to an - swer

D.C.

1. heart that sings.
2. there to save.
3. those who pray.

VERSE 4:

legato

4. God has wa - tered our bar - ren land and

4. spent his mer - ci - ful rain. Now the

4. riv - ers of life run full for an - y -

D.C. al fine

4. one to drink.

Give Me Jesus

VERSES:

1. In the morn-ing when I rise, in the morn-ing when I
2. Now the jour-ney has be - gun, now the jour-ney has be -
3. When the prize is sure - ly won, when the prize is sure - ly

1. rise, in the morn-ing when I rise, }
2. gun, now the jour-ney has be - gun, } give me Je - sus.
3. won, when the prize is sure - ly won, }

REFRAIN:

Descant (last time only)

Give me Je - sus, Je - sus,

Soprano

Alto

Give me Je - sus, give me Je - sus.

Tenor

Bass

all the world. Give me Je - sus.

You may have all this world. Give me Je - sus.

Text: Refrain and verse 1, Traditional; verses 2–3, James Hansen, b. 1937 ©1992, James Hansen. Published by OCP Publications.
Music: Spiritual; choral arr. by James Hansen ©1992, James Hansen. Published by OCP Publications.

Go, Tell It on the Mountain

REFRAIN:

Go, tell it on the moun-tain, O-ver the hills and ev-'ry-where;

Go, tell it on the moun-tain That Je-sus Christ is born.

Fine

VERSES:

1. While shep-herds kept their watch-ing O'er si-lent flocks at night,
2. The shep-herds feared and trem-bled When high a-bove the earth
3. And lo, when they had heard it, They all bowed down and prayed;
4. Down in a low-ly man-ger The hum-ble Christ was born,

D.C.

1. Be-hold, through-out the heav-ens There shone a ho-ly light.
2. Rang out the an-gel cho-rus That hailed our Sav-ior's birth.
3. They trav-eled on to-geth-er To where the Babe was laid.
4. And God sent us sal-va-tion That bless-ed Christ-mas morn.

Text: 76 76 with refrain; *American Negro Songs and Spirituals;* John W. Work, Jr., 1871–1925, alt.
Music: GO TELL IT; Spiritual; harm. by John W. Work, Jr.

God, Beyond All Names

Text: Bernadette Farrell, b. 1957.
Music: Bernadette Farrell.
Text and music ©1990, Bernadette Farrell. Published by OCP Publications.

God of Day and God of Darkness

1. God of day and God of dark - ness, Now we stand be -
2. Still the na - tions curse the dark - ness, Still the rich op -
3. Show us Christ in one an - oth - er, Make us ser - vants
4. You shall be the path that guides us, You the light that
5. Praise to you in day and dark - ness, You our source and

1. fore the night; As the shad - ows stretch and deep - en, Come and
2. press the poor; Still the earth is bruised and bro - ken By the
3. strong and true; Give us all your love of jus - tice, So we
4. in us burns; Shin - ing deep with - in all peo - ple, Yours the
5. you our end; Praise to you who loves and nur - tures us Like a

1. make our dark - ness bright. All cre - a - tion still is groan - ing
2. ones who still want more. Come and wake us from our sleep - ing,
3. do what you would do. Let us call all peo - ple ho - ly,
4. love that we must learn, For our hearts shall wan - der rest - less
5. fa - ther, moth - er, friend; Grant us all a peace-ful rest - ing,

Descant (vs 5 only)

1. For the dawn - ing of your might, When the Sun of peace and
2. So our hearts can - not ig - nore All your peo - ple lost and
3. Let us pledge our lives a - new, Make us one with all the
4. 'Til they safe to you re - turn; Find - ing you in one an -
5. Let each mind and bod - y mend, So we rise re - freshed to -

1. jus - tice Fills the earth with ra - diant light.
2. bro - ken, All your chil - dren at our door.
3. low - ly, Let us all be one in you.
4. oth - er, We shall all your face dis - cern.
5. mor - row, Hearts re - newed to king-dom tend.

Text: 87 87 D; Marty Haugen, b. 1950 ©1985, G.I.A. Publications, Inc.
Music: BEACH SPRING; *The Sacred Harp*, 1844; choral arr. by Marty Haugen ©1985, G.I.A. Publications, Inc.

God Has Chosen Me

Text: Bernadette Farrell, b. 1957.
Music: Bernadette Farrell.
Text and music ©1990, Bernadette Farrell. Published by OCP Publications.

REFRAIN:

And to tell the world that God's king-dom is near, to re-

move op-pres - sion and break down fear, yes God's

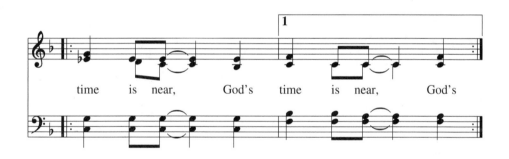

time is near, God's time is near, God's

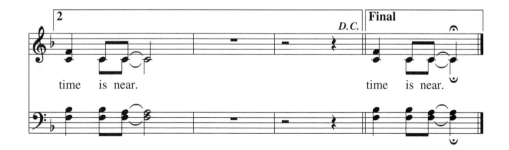

time is near. time is near.

God Rest You Merry, Gentlemen

VERSES:

1. God rest you mer - ry, gen - tle-men, Let noth-ing you dis - may;
2. From God our heav'n-ly Fa - ther A bless-ed an - gel came
3. "Fear not, then," said the an - gel, "Let noth-ing you af - fright;
4. Now to the Lord sing prais - es, All you with-in this place,

1. Re - mem-ber Christ our Sav - ior Was born on Christ-mas Day,
2. And un - to cer - tain shep - herds Brought tid-ings of the same:
3. This day is born a Sav - ior Of Vir-gin pure and bright,
4. And with true love and char - i - ty Each oth - er now em - brace;

1. To save us all from Sa-tan's pow'r When we were gone a - stray.
2. How that in Beth - le - hem was born The Son of God by name.
3. To free all those who trust in him From Sa - tan's pow'r and might."
4. This ho - ly tide of Christ - mas Is filled with heav'n-ly grace.

REFRAIN:

O tid - ings of com - fort and joy, Com-fort and joy;

Text: 86 86 86 with refrain; Trad. English Carol, 18th cent.
Music: GOD REST YOU MERRY; Trad. English Carol; melody fr. *Little Book of Christmas Carols*, ca. 1846.

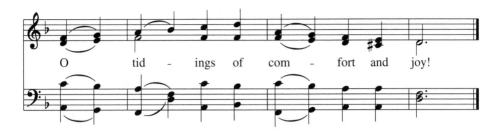

O tid - ings of com - fort and joy!

Good Christians, All, Rejoice

1-3. Good Chris-tians, all, re-joice, With heart and soul and voice;

1. Give ye heed to what we say: Je - sus Christ is born to-day;
2. Now ye hear of end - less bliss; Je - sus Christ was born for this!
3. Now ye need not fear the grave; Je - sus Christ was born to save!

1. Ox and ass be - fore him bow, And he is in the man-ger now.
2. He has o-pened heav-en's door, And we are blest for ev - er-more.
3. Calls you one and calls you all, To gain his ev - er - last-ing hall.

1. Christ is born to - day! Christ is born to - day!
2. Christ was born for this! Christ was born for this!
3. Christ was born to save! Christ was born to save!

Text: 66 77 78 55; Latin and German, 14th cent.; tr. by John M. Neale, 1818–1866, alt.
Music: IN DULCI JUBILO; Klug's *Geistliche Lieder*, Wittenberg, 1533; harm. adapt. fr. John Stainer, 1840–1901.

Hail, Holy Queen

1. Hail, ho-ly Queen en-throned a-bove, O Ma - ri - a! Hail,
2. Our life, our sweet-ness here be-low, O Ma - ri - a! Our
3. And when our life-breath leaves __ us, O Ma - ri - a! Show

1. moth-er of mer-cy and of love, O Ma - ri - a!
2. hope __ in sor-row and in woe, O Ma - ri - a! } Tri-umph, all ye
3. us __ thy Son, Christ Je - sus, O Ma - ri - a!

1-3. cher-u-bim, Sing with us, ye ser-a-phim! Heav'n and earth re-

sing with us, ye

1-3. sound the hymn: Sal - ve, Sal - ve, Sal - ve Re-gi - na!

Text: 84 84 with refrain; *Salve, Regina, Coelitum;* ca. 1080; tr. anon. in *Roman Hymnal,* 1884.
Music: SALVE REGINA COELITUM; Melchior Ludwig's *Choralmelodien zum Heiligen Gesänge,* 1808; choral arr. by
   Randall DeBruyn, b. 1947 ©1995, OCP Publications.

Hail Mary: Gentle Woman

Fine

dove,   teach us wis- dom;   teach us love.

VERSE 1:

1. You were cho - sen   by the Fa- ther;   you were cho -

1. sen   for the Son.   You were cho - sen   from all

D.S.

1. wom- en   and for wom- an,   shin-ing one.

VERSE 2:

2. Bless-ed are you   a-mong wom-en,   blest in turn

2.   all wom-en, too.   Blest are they   with peace-ful

D.S. al fine

2. spir-its.   Bless-ed they   with gen- tle hearts.

Hail, Redeemer, King Divine

VERSES:

1. Hail, re-deem-er, king di-vine! Priest and lamb, the throne is thine;
2. King of ev-er-last-ing might! Be to us e-ter-nal light,

1. King whose reign shall nev-er cease, Prince of ev-er-last-ing peace.
2. Till in peace each na-tion rings With thy prais-es, king of kings.

REFRAIN:

An-gels, saints and na-tions sing: "Praised be Je-sus Christ, our king;

Lord of earth and sky and sea, King of love on Cal-va-ry."

Text: 77 77 D; Patrick Brennen, 1877–1951 © Burns and Oates, Ltd., England.
Music: ST. GEORGE'S WINDSOR; George J. Elvey, 1816-1893.

Hail the Day That Sees Him Rise

1. Hail the day that sees him rise, Al - le - lu - ia!
2. There for him high tri - umph waits; Al - le - lu - ia!
3. High-est heav'n its Lord re - ceives, Al - le - lu - ia!

1. To his throne a - bove the skies; Al - le - lu - ia!
2. Lift your heads, e - ter - nal gates! Al - le - lu - ia!
3. Yet he loves the earth he leaves; Al - le - lu - ia!

1. Christ the Lamb for sin - ners giv'n, Al - le - lu - ia!
2. He has con - quered death and sin; Al - le - lu - ia!
3. Though re - turn - ing to his throne, Al - le - lu - ia!

1. En - ters now the high - est heav'n! Al - le - lu - ia!
2. Take the King of glo - ry in! Al - le - lu - ia!
3. Still he calls us all his own. Al - le - lu - ia!

Text: 77 77 with alleluias; Charles Wesley, 1707–1788.
Music: LLANFAIR; Robert Williams, 1781–1821; choral arr. by Randall DeBruyn, b. 1947 ©1990, OCP Publications.

Hark! The Herald Angels Sing

1. Hark! the her - ald an - gels sing: "Glo - ry to the new-born King;
2. Christ, by high - est heav'n a - dored, Christ, the ev - er - last - ing Lord.
3. Hail the heav'n-born Prince of Peace! Hail the Sun of righ-teous-ness!

1. Peace on earth, and mer - cy mild, God and sin - ners rec - on - ciled!"
2. Late in time, be - hold him come, Off-spring of a vir-gin's womb.
3. Light and life to all he brings, Ris'n with heal - ing in his wings.

1. Joy - ful, all ye na - tions, rise, Join the tri - umph of the skies;
2. Veiled in flesh the God-head see! Hail th'in - car - nate De - i - ty!
3. Mild he lays his glo - ry by, Born that we no more may die,

1. With an - gel - ic hosts pro - claim: "Christ is born in Beth - le - hem!"
2. Pleased as man with us to dwell, Je - sus our Em - man - u - el.
3. Born to raise us from the earth, Born to give us sec - ond birth.

Text: 77 77 D with refrain; Charles Wesley, 1707–1788, alt.
Music: MENDELSSOHN; Felix Mendelssohn, 1809–1847; adapt. by William H. Cummings, 1831–1915, alt.

176

REFRAIN: Parts

Hark! the her-ald an-gels sing, "Glo-ry to the new-born King."

Go to 40

Hear Us Now, Our God and Father

1. Hear us now, our God and Father, Send your
2. Give them joy to light-en sor-row! Give them
3. May the grace of Christ, our Sav-ior, And the

1. Spir-it from a-bove On this Chris-tian man and
2. hope to bright-en life! Go with them to face the
3. Fa-ther's bound-less love, With the Ho-ly Spir-it's

1. wom-an Who here make their vows of love!
2. mor-row, Stay with them in ev-'ry strife.
3. fa-vor Rest up-on them from a-bove.

1. Bind their hearts in true de-vo-tion End-less as the
2. As your Word has prom-ised, ev-er Fill them with your
3. Thus may they a-bide in un-ion With each oth-er

Text: 87 87 D; Verses 1–2, Harry N. Huxhold, b. 1922 ©1978, *Lutheran Book of Worship*. Reprinted by permission of Augsburg Fortress. Verse 3, John Newton, 1725–1807, alt.
Music: HYFRYDOL; Rowland H. Prichard, 1811–1887.

1. sea - shore's sands, Bound - less as the deep - est
2. strength and grace, So that each may serve the
3. and the Lord, And pos - sess in sweet com -

1. o - ceans, Blest and sealed by your own hands.
2. oth - er Till they see you face to face.
3. mun - ion Joys which earth can - not af - ford.

Here I Am, Lord

VERSES: *Moderate tempo, with majesty (♩ = 80)*

1. I, the Lord of sea and sky, I have heard my peo-ple cry.
2. I, the Lord of snow and rain, I have borne my peo-ple's pain.
3. I, the Lord of wind and flame, I will tend the poor and lame.

3. Ah _____ My hand will save.

1. All who dwell in dark and sin my hand will save.
2. I have wept for love of them. They turn a-way.
3. I will set a feast for them. My hand will save.

3. Fin - est bread I will pro-vide till their hearts be

1. I who made the stars of night, I will make their
2. I will break their hearts of stone, give them hearts for
3. Fin-est bread I will pro-vide till their hearts be

3. sat - is - fied. I will give my life to them.

1. dark - ness bright. Who will bear my light to them?
2. love a - lone. I will speak my word to them.
3. sat - is - fied. I will give my life to them.

Text: Based on Isaiah 6; Dan Schutte, b. 1947.
Music: Dan Schutte.
Text and music ©1981, Daniel L. Schutte and New Dawn Music.

REFRAIN:

He Is the Lord

REFRAIN: *With strength*

Sing to the Lord with shouts of joy, let all cre-a-tion re-joice! Come join the song of praise to our God! He is the Lord! He is the Lord!

Fine

VERSES:

Melody

Harmony

1. Cry out with joy to the Lord, ___ all you na - tions! _____ Serve the Lord.
2. Give thanks to God ___ our Fa - ther for his love. _____ Bless our God.
3. Great is the King of cre - a - tion; he is faith - ful. _____ Praise his name.

1. Serve the Lord. _____ Come be - fore him sing - ing for joy! _____
2. Bless our God. _____ His mer - cy is for - ev - er! _____
3. Praise his name. _____ Sing of his sal - va - tion! _____

D.C.

Text: David Haas, b. 1957.
Music: David Haas; choral arr. by Craig Kingsbury, b. 1952.
Text and music ©1981, 1982, OCP Publications.

Hold Me in Life

REFRAIN:

Hold me in life for you are my safe - ty, al - ways my eyes are look - ing for you.

VERSES:

1. Be - cause you are just who you are, don't pass me by, but show me your mer - cy; I will wait for you all ___ my life.
2. Are you the one who is to come, or must we wait and fol - low some oth - er? Lord, my God, I am cer - tain of you.
3. You gave your word to this our world: you are my song, the God of my glad - ness; my de - sire goes ___ out ___ to you.

Fine

D.C.

Text: Psalm 25; Huub Oosterhuis, b. 1933; tr. by David Smith, b. 1933 and Forrest Ingram, b. 1938.
Music: Bernard Huijbers, b. 1922.
Text and music ©1967, Gooi en Sticht, bv., Baarn, The Netherlands. Exclusive agent for English-language countries: OCP Publications.

Holy Darkness

REFRAIN: *Peacefully (♩ = 52)*

Ho - ly dark-ness, bless - ed night, heav - en's an - swer

hid-den from our sight. As we a - wait you, O God of

si - lence, we em-brace your ho - ly night. night.

VERSES 1-3: *Slightly faster*

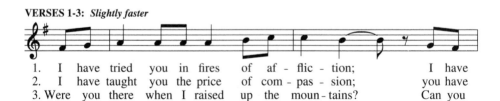

1. I have tried you in fires of af - flic - tion; I have
2. I have taught you the price of com - pas - sion; you have
3. Were you there when I raised up the moun - tains? Can you

Text: Inspired by St. John of the Cross; Dan Schutte, b. 1947.
Music: Dan Schutte; choral arr. by Bob Harrold.
Text and music ©1988, 1993, Daniel L. Schutte. Published by OCP Publications.

1. taught your soul to grieve. In the bar - ren soil of your
2. stood be - fore the grave. Though my love can seem like a
3. guide the morn - ing star? Does the hawk take flight when you

rit. *molto rit.* **D.C.**

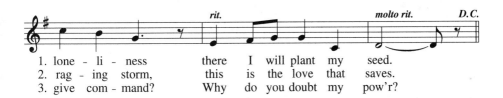

1. lone - li - ness there I will plant my seed.
2. rag - ing storm, this is the love that saves.
3. give com - mand? Why do you doubt my pow'r?

VERSES 4-5: *Faster, with more energy*

4. In your deep - est hour of dark - ness I will
5. As the watch - man waits for morn - ing, and the

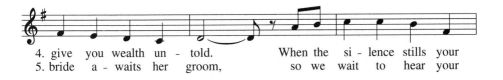

4. give you wealth un - told. When the si - lence stills your
5. bride a - waits her groom, so we wait to hear your

rit. *molto rit.* **D.C.**

4. spir - it, will my rich - es fill your soul.
5. foot - steps as we rest be - neath your moon.

Holy God, We Praise Thy Name

Text: 78 78 77 with repeat; *Te Deum laudamus,* ca. 3rd cent.; *Grosser Gott, wir loben dich,* tr. ascr. to Ignaz Franz, 1719–1790; tr. by
Clarence A. Walworth, 1820–1900.
Music: GROSSER GOTT; *Katholisches Gesangbuch,* Vienna, ca. 1774.

Holy, Holy, Holy

1. Ho-ly, Ho-ly, Ho - ly! Lord ___ God Al-might - y!
2. Ho-ly, Ho-ly, Ho - ly! All the saints a - dore thee,
3. Ho-ly, Ho-ly, Ho - ly! Though the dark-ness hide thee,
4. Ho-ly, Ho-ly, Ho - ly! Lord ___ God Al-might - y!

1. Ear - ly in the morn - ing our song shall rise to thee:
2. Cast - ing down their gold - en crowns a - round the glass - y sea;
3. Though the eye made blind by sin thy glo - ry may not see,
4. All thy works shall praise thy Name in earth and sky and sea;

1. Ho-ly, Ho-ly, Ho - ly! Mer - ci - ful and might - y,
2. Cher - u - bim and ser - a - phim fall - ing down be - fore thee,
3. On - ly thou art ho - ly; there is none be - side thee,
4. Ho-ly, Ho-ly, Ho - ly! Mer - ci - ful and might - y,

1. God in three Per - sons, bless - ed Trin - i - ty.
2. Which were, and are, and ev - er - more shall be.
3. Per - fect in Pow'r, in love, and pur - i - ty.
4. God in three Per - sons, bless - ed Trin - i - ty.

Text: 11 12 12 10; Reginald Heber, 1783–1826, alt.
Music: NICAEA; John B. Dykes, 1823–1876.

187

Holy Is His Name

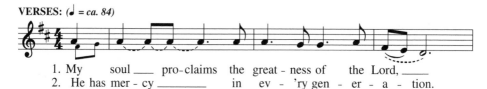

VERSES: (♩ = ca. 84)

1. My soul ___ pro-claims the great-ness of the Lord, ___
2. He has mer - cy ___ in ev - 'ry gen - er - a - tion.

1. and my spir - it ___ ex - alts in God my Sav - ior.
2. He has ___ re - vealed ___ his pow - er and his glo - ry.

1. For he has looked with mer - cy on my low - li - ness,
2. He has cast down the might - y in their ar - ro - gance,

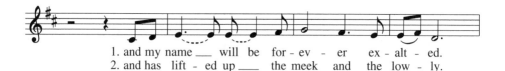

1. and my name ___ will be for - ev - er ex - alt - ed.
2. and has lift - ed up ___ the meek and the low - ly.

Descant (Vs 2 only)

2. He has come to Is - ra - el;

Melody

1. For the might - y God has done great things for me,
2. He has come to help his ser - vant Is - ra - el;

Text: *Magnificat*, based on Luke 1:46–55; John Michael Talbot, b. 1954.
Music: John Michael Talbot; choral arr. by Phil Perkins, b.1948 and Rick Modlin, b.1966.

2. re-mem - ber   our   fa-thers.

1. and his mer-cy _____ will reach from age to   age. ___
2. he   re-mem - bers __ his prom-ise to our fa-thers.

*REFRAIN:

Descant (Final time)

Ho - ly,   ho -

Soprano
Alto

And   ho - ly,   ho -
                ho

Tenor
Bass

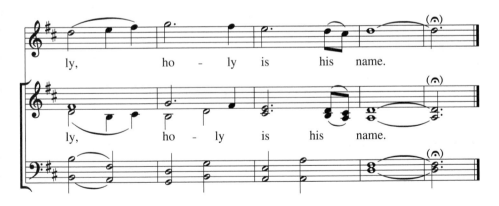

ly,   ho - ly is   his   name.

ly,   ho - ly is   his   name.

*Repeat Final Refrain.

189

Hosea

VERSES 1, 2: *Gently, with movement*

1. Come back to me with all your heart.
2. The wil-der-ness will lead ___ you

1. Don't let fear keep us a-part.
2. to your heart where I will speak. In -

1. Trees do bend, though straight and tall;
2. teg-ri-ty and jus-tice with

1. so must we to oth-ers call.
2. ten-der-ness you shall know.

Text: Based on Hosea; Weston Priory, Gregory Norbet, OSB, b. 1940.
Music: Weston Priory, Gregory Norbet, OSB; choral arr. by Craig S. Kingsbury, b. 1952.
Text and music ©1972, 1986, from the recording *Listen*, The Benedictine Foundation of the State of Vermont, Inc., Weston, VT.

℟ REFRAIN: *SATB*

Long have I wait-ed for your com - ing home to me and liv - ing

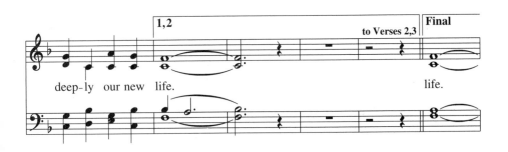

1,2   **to Verses 2,3**   **Final**

deep-ly our new life.   life.

2 *Fine*   **VERSE 3:** *women*

3. You shall sleep   se - cure with peace;

D. S. al fine

3.   faith - ful - ness   will be your joy.

faith - ful - ness will be your joy.

How Can I Keep from Singing

Text: 87 87 with refrain; attr. to Robert Lowry, 1826–1899, alt; verse 3, Doris Plenn ©1957 by SANGA MUSIC, INC. All rights reserved. Used with permission.
Music: HOW CAN I KEEP; Quaker Hymn; attr. to Robert Lowry; choral arr. by Randall DeBruyn, b. 1947 ©1991, OCP Publications.

REFRAIN:

How Great Thou Art

VERSES:

1. O Lord my God! When I in awe-some won - der
2. When through the woods and for - est glades I wan - der
3. And when I think that God, his Son not spar - ing,
4. When Christ shall come with shout of ac - cla - ma - tion

1. Con - si - der all the *worlds thy hands have made,
2. And hear the birds sing sweet - ly in the trees;
3. Sent him to die, I scarce can take it in;
4. And take me home, what joy shall fill my heart!

1. I see the stars, I hear the *roll - ing thun - der,
2. When I look down from lof - ty moun-tain gran - deur
3. That on the cross, my bur - den glad - ly bear - ing,
4. Then I shall bow in hum - ble ad - o - ra - tion

1. Thy pow'r through-out the u - ni - verse dis - played,
2. And hear the brook and feel the gen - tle breeze;
3. He bled and died to take a - way my sin;
4. And there pro - claim, my God, how great thou art!

*Author's original words are "works" and "mighty."

Text: 11 10 11 10 with refrain; Carl Boberg, 1850−1940; tr. by Stuart K. Hine, 1899−1989.
Music: O STORE GUD; Swedish Folk Melody, adapt. by Stuart K. Hine.

REFRAIN:

Then sings my soul, my Sav-ior God to thee; How great thou art, how great thou art! Then sings my soul, my Sav-ior God to thee; How great thou art, how great thou art!

How Lovely Is Your Dwelling Place

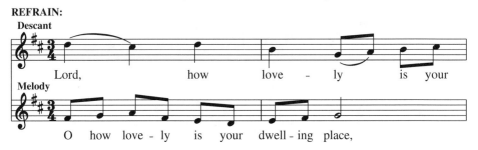

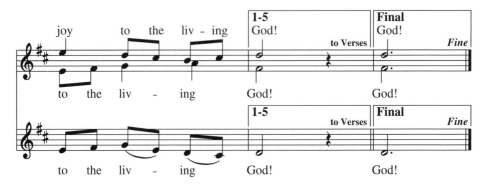

*Optional divisi or top part descant.

Text: Based on Psalm 84; Randall DeBruyn, b. 1947.
Music: Randall DeBruyn.
Text and music ©1981, OCP Publications.

VERSES:

Melody

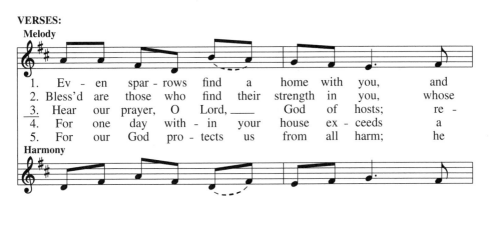

1. Ev - en spar - rows find a home with you, and
2. Bless'd are those who find their strength in you, whose
3. Hear our prayer, O Lord, _____ God of hosts; re -
4. For one day with - in your house ex - ceeds a
5. For our God pro - tects us from all harm; he

Harmony

1. swal-lows lay their young to rest. Bless - ed are _____ those who
2. hearts are high-ways for your will. Bring-ing joy to those a-
3. ceive our lives in - to your hands! Look in - to the hearts of
4. thou-sand spent a - way from you. We would rath - er serve with-
5. gives his fa - vor and his love. All good things will come to

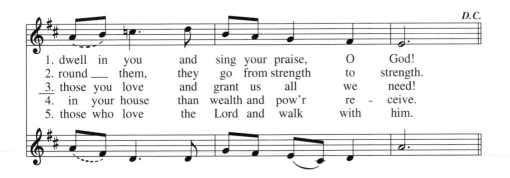

D.C.

1. dwell in you and sing your praise, O God!
2. round _____ them, they go from strength to strength.
3. those you love and grant us all we need!
4. in your house than wealth and pow'r re - ceive.
5. those who love the Lord and walk with him.

How Lovely Is Your Dwelling Place

Text: Psalm 84; refrain and verses 1,3 and 4 ©1963, The Grail (England). Used with permission of G.I.A. Publications, Inc., agent.
Verses 2 and 5, Christopher Walker, b. 1947 ©1991, Christopher Walker. Published by OCP Publications.
Music: Christopher Walker ©1991, Christopher Walker. Published by OCP Publications.

VERSES:

Più mosso **Cantor/Semichorus:**

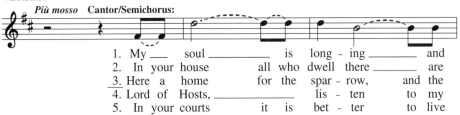

1. My __ soul ____ is long - ing ____ and
2. In your house all who dwell there ____ are
3. Here a home for the spar - row, and the
4. Lord of Hosts, ____ lis - ten to my
5. In your courts it is bet - ter to live

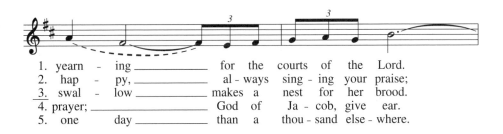

1. yearn - ing ____ for the courts of the Lord.
2. hap - py, ____ al - ways sing - ing your praise;
3. swal - low ____ makes a nest for her brood.
4. prayer; ____ God of Ja - cob, give ear.
5. one day ____ than a thou - sand else - where.

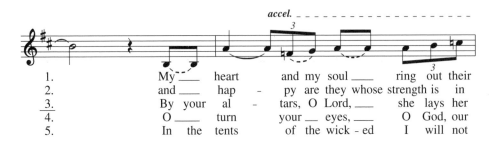

accel.

1. My __ heart and my soul __ ring out their
2. and __ hap - py are they whose strength is in
3. By your al - tars, O Lord, __ she lays her
4. O __ turn your __ eyes, __ O God, our
5. In the tents of the wick - ed I will not

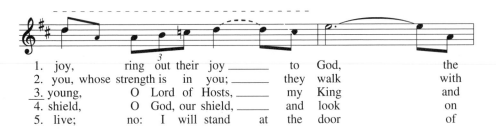

1. joy, ring out their joy ____ to God, the
2. you, whose strength is in you; ____ they walk with
3. young, O Lord of Hosts, ____ my King and
4. shield, O God, our shield, ____ and look on
5. live; no: I will stand at the door of

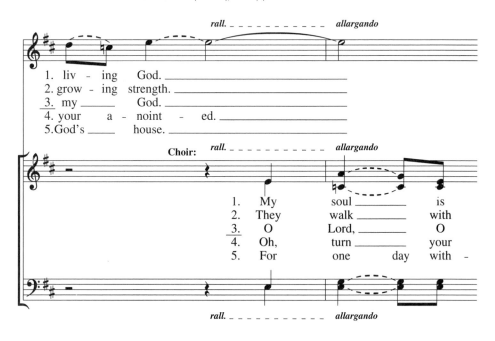

Humbly, Lord, We Worship You

1. Hum-bly, Lord, we wor-ship you, our E-ter-nal King.
2. Je-sus, Lord, we of-fer you ev-'ry act this day.
3. Lord, for-give us all our faults, oth-ers we for-give.
4. May we love you in each soul and each soul in you;

1. You who died to give us life, hear us as we sing.
2. May we live our love for you and your will o-bey.
3. May we strive with all our souls, Chris-tian lives to live.
4. One in our e-ter-nal goal, one in all we do.

1-4. Je-sus, God and Lord of all, come to us, we pray.

1-4. Thus u-nit-ed in your love, may we live this day.

Text: 12 12 12 12; Jeanne Frolick, SFCC ©1973, Jeanne Frolick, SFCC. Published by OCP Publications.
Music: ADORO TE DEVOTE; Mode V, Paris Processional, 1697; choral arr. by Randall DeBruyn, b. 1947 ©1990, OCP Publications.

I Am the Bread of Life

VERSES:

1.   I am the Bread of life. ___ You who come to me
2. The bread that ___ I will give ___ is my flesh for the
3. Un - less ___ you ___ eat ___ of the flesh of the
4. ♪ I am the Res - ur - rec - tion, ___ I ___
5. Yes, Lord, ___ I be - lieve ___ that ___ you ___

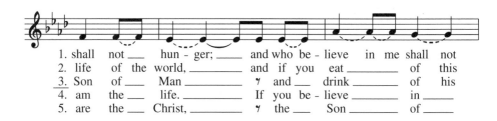

1. shall not ___ hun - ger; ___ and who be - lieve in me shall not
2. life of the world, ___ and if you eat ___ of this
3. Son of ___ Man ___ ♪ and ___ drink ___ of his
4. am the ___ life. ___ If you be - lieve ___ in ___
5. are the ___ Christ, ___ ♪ the ___ Son ___ of ___

1. thirst. ___ No one can come to me un -
2. bread, ___ you shall ___ live for ev - er,
3. blood, and drink ___ of his blood, you
4. me, ___ e - ven though you die, ___
5. God, ___ who ___ have ___ come in -

Soprano

REFRAIN:

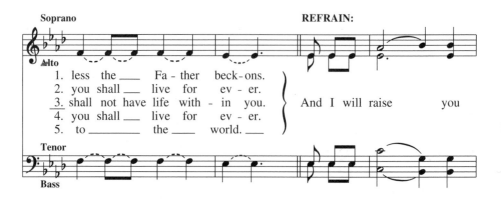

Alto

1. less the ___ Fa - ther beck - ons.
2. you shall ___ live for ev - er.
3. shall not have life with - in you.
4. you shall ___ live for ev - er.
5. to ___ the ___ world. ___

And I will raise you

Tenor

Bass

Text: Based on John 6, 11; Suzanne Toolan, SM, b. 1927.
Music: Suzanne Toolan, SM.
Text and music ©1970, G.I.A. Publications, Inc.

up,   and I will raise   you   up,   and I will

raise   you   up   on   the   last   day.

I Am the Light of the World

REFRAIN:

"I am the Light of the world," says the Lord,

"They who fol-low me will have the light of

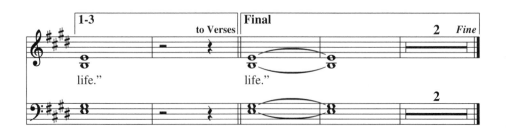

1-3 *to Verses* | Final | 2 *Fine*

life." life."

VERSES 1, 2:

Descant

Melody

1. "A - rise," says the Lord, ? "Have no fear with -
2. ? "Walk in the light, there is no cause to

1. in you; for in my pres - ence there will be no
2. stum - ble; ? I have come to light the path be -

Text: Based on John 8:12, Matthew 5:14, Ephesians 5:14, John 2:10; Greg Hayakawa, b. 1953.
Music: Greg Hayakawa; choral arr. by Craig S. Kingsbury, b. 1952.
Text and music ©1978, 1979, 1985, Greg Hayakawa. Published by OCP Publications.

D.C.

1. dark - ness.   I   am   the Light   of the world."
2. - fore   you.   I   am   the Light   of the world."

VERSE 3:

3. "Lis-ten   to   my   words;   they   are from the One who

3. sent   me: For you,   my friends, are   called to share   God's

D.C.

3. glo - ry.   You   are the Light   of the world."

I Have Loved You

REFRAIN: *Lyric and expansive* (♩ = 72)

Text: Based on Jeremiah 31:3, Psalm 24:3; Michael Joncas, b. 1951.
Music: Michael Joncas.
Text and music ©1979, New Dawn Music.

VERSES 1, 2:

Melody

1-2. Seek the face of the Lord and long for him:

Harmony

D.C.

1. he will bring you his light and his peace.
2. he will bring you his joy and his hope.

VERSE 3:

S/Melody

A

3. Seek the face of the Lord and long for him:

T

B

D.C.

3. he will bring you his care and his love.

I Am the Living Bread

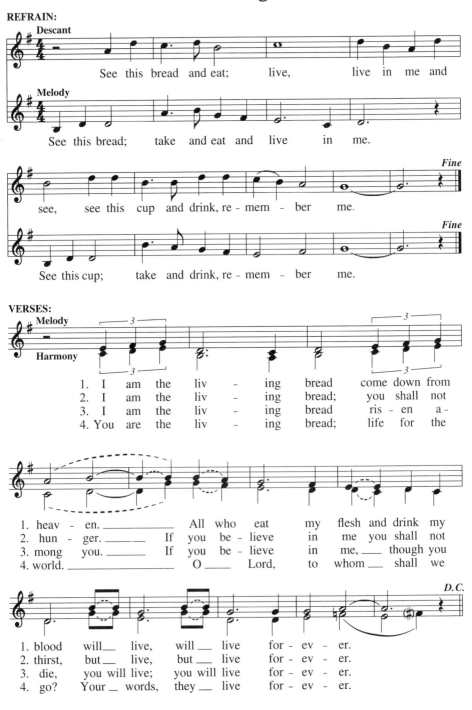

Text: Based on John 6; David Haas, b. 1957.
Music: David Haas.
Text and music ©1985, David Haas. Published by OCP Publications.

I Heard the Voice of Jesus

1. I heard the voice of Je-sus say, "Come un-to me and rest;
2. I heard the voice of Je-sus say, "Be-hold, I free-ly give
3. I heard the voice of Je-sus say, "I am this dark world's light;

1. Lay down, thou wea-ry one, lay down Thy head up-on my breast."
2. The liv-ing wa-ter; thirst-y one, Stoop down, and drink, and live."
3. Look un-to me, thy morn shall rise, And all thy day be bright."

1. I came to Je-sus as I was, Wea-ry and worn and sad;
2. I came to Je-sus, and I drank Of that life-giv-ing stream;
3. I looked to Je-sus, and I found In him my — star, my sun;

1. I found in him a rest-ing place, And he has made me glad.
2. My thirst was quenched, my soul re-vived, And now I live in him.
3. And in that light of life I'll walk Till trav-'ling days are done.

Text: CMD; Horatius Bonar, 1808–1889.
Music: KINGSFOLD; Trad. English Melody; adapt. by Ralph Vaughan Williams, 1872–1958 © Oxford University Press, London.

I Know That My Redeemer Lives

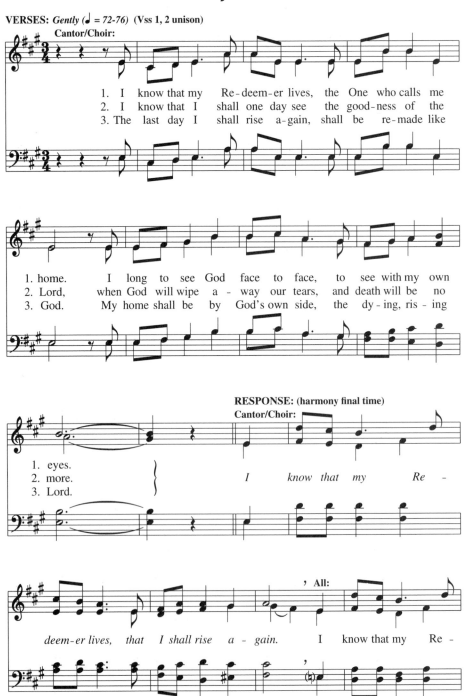

Text: Based on Job 19, Psalm 27, Isaiah 25; Scott Soper.
Music: Scott Soper.
Text and music ©1990, Scott Soper. Published by OCP Publications.

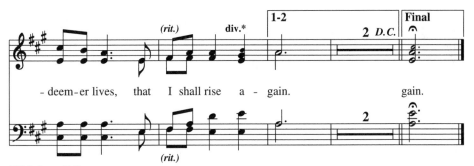

- deem-er lives, that I shall rise a - gain.   gain.

*Melody - middle notes

I Know That My Redeemer Lives

1. I know that my Re - deem - er lives!
2. He lives tri - um - phant from the grave;
3. He lives to si - lence all my fears;
4. He lives all glo - ry to his name!

1. What joy the blest as - sur - ance gives!
2. He lives e - ter - nal - ly to save;
3. He lives to wipe a - way my tears;
4. He lives my Sav - ior, still the same;

1. He lives, he lives, who once was dead;
2. He lives in maj - es - ty a - bove;
3. He lives to calm my trou - bled heart;
4. What joy this blest as - sur - ance gives;

1. He lives my ev - er - liv - ing head!
2. He lives to guide his church in love.
3. He lives all bless - ings to im - part.
4. I know that my Re - deem - er lives!

Text: LM; Based on Job 19:25; Samuel Medley, 1738–1799.
Music: DUKE STREET; John Hatton, ca. 1710–1793.

I Sing the Mighty Power of God

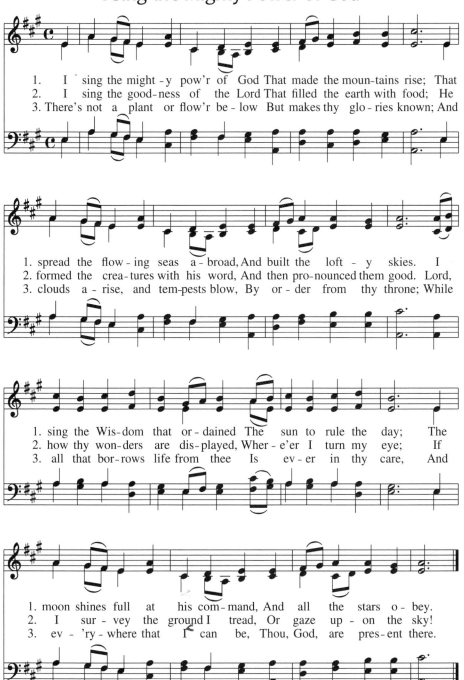

1. I sing the might-y pow'r of God That made the moun-tains rise; That
2. I sing the good-ness of the Lord That filled the earth with food; He
3. There's not a plant or flow'r be-low But makes thy glo-ries known; And

1. spread the flow-ing seas a-broad, And built the loft-y skies. I
2. formed the crea-tures with his word, And then pro-nounced them good. Lord,
3. clouds a-rise, and tem-pests blow, By or-der from thy throne; While

1. sing the Wis-dom that or-dained The sun to rule the day; The
2. how thy won-ders are dis-played, Wher-e'er I turn my eye; If
3. all that bor-rows life from thee Is ev-er in thy care, And

1. moon shines full at his com-mand, And all the stars o-bey.
2. I sur-vey the ground I tread, Or gaze up-on the sky!
3. ev-'ry-where that I can be, Thou, God, are pres-ent there.

Text: CMD; Isaac Watts, 1674–1748, alt.
Music: ELLACOMBE; *Gesangbuch der Herzogl. Wirtembergischen katholischen Hofkapelle*, 1784, alt.

I Lift Up My Soul

REFRAIN: *Slowly and smoothly (♩ = 66)*

Descant

To you, Yah-weh, I lift up my soul, O my

Melody

To you, Yah-weh, I lift up my soul, O my

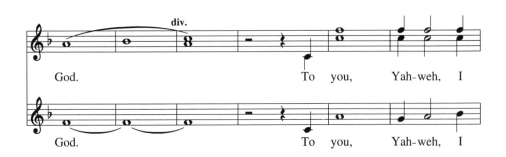

God. To you, Yah-weh, I

God. To you, Yah-weh, I

lift up my soul, O my God. *(⌒) Fine*

lift up my soul, O my God. *(⌒) Fine*

VERSES 1, 3:

1. Yah - weh,_____ show your ways to me.
3. All day long I hope in your good-ness. Re -

Text: Based on Psalm 25; Tim Manion.
Music: Tim Manion.
Text and music ©1976, 1979, Timothy J. Manion and New Dawn Music.

1. Teach me your paths and keep me in the ways of your
3. -mem-ber your love, the love that you prom-ised long a-

1. truth, for you ___ are the God that ___
3. go, and the kind-ness that you gave from of

1. saves me. ___
3. old. ___

VERSE 2:

2. The Lord is so good, so ho-ly,

2. sin-ners find the way, and in all that is right he guides the

2. hum-ble. The poor he leads in his

2. path-ways.

I, the Lord

I, the Lord, am with you, al - ways by your side.

Come and take my hand, for I will lead you home. Fol-low

me, fol-low me.

Fol-low me, fol-low me.

Text: Based on John 6:35–58; Tom Kendzia.
Music: Tom Kendzia.
Text and music ©1983, Tom Kendzia and North American Liturgy Resources (N.A.L.R.).

VERSE 1:

Solo 1. I am the res - ur - rec - tion, and I am the life; if

slight rall.- -

D.C.

1. you be-lieve in me, you shall live for - ev - er.

VERSE 2: SA

Soprano (Melody)

Alto

2. You shall have new life and live it to the full.

Tenor

Bass

slight rall.- -

D.C.

2. Turn your sor - row in - to joy, for life has just be - gun.

I Will Lift Up My Eyes

REFRAIN:

Descant: I will lift up my eyes at the name

Soprano / Alto: I will lift up my eyes at the name

of the one who knows me well. *Fine*

of the one who knows me well. *Fine*

VERSE 1:

1. You are my God, whom I seek with my life; for you I

1. thirst, as the dry earth for wa - ter. Life - less and

1. parched, with-out you I am no - where, no one at all. *D.C.*

Text: Based on Psalm 63; Tom Conry, b. 1951.
Music: Tom Conry; choral arr. by Randall DeBruyn, b. 1947.
Text and music ©1984, TEAM Publications. Published by OCP Publications.

VERSE 2:

2. Thus have I seen you in your ho-ly house, with my own eyes, how faith-ful and

2. sure. More than my life, your mer-cy en-dures long-er than time.

VERSE 3:

Melody

Harmony

3. Thus shall I bless you while I am a-live; call-ing on you, my breath and my

3. bread. And with a song through day and the dark-ness cling-ing to you.

VERSE 4:

4. And I shall see that day when your jus-tice and pow'r will

4. break the chains that bind me. And mine en-e-mies' lies strewn

4. brok-en and emp-ty: your might-y hand, that aw-ful grace.

I Will Not Die

Text: Tom Conry, b. 1951.
Music: Tom Conry.
Text and music ©1984, 1990, TEAM Publications. Published by OCP Publications.

Soprano/Alto

I will not die be-fore I've lived to see that land; firm as the

Tenor/Bass

I will not

earth, your own prom-ise. I'll not let go un-til I've

die be-fore I've lived to see that land; firm as the earth,

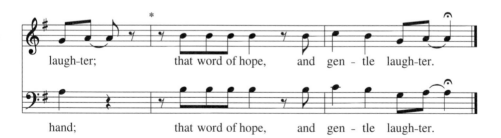

held it in my hand; that word of hope, and gen - tle

your own prom-ise. I'll not let go un-til I've held it in my

laugh-ter; that word of hope, and gen - tle laugh-ter.

hand; that word of hope, and gen - tle laugh-ter.

*Accompaniment books end here. Last 2 bars must be repeated to match choral canon.

Immaculate Mary

VERSES:

1. Im - mac - u - late Ma - ry, your prais - es we sing; You
2. In heav - en the bless - ed your glo - ry pro - claim; On
3. We pray for our Moth - er, the Church up - on earth; And

1. reign now in heav - en with Je - sus our King.
2. earth we, your chil - dren, in - voke your fair name.
3. bless, Ho - ly Ma - ry, the land of our birth.

REFRAIN:

A - ve, A - ve, A - ve, Ma - ri - a!

A - ve, A - ve, Ma - ri - a!

Text: 11 11 with refrain; Anon. in *Parochial Hymn Book*, Boston, 1897; rev. of *Hail Virgin of Virgins*; Jeremiah Cummings, 1814–1866.
Music: LOURDES HYMN; Trad. Pyrenean Melody pub. Grenoble, 1882; alt. by Augustus E. Tozer, 1857–1910; choral arr. by Randall
 DeBruyn, b. 1947 ©1990, OCP Publications.

In Christ There Is No East or West

1. In Christ there is no east or west, In him no south or north, But one great fam - 'ly bound by love Through - out the whole wide earth.

2. In him shall true hearts ev - 'ry - where Their high com - mun - ion find; His ser - vice is the gold - en cord Close - bind - ing hu - man - kind.

3. Join hands, dis - ci - ples in the faith, What - e'er your race may be! Who serve each oth - er in Christ's love Are sure - ly kin to me.

4. In Christ now meet both east and west, In him meet south and north, All Christ - ly souls are one in him, Through - out the whole wide earth.

Text: CM; Galatians 3:28; John Oxenham, 1852–1941.
Music: MC KEE; Spiritual; adapt. and harm. by Harry T. Burleigh, 1866–1949.

In Perfect Charity

Gently; with feeling (♩ = 60)

1. O most high and glo-rious God, cast your
2. O most high and glo-rious God, o-pen
3. Then most high and thank-ful praise I will

1. light in-to the dark-ness of my heart. Give me right
2. wide the door that leads me to your love. Give me your
3. sing un-to the glo-ry of your name. To Fa-ther,

1. faith, and cer-tain hope, and __ per-fect, per-fect char-i-
2. firm, yet gen-tle strength; may I live that per-fect char-i-
3. Son, and Spir-it bright, Liv-ing Pres-ence, Per-fect Char-i-

1. ty. Give me true in-sight, Lord, and wis-dom, that
2. ty. Lord, may your peace be ev-er in me, that
3. ty. Praise to the Love that shines in splen-dor, that

Text: Verse 1, St. Francis of Assisi, 1182–1226, alt. by Randall DeBruyn, b. 1947; verses 2–3, Randall DeBruyn.
Music: Randall DeBruyn.
Text and music ©1982, Randall DeBruyn. Published by OCP Publications. From Leonardo Difilippis' *St. Francis: Troubadour of God's Peace.*

1. I may al - ways live with - in your ev - er ho - ly
2. I may al - ways seek to serve your chil - dren here on
3. lights the path - ways of my heart, and brings me close to

1. will. Lord, may your light with - in me
2. earth; that I may find my home with
3. you. O Ho - ly One, in - vite me

1. burn, shin - ing out in per - fect char - i - ty.
2. you, and ___ live in per - fect char - i - ty.
3. in, where you live in per - fect char - i - ty.

Isaiah 49

Text: Based on Isaiah 49:15; Carey Landry, b. 1944.
Music: Carey Landry; choral arr. by Louise Anderson.
Text and music ©1975, Carey Landry and North American Liturgy Resources (N.A.L.R.).

VERSE 2:

2. Does a moth-er   for - get   her   ba - by?

2. Or   a   wo-man   the child with-in   her   womb?

2. Yet   e – ven   if   these for - get, yes,   e - ven   if

(Repeat Verse 1)
D.C. al fine

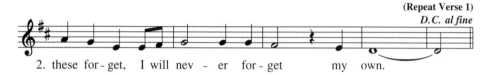

2. these for - get,   I will nev – er   for - get   my   own.

227

It Came upon the Midnight Clear

1. It came up-on the mid-night clear, That glo-rious
2. Still through the clo-ven skies they come With peace-ful
3. And ye, be-neath life's crush-ing load, Whose forms are
4. For lo! the days are has-tening on, By proph-et

1. song of old, From an-gels bend-ing
2. wings un-furled, And still their heav'n-ly
3. bend-ing low, Who toil a-long the
4. bards fore-told, When with the ev-er-

1. near the earth To touch their harps of gold:
2. mu-sic floats O'er all the wea-ry world;
3. climb-ing way With pain-ful steps and slow,
4. cir-cling years Comes 'round the age of gold,

1. "Peace on the earth, good will to all, From
2. A-bove its sad and low-ly plains They
3. Look now! for glad and gold-en hours Come
4. When peace shall o-ver all the earth Its

Text: CMD; Edmund H. Sears, 1810–1876, alt.
Music: CAROL; Richard S. Willis, 1819–1900.

1. heav'n's all gra - cious King"; The world in sol - emn
2. bend on hov - 'ring wing, And ev - er o'er its
3. swift - ly on the wing; O rest be - side the
4. an - cient splen - dors fling, And all the world give

1. still - ness lay To hear the an - gels sing.
2. Ba - bel - sounds The bless - ed an - gels sing.
3. wea - ry road And hear the an - gels sing.
4. back the song Which now the an - gels sing.

In the Breaking of the Bread/
Cuando Partimos el Pan del Señor

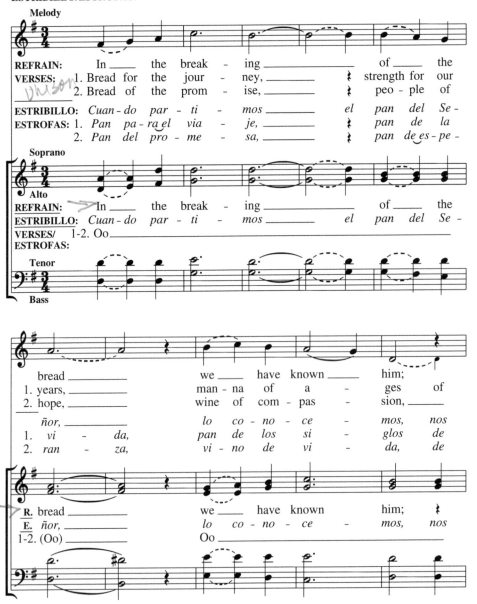

Text: English text by Bob Hurd, b. 1950 and Michael Downey ©1987, Bob Hurd and Michael Downey; Spanish text by Stephen Dean and Kathleen Orozco ©1989, OCP Publications.
Music: Bob Hurd; choral arr. by Craig S. Kingsbury, b. 1952 ©1984, 1985, Bob Hurd. Published by OCP Publications.

we have been fed. _____ Je - sus the __
1. strug - gle and tears. _____ Cup of sal -
2. life for the world. _____ Gath-ered at __

da de co - mer. _____ Je - sús des - co - no -
1. lu - cha y do - lor, _____ y es - te __
2. su com - pa - sión, _____ en es - ta __

R. we have been fed. _____ Je - sus the __
E. da de co - mer. _____ Je - sús des - co - no -
1-2. (Oo) _____ Oo _____

stran - ger, _____ Je - sus the Lord, _____
1. va - tion, _____ fruit of the land, _____
2. ta - ble, _____ joined as his bod -

ci - do, _____ Je - sús, __ Se - ñor, _____
1. vi - no, _____ fru - to de la tie -
2. me - sa _____ un so - lo cuer -

R. stran - ger, _____ Je - sus the Lord, _____
E. ci - do, _____ Je - sús, __ Se - ñor, _____
1-2. (Oo) _____

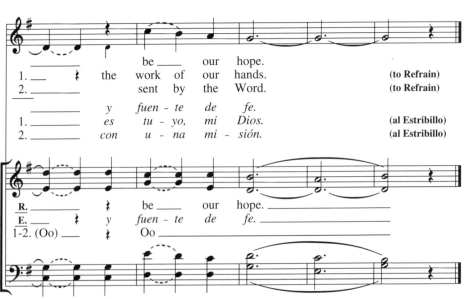

Jerusalem, My Happy Home

1. Je - ru - sa - lem, my hap - py home, When
2. O hap - py har - bor of the saints, O
3. Your gar - dens and your gal - lant walks Con -
4. There trees for - ev - er - more bear fruit And
5. Je - ru - sa - lem, Je - ru - sa - lem, God

1. shall I come to thee? When shall my sor - rows
2. sweet and pleas - ant soil! In you no sor - row
3. tin - ual - ly are green; There grow such sweet and
4. ev - er - more do spring; There ev - er - more the
5. grant that I may see Your end - less joy, and

1. have an end? Your joys when shall I see?
2. may be found, No grief, no care, no toil.
3. pleas - ant flow'rs As no - where else are seen.
4. an - gels sit And ev - er - more do sing.
5. of the same Par - tak - er ev - er be!

Text: CM; Joseph Bromehead, 1747–1826, alt.
Music: LAND OF REST; Trad. American Melody; adapt. and harm. by Annabel Morris Buchanan, 1888–1983 ©1938, J. Fischer & Bro.,
   a division of Belwin-Mills Publishing Corp. Copyright renewed 1966.

Jesu, Joy of Our Desiring

1. Je - su, joy of our de - sir - ing,
2. Through the way where hope is guid - ing,

Ho - ly
Hear what

1. wis - dom, love most bright, Drawn by you, our
2. peace - ful mu - sic rings; Where the flocks in

1. souls as - pir - ing, Soar to un - cre - a - ted Light.
2. you con - fid - ing, Drink of joy from death - less springs!

1. Word of God, our flesh that fash - ioned With the fire of
2. Theirs is beau - ty's fair - est pleas - ure; Theirs is wis - dom's

Text: 87 87 88 77; *Jesu, Joy Of Man's Desiring*; Martin Jahn, ca. 1620–1682; tr. by Robert S. Bridges, 1844–1930, rev.
Music: WERDE MUNTER; *Himmlische Lieder*, 1642; Johann P. Schop, ca. 1590–1664; arr. by Johann S. Bach, 1685–1750, alt.

234

1. life im - pas-sioned, Striv - ing still to truth un -
2. ho - liest treas-ure; You do ev - er lead your

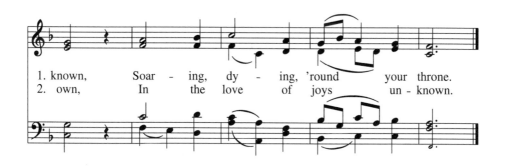

1. known, Soar - ing, dy - ing, 'round your throne.
2. own, In the love of joys un - known.

Jesus Christ Is Risen Today

1. Je - sus Christ is ris'n to - day,
2. Hymns of praise then let us sing,
3. But the pains which he en-dured,
4. Sing we to our God a - bove,

Al - le - lu - ia!

1. Our tri - um - phant ho - ly day,
2. Un - to Christ, our heav'n - ly King,
3. Our sal - va - tion have pro - cured;
4. Praise e - ter - nal as his love;

Al - le - lu - ia!

1. Who did once up - on the cross,
2. Who en - dured the cross and grave,
3. Now he reigns a - bove as King,
4. Praise him, all ye heav'n - ly host,

Al - le - lu - ia!

1. Suf - fer to re - deem our loss.
2. Sin - ners to re - deem and save.
3. Where the an - gels ev - er sing.
4. Fa - ther, Son, and Ho - ly Ghost.

Al - le - lu - ia!

Text: 77 77 with alleluias; verse 1, Latin, 14th cent., para. in *Lyra Davidica*, 1708, alt.; verses 2–3, *The Compleat Psalmosdist*, ca. 1750, alt.; verse 4, Charles Wesley, 1707–1788.
Music: EASTER HYMN; later form of melody fr. *Lyra Davidica*, 1708.

Jesus, Come to Us

REFRAIN: *Slow, with movement*

Descant

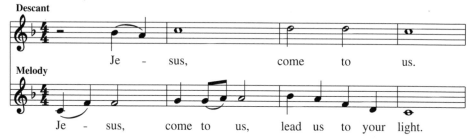

Je - sus, come to us.

Melody

Je - sus, come to us, lead us to your light.

Je - sus, we need you.

Je - sus, be with us, for we need you.

VERSES:

1. Lord, we come be - fore you,_____ lis - ten to our prayer.
2. Lord, we come to praise you for your faith - ful - ness through night.
3. Lord, you give us won - ders,___ your glo - ry to all.

1. Fill us all with hope, and your love.
2. You will be with us, this we know.
3. We be - lieve in you, come to us.

Text: David Haas, b. 1957.
Music: David Haas.
Text and music ©1981, 1982, 1988, OCP Publications.

Jesus Is Risen

1. Je - sus is ris - en! Let us sing! Praise to the ev -
2. On this most ho - ly day of days, Let us to - geth -
3. To God the Fa - ther let us sing, To God the Son,

1. er - liv - ing King! Al - le - lu - ia! Al - le -
2. er sing his praise! Al - le - lu - ia! Al - le -
3. our ris - en King! Al - le - lu - ia! Al - le -

1. lu - ia! Praise him in song, ye Ser - a - phim! Praise
2. lu - ia! Raise joy - ful voic - es to the sky! Sing
3. lu - ia! And e - qual - ly let us a - dore The

1. him with joy, ye Cher - u - bim! (Melody)
2. out, ye heav - ens, in re - ply: 1-3. Al - le -
3. Ho - ly Spir - it ev - er - more! 1-3. Al -

Text: LM with additions; composite.
Music: LASST UNS ERFREUEN; melody fr. *Auserlesene, Catholische, Geistliche Kirchengesäng*, Cologne, 1623; choral arr. by Randall DeBruyn, b. 1947 ©1994, OCP Publications.

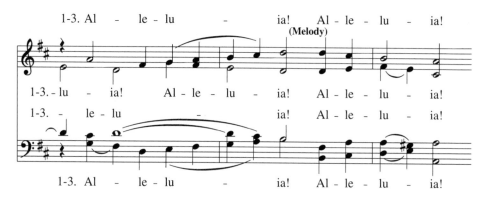

Jesus, the Bread of Life

REFRAIN: *Largo, steady (♩ = ca. 60)*

Je - sus, the Bread of life, Je -

sus, the Bread of life. All who eat and

drink of him will nev - er die,

Fine

will nev - er die.

Text: Based on John 6:51, 14:23; Grayson Warren Brown, b. 1948.
Music: Grayson Warren Brown.
Text and music ©1981, Grayson Warren Brown. Published by OCP Publications.

VERSES:

1. I am the Bread that came down from heav-en. I will
2. All who come to me will not hun-ger nor will
3. All who love and keep my com-mand-ments will be

Mm   Mm

1. be ___ your food. ___ All who put their
2. they ev-er thirst. ___ If you turn to
3. loved by my Fa - ther. And we shall both

(Mm) ___ Mm ___

1. trust in me will nev - er die.
2. me in faith I'll nev-er turn a-way.
3. com-fort them and make our home in them.

(Mm) ___

D.C.

Jesus the Lord

Text: Based on Jesus' Prayer, Philippians 2, Acts 17; Roc O'Connor, SJ, b.1949.
Music: Roc O'Connor, SJ.
Text and music ©1981, Robert F. O'Connor, SJ and New Dawn Music.

VERSES: Cantor

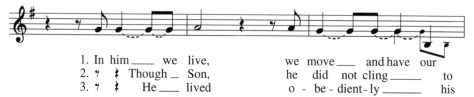

1. In him ___ we live, we move ___ and have our
2. ⁊ ⁊ Though ___ Son, he did not cling ___ to
3. ⁊ ⁊ He ___ lived o - be - dient - ly ___ his

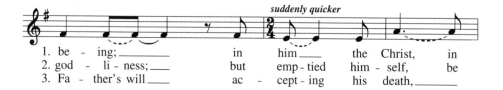

suddenly quicker

1. be - ing; ___ in him ___ the Christ, in
2. god - li - ness; ___ but emp - tied him - self, be
3. Fa - ther's will ___ ac - cept - ing his death, ___

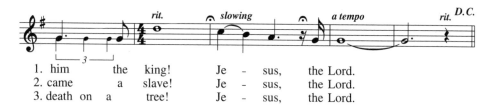

rit.   *slowing*   *a tempo*   *rit.* **D.C.**

1. him the king! Je - sus, the Lord.
2. came a slave! Je - sus, the Lord.
3. death on a tree! Je - sus, the Lord.

Join in the Dance

REFRAIN: *Joyfully (𝅗𝅥. = ca. 94)*

Descant

Join the dance of ju - bi - la - tion! This the

Melody

Join in the dance of the earth's ju - bi - la - tion! This is the

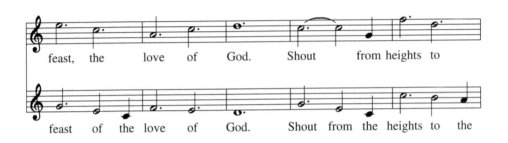

feast, the love of God. Shout from heights to

feast of the love of God. Shout from the heights to the

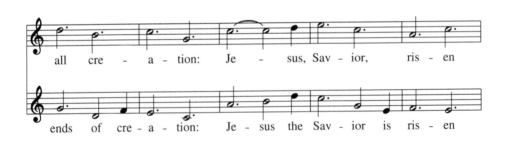

all cre - a - tion: Je - sus, Sav - ior, ris - en

ends of cre - a - tion: Je - sus the Sav - ior is ris - en

from the grave!

from the grave!

Text: Dan Schutte, b. 1947.
Music: Dan Schutte.
Text and music ©1991, Daniel L. Schutte. Published by OCP Publications.

VERSES:

1. Wake, O peo - ple; sleep no long - er: greet the
2. All cre - a - tion, like a moth - er, la - bors
3. Now our shame be - comes our glo - ry on this
4. None on earth, no prince or pow - er, nei - ther
5. Love's tri - um - phant day of vic - t'ry heav - en
6. Christ for ev - er, Lord of a - ges, Love be -

1. break - ing day! Christ, Re - deem - er,
2. to give birth. Soon the pain will
3. ho - ly tree. Now the reign of
4. death nor life, noth - ing now can
5. o - pens wide. On the tree of
6. yond our dreams: Christ, our hope of

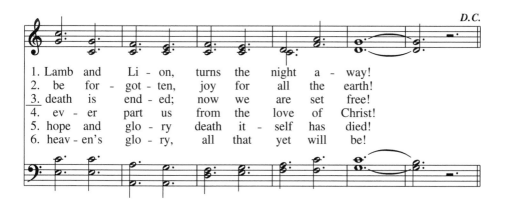

D.C.

1. Lamb and Li - on, turns the night a - way!
2. be for - got - ten, joy for all the earth!
3. death is end - ed; now we are set free!
4. ev - er part us from the love of Christ!
5. hope and glo - ry death it - self has died!
6. heav - en's glo - ry, all that yet will be!

Jesus, Remember Me

Je - sus, re - mem - ber me when you come in-to your king - dom.

Je - sus, re - mem - ber me when you come in - to your king - dom.

Text: Luke 23:42; Taizé Community.
Music: Jacques Berthier, 1934–1994.
Text and music ©1981, *Ateliers et Presses de Taizé* (France). Used by permission of G.I.A. Publications, Inc., agent.

Joy to the World

1. Joy to the world! the Lord is come; Let earth re-ceive her King;
2. Joy to the earth! the Sav - ior reigns; Let us our songs em - ploy;
3. He rules the world with truth and grace, And makes the na - tions prove

1. Let ev - 'ry heart pre - pare him room,
2. While fields and floods, rocks, hills and plains
3. The glo - ries of his righ - teous - ness,

1. And heav'n and na - ture sing, And heav'n and na - ture
2. Re - peat the sound-ing joy, Re - peat the sound-ing
3. And won - ders of his love, And won - ders of his

1. And heav'n and na - ture sing,
2. Re - peat the sound-ing joy,
3. And won - ders of his love,

1. And heav'n and na - ture sing, and
2. Re - peat the sound-ing joy, re -
3. And won - ders of his love, and

1. sing, And heav'n, and heav'n and na - ture sing.
2. joy, Re - peat, re - peat the sound-ing joy.
3. love, And won - ders, won - ders of his love.

1. heav'n and na - ture sing,
2. peat the sound-ing joy,
3. won - ders of his love,

Text: CM with repeats; Based on Psalm 98; Isaac Watts, 1674–1748.
Music: ANTIOCH; T. Hawkes' *Collection of Tunes*, 1833; George F. Handel, 1685–1759; adapt. and arr. by Lowell Mason, 1792–1872, alt.

Joyful, Joyful, We Adore Thee

1. Joy- ful, joy- ful, we a - dore thee, God of glo- ry, Lord of love;
2. All thy works with joy sur- round thee, Earth and heav'n re - flect thy rays,
3. Thou art giv- ing and for - giv - ing, Ev - er bless- ing, ev - er blest,

1. Hearts un - fold like flow'rs be - fore thee, O-p'ning to the sun a - bove.
2. Stars and an - gels sing a - round thee, Cen - ter of un - bro- ken praise;
3. Well-spring of the joy of liv - ing, O - cean depth of hap-py rest!

1. Melt the clouds of sin and sad - ness; Drive the dark of doubt a - way;
2. Field and for - est, vale and moun-tain, Flow-'ry mead-ow, flash - ing sea,
3. Thou our Fa - ther, Christ our broth- er, All who live in love are thine;

1. Giv- er of im - mor- tal glad-ness, Fill us with the light of day.
2. Chant-ing bird and flow-ing foun-tain, Call us to re - joice in thee.
3. Teach us how to love each oth - er, Lift us to the joy di - vine.

Text: 87 87 D; Henry van Dyke, 1852–1933.
Music: HYMN TO JOY; Ludwig van Beethoven, 1770–1827; adapt. by Edward Hodges, 1796–1867.

Let All Mortal Flesh Keep Silence

1. Let all mor-tal flesh keep si - lence, And with fear and
2. King of kings, yet born of Ma - ry, As of old on
3. Rank on rank the host of heav - en Spreads its van-guard
4. At his feet the six - winged ser - aph; Cher - u - bim with

1. trem-bling stand; Pon-der noth-ing earth - ly mind - ed,
2. earth he stood, Lord of lords, in hu - man ves - ture,
3. on the way, As the Light of light de - scend-eth
4. sleep-less eye, Veil their fac - es to the Pres-ence,

1. For with bless-ing in his hand Christ our God to earth de -
2. In the Bod - y and the Blood He will give to all the
3. From the realms of end - less day, That the pow'rs of hell may
4. As with cease-less voice they cry, "Al - le - lu - ia, al - le -

1. scend - eth, Our full hom-age to de - mand.
2. faith - ful His own self for heav'n-ly food.
3. van - ish As the dark-ness clears a - way.
4. lu - ia! Al - le - lu - ia, Lord most high!"

Text: 87 87 87; Liturgy of St. James, 5th cent.; para. by Gerard Moultrie, 1829–1885.
Music: PICARDY; French, 17th cent.; melody fr. *Chansons populaires des Provinces de France*, 1860; choral arr. by Randall DeBruyn, b. 1947 ©1990, OCP Publications.

Lead Me, Lord

VERSES: (♩ = 120)

1. Bless-ed are the poor in spir-it, long-ing for their Lord, for God's
2. Bless-ed are the mer-ci-ful, for mer-cy shall be theirs, and the
3. Blest are they who through their life-times sow the seeds of peace, all will

1. com-ing king-dom shall be theirs.
2. pure in heart shall see their God.
3. call them chil-dren of the Lord.

Bless-ed are the sor-row-ing, for
Blest are they whose hun-ger on-ly
Blest are you, though per-se-cu-ted

1. they shall be con-soled, and the meek shall come to rule the world.
2. ho-li-ness can fill, for I say they shall be sat-is-fied.
3. in your ho-ly life, for in heav-en, great is your re-ward.

REFRAIN:
Melody (Assembly)

Lead me, Lord, lead me, Lord, by the light of truth to

Soprano
Alto

Lead me, Lord, by the light of

Tenor
Bass

seek and to find the nar-row way. Be my way;

truth to seek and find the nar-row way.

Text: Based on Matthew 5, 7, John 14; John D. Becker, b. 1953.
Music: John D. Becker.
Text and music ©1987, John D. Becker. Published by OCP Publications.

be my truth; be my life, my Lord, and

Be my way, my truth, my life, Lord,

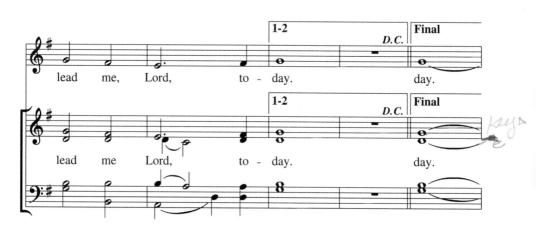

lead me, Lord, to - day. day.

lead me Lord, to - day. day.

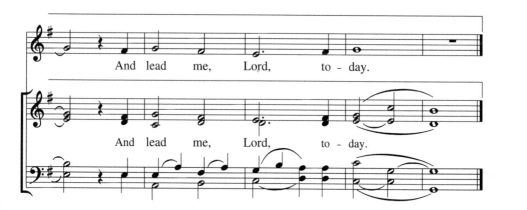

And lead me, Lord, to - day.

And lead me, Lord, to - day.

Let Heaven Rejoice

REFRAIN: *Lightly (♩. = 60)*

Descant

Al - le - lu - ia. Al - le - lu - ia.

Melody

Let heav-en re-joice and earth be glad; let all cre-a - tion sing. Let

Chil - dren sing, "Ho - san - na to our king."

chil-dren pro-claim through ev - 'ry land: "Ho - san - na to our king."

VERSES:

1. Sound the trum - pet in - to the night; the day of the
2. Rise in splen - dor; shake off your sleep; put on your
3. Raise your voic - es, be not a - fraid. Pro - claim it in

1. Lord is near. Wake your peo - ple,
2. robes of joy. And in the morn - ing
3. ev - 'ry land. Christ has died, but

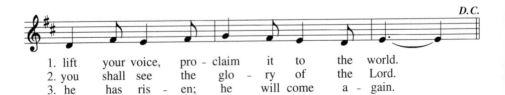

1. lift your voice, pro - claim it to the world.
2. you shall see the glo - ry of the Lord.
3. he has ris - en; he will come a - gain.

Text: Bob Dufford, SJ, b. 1943.
Music: Bob Dufford, SJ.
Text and music ©1972, 1974, Robert J. Dufford, SJ. Administered by New Dawn Music.

VERSE 4:

4. Sing a new song un - to the Lord, whose la - bor has

4. led us to life. With grate - ful hearts and

D.C. al fine

4. joy - ful danc - ing, play be - fore the Lord.

Let the Heavens Be Glad

*Choral descant is sung as the refrain is sung each time. If feasible, the song may begin with the descant sung *a cappella*. For simplicity, the descant may be sung using only the melody line.

Text: Based on Psalm 96:11–13; Dan Feiten.
Music: Dan Feiten.
Text and music ©1982, EKKLESIA MUSIC, INC.

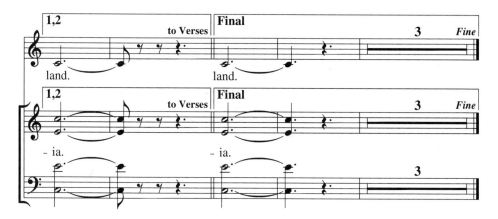

land.   land.

- ia.   - ia.

VERSES:

1. Then shall   the trees,   the   trees of the for-est ex - ult
2. The Lord   shall rule   with jus-tice for all of the earth.

Descant

(Melody)

1. be-fore   the Lord,   who comes now to rule   the earth.
2. In con-stant love   he   comes now to rule   the earth.

Let the King of Glory Come

Text: Based on Psalm 24, "O" Antiphons; Michael Joncas, b. 1951.
Music: Michael Joncas.
Text and music ©1979, New Dawn Music.

D.C.

2. Come, O come, you Lord of might: Ban-ish death and fear!
3. Come, O come, you Day - spring: Love, un-close our eyes!

VERSE 4:

4. Come, you Key of Da - vid, come: O-pen our heav-en-ly home!

D.C.

4. Come, De - sire of na - tions, come: Bring us in-to your peace!

CODA

Let the King of glo - ry come!

Let the Valleys Be Raised

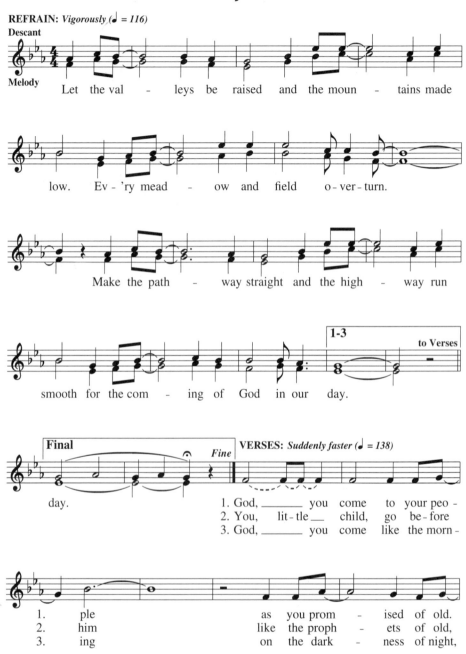

REFRAIN: *Vigorously (♩ = 116)*

Descant

Melody

Let the val - leys be raised and the moun - tains made

low. Ev - 'ry mead - ow and field o - ver - turn.

Make the path - way straight and the high - way run

1-3 to Verses

smooth for the com - ing of God in our day.

Final *Fine* **VERSES:** *Suddenly faster (♩ = 138)*

day.
1. God, _____ you come to your peo -
2. You, lit - tle ___ child, go be - fore
3. God, _____ you come like the morn -

1. ple as you prom - ised of old.
2. him like the proph - ets of old,
3. ing on the dark - ness of night,

Text: Based on Isaiah 40:3–5; Luke 1:68–79; Dan Schutte, b. 1947.
Music: Dan Schutte.
Text and music ©1977, Daniel L. Schutte and New Dawn Music.

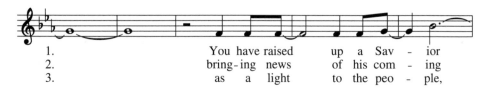

1. You have raised up a Sav - ior
2. bring-ing news of his com - ing
3. as a light to the peo - ple,

a tempo
D.C.

1. in the sight of us all.
2. by the mer - cy of God.
3. like the break - ing of day.

Let There Be Peace on Earth

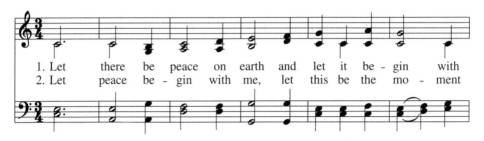

1. Let there be peace on earth and let it be - gin with
2. Let peace be - gin with me, let this be the mo - ment

1. me. Let there be peace on earth, the
2. now. With ev - 'ry step I take, let

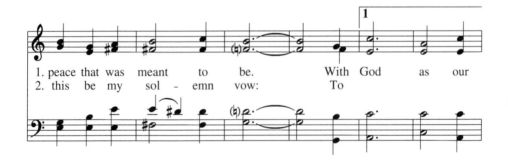

1. peace that was meant to be. With God as our
2. this be my sol - emn vow: To

1. Fa - ther, broth - ers all are we;
(optional text) we are fam - i - ly.

Text: Sy Miller, 1908–1971 and Jill Jackson, 1913–1995.
Music: Sy Miller and Jill Jackson; choral arr. by Dennis Richardson, b. 1947.
Text and music ©1955, 1982, renewed 1983, Jan-Lee Music.

1. Let me walk with my broth-er in per-fect har - mo -
Let us walk with each oth - er

1. ny. 2. take each mo-ment and live each mo-ment in

2. peace e - ter - nal - ly. Let there be

2. peace on earth and let it be - gin with me.

Repeat Verses 1 & 2

Final

2. let it be - gin with me.

poco rit.

poco rit.

Let Us Break Bread Together

Descant

3. Praise God on our

Melody

1. Let us break bread to - geth - er on our knees;
2. Let us drink wine to - geth - er on our knees;
3. Let us praise God to - geth - er on our knees;

3. knees; Praise God on our knees, on our knees;

1. Let us break bread to - geth - er on our knees;
2. Let us drink wine to - geth - er on our knees;
3. Let us praise God to - geth - er on our knees;

3. When I fall with my face to the

1-3. When I fall on my knees, with my face to the ris - ing

3. sun, O Lord, have mer - cy on me.

1-3. sun, O Lord, have mer-cy on me.

Text: 10 10 with refrain; Spiritual.
Music: LET US BREAK BREAD; Spiritual; descant by Randall DeBruyn, b. 1947 ©1996, OCP Publications.

Lift High the Cross

REFRAIN:

Descant

Lift high, lift high, the cross pro - claim

Melody

Lift high the cross, the love of Christ pro - claim till

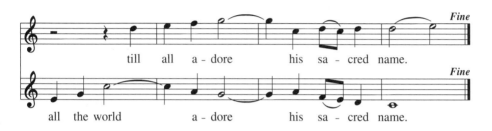

Fine

till all a - dore his sa - cred name.

Fine

all the world a - dore his sa - cred name.

VERSES:

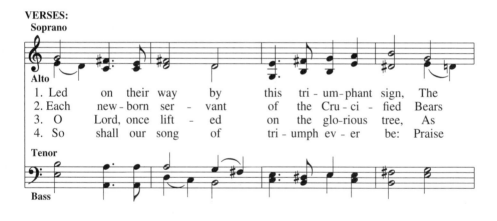

Soprano

Alto

1. Led on their way by this tri - um-phant sign, The
2. Each new - born ser - vant of the Cru - ci - fied Bears
3. O Lord, once lift - ed on the glo - rious tree, As
4. So shall our song of tri - umph ev - er be: Praise

Tenor

Bass

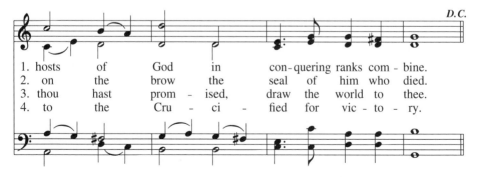

D.C.

1. hosts of God in con - quering ranks com - bine.
2. on the brow the seal of him who died.
3. thou hast prom - ised, draw the world to thee.
4. to the Cru - ci - fied for vic - to - ry.

Text: 10 10 with refrain; Based on 1 Corinthians 1:18; George W. Kitchin, 1827−1912; rev. by Michael R. Newbolt, 1874−1956.
Music: CRUCIFER; Sydney H. Nicholson, 1875−1947; descant by Randall DeBruyn, b, 1947.

263

Lift Up Your Hearts

*Optional repeat after Verse 4.

Text: Based on Psalm 66; Roc O'Connor, SJ, b. 1949.
Music: Roc O'Connor, SJ; choral arr. by Bob Dufford, SJ, b. 1943.
Text and music ©1981, 1993, Robert F. O'Connor, SJ and New Dawn Music.

264

VERSES:

1. Shout with joy   to   the   Lord,   all   the earth!
2. Let   the earth   wor - ship,   sing - ing   your praise.
3. God's right hand   made   a   path   through the night,
4. Lis - ten now,   all   you   ser - vants   of   God,

1. Praise the name   a - bove   all   names!   Say   to God, "How
2. Praise the glo - ry   of   your   name!   Come and see   the
3. split   the wa - ters   of   the   sea.   All   cre - a - tion,
4. as   I   tell   of these great works.   Bless - ed be   the

D.C.

1. won - drous your works,   how   glo - rious your name!"
2. deeds   of   the   Lord;   bless   God's   ho - ly   name!
3. lift   up   your voice: "Our   God   set   us   free!"
4. Lord   of   my   life,   whose love   shall   en - dure!

Like a Shepherd

REFRAIN: *Gently, not too fast (♩ = 100-104)*

Like a shep-herd he feeds his flock and gath-ers the

lambs in his arms, hold-ing them care-ful-ly

close to his heart, lead-ing them home.

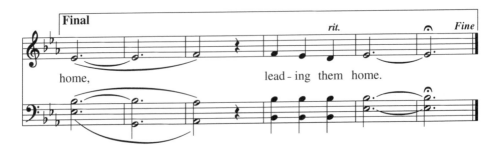

home, lead-ing them home.

Text: Based on Isaiah 40:9ff, Ezekiel 34:11ff; Matthew 12:28ff; Bob Dufford, SJ, b. 1943.
Music: Bob Dufford, SJ.
Text and music ©1976, Robert J. Dufford, SJ and New Dawn Music.

VERSES 1,2: *Slightly faster (♩ = 104)*

Melody

Harmony

1. Say to the cit-ies of Ju – dah: Pre-pare _ the
2. I _ my - self _ will shep-herd them, for oth-ers have

1. way of the Lord. Go to the moun-tain-top,
2. led them a - stray. The lost I will res - cue and

D.C.

1. lift your voice: Je - ru - sa - lem, here is your God.
2. heal their wounds and pas - ture them, giv-ing them rest.

VERSE 3: *Slightly faster (♩ = 104)*

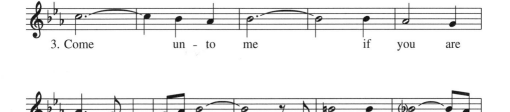

3. Come un - to me if you are

3. heav - i - ly bur - dened, and take my yoke up-

D.C.

3. on your shoul-ders. I will give you rest.

Litany of the Saints

Gently flowing (♩ = 100)

Presider/Cantor
Lord, have mer - cy. Christ, have

Choir/Assembly
Lord, have mer - cy.

mer - cy. Lord, have mer - cy.

Christ, have mer - cy. Lord, have mer - cy.

1. Ma - ry and Jo - seph, __
2. An - drew, __
3. - so - go - nus,
4. - se - bi - us,
5. mer - ci - ful.
6. new life. __

1-4. Pray for
5. Save your
6. Hear our

1. Mi - chael _____ and all an - gels,
2. James, __ John and all a - pos - tles,
3. In - no - cent __ and __ Bon - i - face,
4. Scho - las - ti - ca and __ Ben - e - dict,
5. From __ all __ e - vil
6. To __ these __ cho - sen,

1-4. us. _____
5. peo - ple.
6. prayer. ____

Pray for
Save your
Hear our

Text: ©1973, I.C.E.L., Inc.
Music: John D. Becker, b. 1953 ©1987, John D. Becker. Published by OCP Publications.

1. An - na, Jo - a-chim, E - liz - a-beth, E - li-jah,
2. Ma - ry Mag-de-lene, Ve - ron - i - ca,
3. Hip - po - ly - tus and Or - i - gen, A - tha-
4. Am-brose, Mon - i - ca, Au - gus - tine,
5. From ev - 'ry sin. From
6. By the grace of bap - tism. O Je-sus,

1-4. us. Pray for us.
5. peo - ple. Save your peo - ple.
6. prayer. Hear our prayer.

1. Mo - ses, John the Bap - tist, I - saac, Sa-rah,
2. Bar - na - bas, Mat - thi - as, Ste-phen, Phi - lip and Cor-
3. na - sius and Ba - sil, Fe - li - ci - ty, Per-
4. Mar - tin and Gre-go-ry, Clare, Fran - cis, and
5. ev - er - last-ing death, By your in-car-
6. Son of the liv-ing God. Send your

1-4. Pray for us.
5. Save your peo - ple.
6. Hear our prayer.

1. A - bra-ham, Ja - cob, Jo - seph,
2. ne - li - us, Pris - ca and A -
3. pe - tu - a, Cos - mos and
4. Dom - i - nic, Fran - cis Xa - vier, Ig -
5. na - tion. By your death and re - sur -
6. Spir - it. In its

1-4. Pray for us.
5. Save your peo - ple.
6. Hear our prayer.

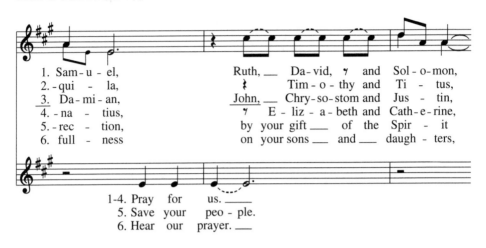

1. Sam-u-el,
2. -qui - la,
3. Da-mi-an,
4. -na - tius,
5. -rec - tion,
6. full - ness

Ruth, __ Da-vid, and Sol-o-mon,
Tim-o-thy and Ti - tus,
John, __ Chry-so-stom and Jus - tin,
E - liz - a - beth and Cath-e-rine,
by your gift __ of the Spir - it
on your sons __ and __ daugh-ters,

1-4. Pray for us. __
5. Save your peo - ple.
6. Hear our prayer. __

1.
2.
3.
4.
5.
6.

I - sai-ah, Jer-e-mi - ah,
Li-nus, Cle-tus and __ Cle - ment,
Lu-cy, A-ga-tha and Ag - nes,
Lou-is and __ Wen-ce-slaus,
have mer-cy on us sin - ners.
who be-lieve __ and pro-fess you.

1-4. Pray for us. __
5. Save your peo-ple.
6. Hear our prayer. __

Pray for us. __
Save your peo-ple.
Hear our prayer. __

1-4. All you ho - ly men and wo-men, pray for
5-6. Christ, __ hear us; Lord, __ Je - sus, hear our

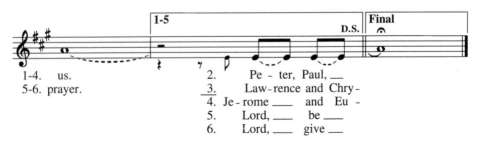

1-5

Final
D.S.

1-4. us.
5-6. prayer.

2. Pe - ter, Paul, __
3. Law-rence and Chry-
4. Je-rome __ and Eu -
5. Lord, __ be __
6. Lord, __ give __

270

Lift Up Your Heads, Ye Mighty Gates

1. Lift up your heads, ye might - y gates; Be-
2. O blest the land, the cit - y blest, Where
3. Fling wide the por - tals of your heart; Make
4. So come, my Sov - 'reign; en - ter in! Let

1. hold the King of glo - ry waits! The
2. Christ the rul - er is con - fest! O
3. it a tem - ple, set a - part From
4. new and no - bler life be - gin; Thy

1. King of kings is draw - ing near; The
2. hap - py hearts and hap - py homes To
3. earth - ly use for heav'n's em - ploy, A-
4. Ho - ly Spir - it guide us on, Un-

1. Sav - ior of the world is here.
2. whom this King of tri - umph comes!
3. dorned with prayer and love and joy.
4. til the glo - rious crown be won.

Text: LM; George Weissel, 1590–1635; tr. by Catherine Winkworth, 1827–1878.
Music: TRURO; Williams' *Psalmodia Evangelica, Part II*, 1789; harm. by Lowell Mason, 1792–1872, alt.

Lo, How a Rose E'er Blooming

1. Lo, how a Rose e'er bloom - ing From ten - der
2. I - sai - ah 'twas fore - told it, This Rose I

1. stem hath sprung! Of Jes - se's lin - eage com - ing, As
2. have in mind, With Ma - ry we be - hold it, The

1. those of old have sung. It came, a flow - er bright, A-
2. Vir - gin Moth - er kind. To show God's love a - right, She

1. mid the cold of win - ter, When half spent was the night.
2. bore to us a Sav - ior, When half spent was the night.

Text: 76 76 6 76; German carol, 15th cent.; based on Isaiah 11:1; tr. by Theodore Baker, 1851–1934.
Music: ES IST EIN' ROS' ENTSPRUNGEN; melody fr. *Alte Catholische Geistliche Kirchengesäng*, Cologne, 1599; harm. by Michael Praetorius, 1571–1621.

Lord of All Hopefulness

1. Lord of all hope - ful - ness, Lord of all joy, Whose
2. Lord of all ea - ger - ness, Lord of all faith, Whose
3. Lord of all kind - li - ness, Lord of all grace, Your
4. Lord of all gen - tle - ness, Lord of all calm, Whose

1. trust, ev - er child - like, no cares can de - stroy, Be
2. strong hands were skilled at the plane and the lathe, Be
3. hands swift to wel - come, your arms to em - brace, Be
4. voice is con - tent - ment, whose pres - ence is balm, Be

1. there at our wak - ing, and give us, we pray, Your
2. there at our la - bors, and give us, we pray, Your
3. there at our hom - ing, and give us, we pray, Your
4. there at our sleep - ing, and give us, we pray, Your

1. bliss in our hearts, Lord, at the break of the day.
2. strength in our hearts, Lord, at the noon of the day.
3. love in our hearts, Lord, at the eve of the day.
4. peace in our hearts, Lord, at the end of the day.

Text: 10 11 11 12; Jan Struther, 1901–1953 © Oxford University Press, London.
Music: SLANE; Trad. Irish Melody; choral arr. by Randall DeBruyn, b. 1947 ©1990, OCP Publications.

Look Beyond

Text: Darryl Ducote, b. 1945.
Music: Darryl Ducote.
Text and music ©1969, 1979, Damean Music.

VERSES 2, 3:

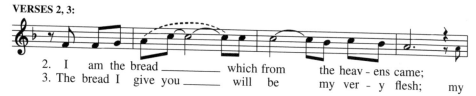

2. I am the bread _____ which from the heav - ens came;
3. The bread I give you _____ will be my ver - y flesh; my

2. those who eat this bread will nev - er die.
3. blood _____ will tru - ly be your drink.

VERSES 4, 5:

4. This man speaks harsh - ly; _____ who can lis - ten to his word?
5. You, my dis - ci - ples, _____ will you _____ al - so leave?

4. We shall no long - er fol - low him.
5. Lord, _____ to whom _____ can we go?

(Melody)

4. We shall no long - er fol - low him.
5. Lord, _____ to whom _____ can we go?

Lord of Glory

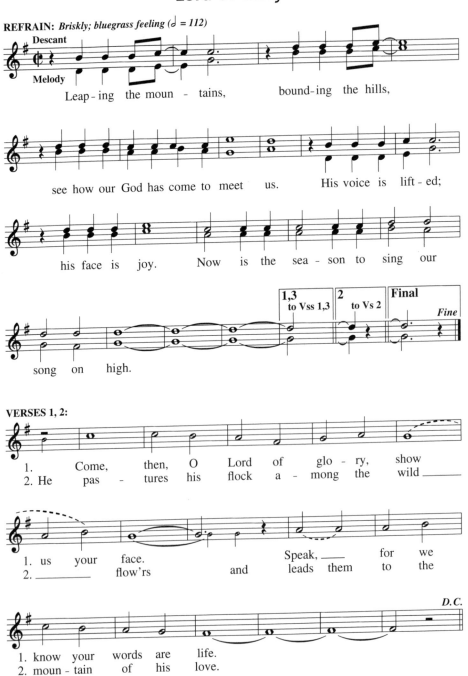

REFRAIN: *Briskly; bluegrass feeling (♩ = 112)*

Descant / Melody

Leap-ing the moun - tains, bound-ing the hills,

see how our God has come to meet us. His voice is lift-ed;

his face is joy. Now is the sea-son to sing our

1,3 to Vss 1,3   **2** to Vs 2   **Final**   *Fine*

song on high.

VERSES 1, 2:

1. Come, then, O Lord of glo - ry, show
2. He pas - tures his flock a - mong the wild _____

1. us your face. Speak, _____ for we
2. _____ flow'rs and leads them to the

D.C.

1. know your words are life.
2. moun - tain of his love.

Text: Based on Song of Songs; Tim Manion.
Music: Tim Manion.
Text and music ©1976, Timothy J. Manion and New Dawn Music.

VERSE 3:

3. All through the day, all through the

3. night, seek for the Lord and

3. sing his love.

D.C.

Lord of the Dance

Text: Sydney Carter, b. 1915.
Music: SHAKER SONG; 19th cent. Shaker tune; adapt. by Sydney Carter.
Text and music ©1963, Stainer & Bell Ltd., London, England. Used by permission of Hope Publishing Co.

I am the Lord of the Dance, said he. I'll

lead you all wher - ev - er you may be, I will

lead you all in the Dance, said he. Dance, said he.

Lord, Who at Thy First Eucharist

1. Lord, who at thy first Eucharist did pray That all thy Church might be for-ev-er one, Grant us at ev-'ry Eucharist to say, With long-ing heart and soul, "Thy will be done." O
2. For all thy Church, O Lord, we in-ter-cede; Make thou our sad di-vi-sions soon to cease; Draw us the near-er each to each we plead, By draw-ing all to thee, O Prince of Peace; Thus
3. We pray thee, too, for wan-d'rers from thy fold; O bring them back, Good Shep-herd of the sheep, Back to the faith which saints be-lieved of old, Back to the Church which still that faith doth keep; Soon
4. So, Lord, at length when sac-ra-ments shall cease, May we be one with all thy Church a-bove, One with thy saints in one un-bro-ken peace, One with thy saints in one un-bound-ed love; More

Text: 10 10 10 10 10 10; William H. Turton, 1856–1938.
Music: UNDE ET MEMORES; William H. Monk, 1823–1889, alt.

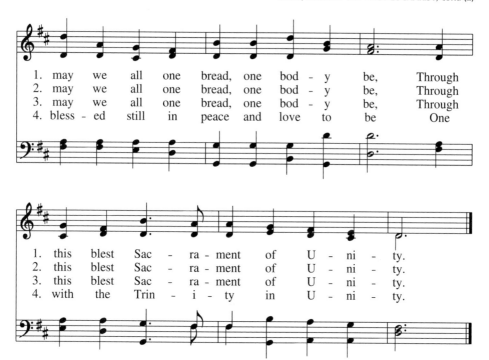

1. may we all one bread, one bod - y be, Through
2. may we all one bread, one bod - y be, Through
3. may we all one bread, one bod - y be, Through
4. bless - ed still in peace and love to be One

1. this blest Sac - ra - ment of U - ni - ty.
2. this blest Sac - ra - ment of U - ni - ty.
3. this blest Sac - ra - ment of U - ni - ty.
4. with the Trin - i - ty in U - ni - ty.

Lord, You Give the Great Commission

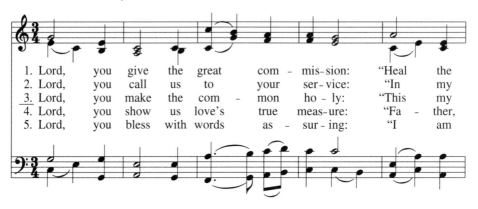

1. Lord, you give the great com-mis-sion: "Heal the
2. Lord, you call us to your ser-vice: "In my
3. Lord, you make the com - mon ho - ly: "This my
4. Lord, you show us love's true meas-ure: "Fa - ther,
5. Lord, you bless with words as - sur-ing: "I am

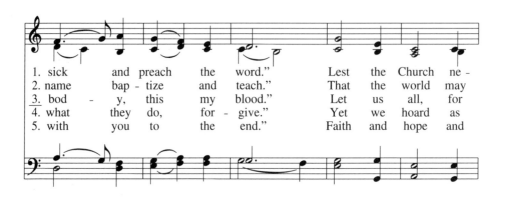

1. sick and preach the word." Lest the Church ne -
2. name bap - tize and teach." That the world may
3. bod - y, this my blood." Let us all, for
4. what they do, for - give." Yet we hoard as
5. with you to the end." Faith and hope and

1. glect its mis - sion And the Gos - pel
2. trust your prom - ise, Life a - bun - dant
3. earth's true glo - ry, Dai - ly lift life
4. pri - vate treas - ure All that you so
5. love re - stor - ing, May we serve as

1. go un - heard, Help us wit - ness to your
2. meant for each, Give us all new fer - vor,
3. heav - en - ward, Ask - ing that the world a -
4. free - ly give, May your care and mer - cy
5. you in - tend, And, a - mid the cares that

1. pur - pose With re - newed in - teg - ri - ty;
2. draw us Clos - er in com - mu - ni - ty;
3. round us Share your chil - dren's lib - er - ty;
4. lead us To a just so - ci - e - ty;
5. claim us, Hold in mind e - ter - ni - ty;

1-5. With the Spir - it's gifts em - pow'r us

1-5. For the work of min - is - try.

Lord, You Have Come/Pescador de Hombres

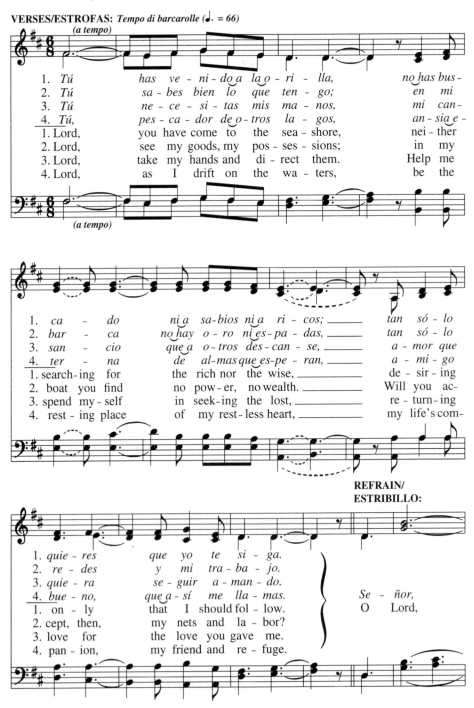

VERSES/ESTROFAS: *Tempo di barcarolle (♩. = 66)*
(a tempo)

1. Tú has ve-ni-do a la o-ri-lla, no has bus-
2. Tú sa-bes bien lo que ten-go; en mi
3. Tú ne-ce-si-tas mis ma-nos, mi can-
4. Tú, pes-ca-dor de o-tros la-gos, an-sia e-
1. Lord, you have come to the sea-shore, nei-ther
2. Lord, see my goods, my pos-ses-sions; in my
3. Lord, take my hands and di-rect them. Help me
4. Lord, as I drift on the wa-ters, be the

1. ca-do ni a sa-bios ni a ri-cos; ___ tan só-lo
2. bar-ca no hay o-ro ni es-pa-das, ___ tan só-lo
3. san-cio que a o-tros des-can-se, ___ a-mor que
4. ter-na de al-mas que es-pe-ran, ___ a-mi-go
1. search-ing for the rich nor the wise, ___ de-sir-ing
2. boat you find no pow-er, no wealth. ___ Will you ac-
3. spend my-self in seek-ing the lost, ___ re-turn-ing
4. rest-ing place of my rest-less heart, ___ my life's com-

REFRAIN/ESTRIBILLO:

1. quie-res que yo te si-ga.
2. re-des y mi tra-ba-jo.
3. quie-ra se-guir a-man-do.
4. bue-no, que a-sí me lla-mas. Se-ñor,
1. on-ly that I should fol-low. O Lord,
2. cept, then, my nets and la-bor?
3. love for the love you gave me.
4. pan-ion, my friend and re-fuge.

Text: Spanish by Cesáreo Gabaráin, 1936–1991; tr. by Robert C. Trupia.
Music: Cesáreo Gabaráin; choral arr. by Joseph Abell.
Text and music ©1979, 1987, Cesáreo Gabaráin. Published by OCP Publications.

me has mi - ra-do a los o - jos, son - ri - en - do ___
with your eyes set up - on me, gent - ly smil - ing, ___

___ has di-cho mi nom - bre, ___ en la a - re - na
___ you have spo-ken my name; ___ all I longed for

he de - ja - do mi bar - ca, jun - to a
I have found by the wa - ter, at your

rit.

Ti bus - ca - ré o - tro mar.
side, I will seek oth - er shores.

rit.

Lord, You Have the Words

Harmony (handwritten)

REFRAIN: (♩ = ca. 76) — Fine

Lord, you have the words of ev-er-last - ing life.

Cantor all 3 verses (handwritten)

VERSE 1: *Slightly faster* (♩ = ca. 100)

1. The law of the Lord is per-fect, re-fresh-ing the soul, the de-

rall. *D.C.*

1. cree of the Lord is trust-worth-y, giv-ing wis-dom to the sim-ple.

VERSE 2: *Slightly faster* (♩ = ca. 100)

2. The pre-cepts of the Lord are right, re-joic-ing the heart;

rall. *D.C.*

2. the com-mand of the Lord is clear, en-light-'ning the eye.

Text: John 6:68; Psalm 19:8–11; Michael Joncas, b. 1951.
Music: Michael Joncas.
Text and music ©1981, 1990, Michael Joncas. Published by Cooperative Ministries, Inc. Exclusive agent: OCP Publications.

VERSE 3: *Slightly faster (♩ = ca. 100)*

3. The fear of the Lord is pure, en - dur-ing for - ev - er,

3. the ord'- nan-ces of the Lord are true, all of them just.

VERSE 4: *Slightly faster (♩ = ca. 100)*

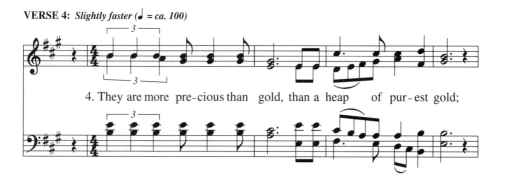

4. They are more pre-cious than gold, than a heap of pur-est gold;

4. sweet - er al - so than syr-up or hon - ey from the comb.

Love Divine, All Loves Excelling

1. Love di - vine, all loves ex - cel - ling, Joy of
2. Come, al - might - y to de - liv - er, Let us
3. Fin - ish then your new cre - a - tion, Pure and

1. heav'n to earth come down! Fix in us your
2. all your life re - ceive; Sud - den - ly re -
3. spot - less, gra - cious Lord, Let us see your

1. hum - ble dwell - ing, All your faith - ful
2. turn and nev - er, Nev - er more your
3. great sal - va - tion Per - fect - ly in

1. mer - cies crown. Je - sus, source of all com-
2. tem - ples leave. Lord, we would be al - ways
3. you re - stored. Changed from glo - ry in - to

Text: 87 87 D; Charles Wesley, 1707–1788, alt.
Music: HYFRYDOL; Rowland H. Prichard, 1811–1887.

1. -pas - sion, Love un - bound - ed, love all
2. bless - ing, Serve you as your hosts a -
3. glo - ry, Till in heav'n we take our

1. pure; Vis - it us with your sal -
2. bove, Pray, and praise you with - out
3. place, Till we sing be - fore the al -

1. va - tion, Let your love in us en - dure.
2. ceas - ing, Glo - ry in your pre - cious love.
3. might - y Lost in won - der, love and praise.

Love One Another

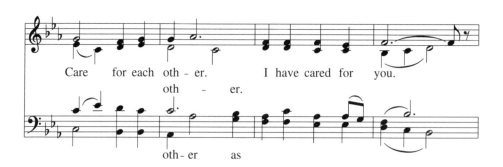

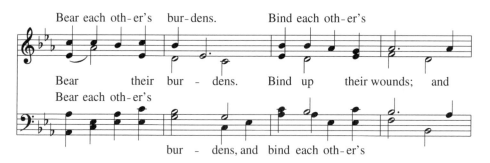

Text: Based on John 14–16, 1 Corinthians 13; Bob Dufford, SJ, b. 1943.
Music: Bob Dufford, SJ.
Text and music ©1987, 1996, Robert J. Dufford, SJ. Published by OCP Publications.

VERSE 1: *Faster (♩ = ca. 112)*

1. My friends, do you know what I have done for you?

1. I have washed your feet with my hands. If

slower   *accel.*

1. I, your Lord, have knelt at your feet, you should do at each

rit.   *D.C.*

1. oth-er's feet as I have done for you.

VERSE 2: *Faster (♩ = ca. 112)*

2. When the world will hate you and re - vile you,

2. when they laugh at your care for the poor,

2. when they hold you in dark-ness and im - pris - on your

rit.   *D.C.*

2. tongues, re - mem-ber how they lis-tened to me.

VERSE 3: *Faster (♩ = ca. 112)*

3. Let not your hearts be trou-bled. Put your trust in

3. God and in me. In my Fa - ther's home I pre -

rit.   **D.C.**

3. pare your room, that where I am you may be.

VERSE 4: *Slower (♩ = ca. 98)*

4. This bread which I give is my bod - y. This cup holds the

rit.   *a tempo*

4. blood of my life. And all will be bro-ken that

rit.   **D.C.**

4. you may have life, that you may learn to for - give.

VERSE 5: *Faster (♩ = ca. 112)*

5. I am the vine, you are the branch - es.

rit.   **D.C.**

5. Re - main in my love and bring forth fruit.

VERSE 6: *Faster (♩ = ca. 112)*

6. For love is pa - tient, love is kind,

6. love is al - ways there to for - give, to en -

6. dure. All the world will crum - ble, but love will re -

rit. **D.C.**

6. main; for Love's own self is God.

VERSE 7: *Faster (♩ = ca. 112)*

7. You will weep in pain while the world re -

7. joic - es, but your grief will be changed in - to joy.

7. For the world will for - get you, but have cour - age, my

rit. **D.C. al fine**

7. friends, for I have o - ver - come the world.

Loving and Forgiving

REFRAIN: (♩ = ca. 80)

Lov-ing and for - giv - ing are you, O Lord;

Lov - ing, for - giv - ing are you, O Lord;

slow to an - ger, rich in kind - ness, lov - ing and for -

slow to an - ger, lov - ing, for -

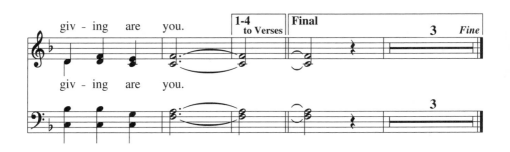

giv - ing are you. 1-4 to Verses Final 3 Fine

giv - ing are you.

VERSES: Cantor(s)

Melody

Harmony

1. All my be - ing, bless the Lord, _____ bless the ho - ly
2. God for-gives us all our sins, _____ heal-ing those who
3. Good and gra - cious is the Lord, _____ slow to an - ger,
4. As heav - en soars a - bove the earth, so great the love of

Text: Based on Psalm 103; Scott Soper.
Music: Scott Soper.
Text and music ©1992, Scott Soper. Published by OCP Publications.

1. name of God. _____ All my be - ing, bless the Lord, re -
2. live in pain, _____ sav - ing us from fi - nal death. God
3. rich in love. _____ God re - mem - bers not our sins; for -
4. God for us. As far as east is from the west, the

rit.   *D.C.*

1. mem - b'ring the good - ness of God.
2. fills us with good - ness and love.
3. giv - ing and lov - ing is God.
4. Lord takes our sins _____ from us.

Lord, Who throughout These Forty Days

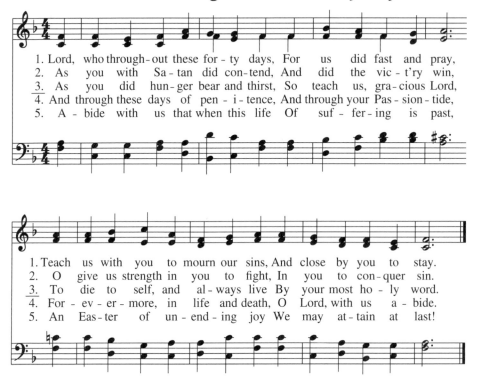

1. Lord, who through-out these for - ty days, For us did fast and pray,
2. As you with Sa - tan did con-tend, And did the vic - t'ry win,
3. As you did hun - ger bear and thirst, So teach us, gra - cious Lord,
4. And through these days of pen - i - tence, And through your Pas - sion-tide,
5. A - bide with us that when this life Of suf - fer - ing is past,

1. Teach us with you to mourn our sins, And close by you to stay.
2. O give us strength in you to fight, In you to con - quer sin.
3. To die to self, and al - ways live By your most ho - ly word.
4. For - ev - er - more, in life and death, O Lord, with us a - bide.
5. An Eas - ter of un - end - ing joy We may at - tain at last!

Text: CM; Claudia F. Hernaman, 1838–1898, alt.
Music: ST. FLAVIAN; *John Day's Psalter*, 1562.

Mary, Full of Grace

1. Ma - ry, full of grace, Splen - dor of our race,
2. Moth - er, Vir - gin pure, Hope and ref - uge sure,

1. Ho - ly Vir - gin Ma - ri - a!
2. Lead us safe - ly to Je - sus!

1. Pray for us to Christ, your Son, Now and when our life is done!
2. Spir - it filled and low - ly, Mir - ror of the Ho - ly!

1-2. O - ra, O - ra pro no - bis!

Text: 55 7 77 7; *O Sanctissima,* alt.; tr. by Jeanne Frolick, SFCC ©1973 Jeanne Frolick, SFCC. Published by OCP Publications.
Music: O DU FRÖLICHE; Tatersall's *Improved Psalmody,* 1794; choral arr. by Randall DeBruyn, b. 1947 ©1991, OCP Publications.

Mary's Song

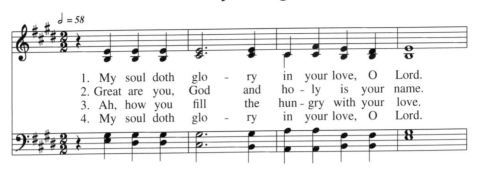

1. My soul doth glo - ry in your love, O Lord.
2. Great are you, God and ho - ly is your name.
3. Ah, how you fill the hun - gry with your love.
4. My soul doth glo - ry in your love, O Lord.

1. My soul doth glo - ry in your love, O Lord. For you
2. Your mer - cy reach - es to the end of time. Ah, the
3. With emp - ty hands the rich are sent a - way. You will
4. My soul doth glo - ry in your love, O Lord. For you

with com - pas - sion,
to the heav - ens,
of your mer - cy,
with com - pas - sion,

1. gazed on your ser - vant with com - pas -
2. low - ly you raise ___ to the heav -
3. al - ways be mind - ful of your mer -
4. smiled on your ser - vant with com - pas -

Text: Luke 1:46 – 55; Millie Rieth.
Music: Millie Rieth; choral arr. by Randall DeBruyn.
Text and music © 1977, 1982, Mildred F. Rieth. Published by OCP Publications.

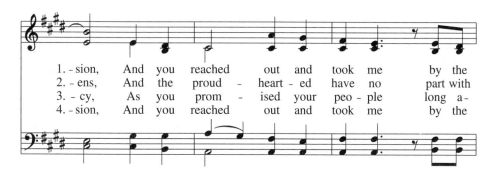

1. - sion, And you reached out and took me by the
2. - ens, And the proud - heart - ed have no part with
3. - cy, As you prom - ised your peo - ple long a-
4. - sion, And you reached out and took me by the

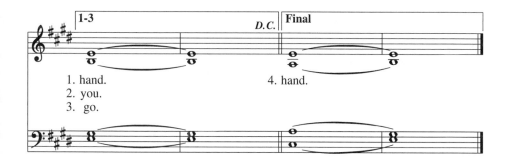

1-3   *D.C.*   **Final**

1. hand.   4. hand.
2. you.
3. go.

Mary's Song

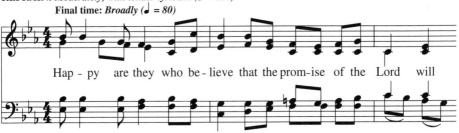

REFRAIN: *Moderately; with tender lyricism* (♩ = 112)
Final time: *Broadly* (♩ = 80)

Hap - py are they who be - lieve that the prom - ise of the Lord will

be ful - filled. / filled. / filled.

1 | 2-6 to Verses | Final Fine

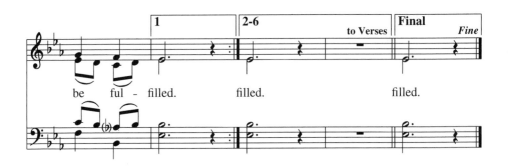

VERSES 1, 2, 5:

Melody

1. I sing with all my soul and praise the Lord.
2. I may hence-forth re-gard my - self as hap - py,
5. His ser - vant Is - ra - el he has re- mem-ber'd.

Harmony

1. I sing to praise the Lord. __
2. I count my-self as hap-py
5. Re-mem-ber'd Is - ra - el; __

Text: Based on Luke 1:45–55; Huub Oosterhuis, b. 1933; tr. by David Smith, b. 1933 ©1967, Gooi en Sticht, bv., Baarn, The Netherlands. Exclusive agent for English-language countries: OCP Publications.
Music: Michael Joncas, b. 1951 ©1979, New Dawn Music.

1. My heart is glad be-cause of God, my Sav - ior;
2. be - cause my God has done great things for me, _____
5. He has been mer - ci - ful to all his peo - ple,

1. My heart is glad be - cause of God, my Sav - ior;
2. be - cause my God has done great things for me, _____
5. he has been mer - ci - ful to all his peo - ple,

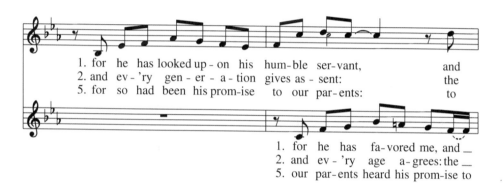

1. for he has looked up - on his hum - ble ser - vant, and
2. and ev - 'ry gen - er - a - tion gives as - sent: the
5. for so had been his prom - ise to our par - ents: to

1. for he has fa - vored me, and __
2. and ev - 'ry age a - grees: the __
5. our par - ents heard his prom - ise to

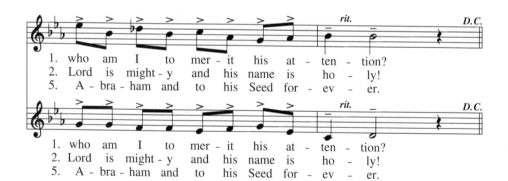

1. who am I to mer - it his at - ten - tion?
2. Lord is might - y and his name is ho - ly!
5. A - bra - ham and to his Seed for - ev - er.

1. who am I to mer - it his at - ten - tion?
2. Lord is might - y and his name is ho - ly!
5. A - bra - ham and to his Seed for - ev - er.

VERSES 3, 4:

Melody

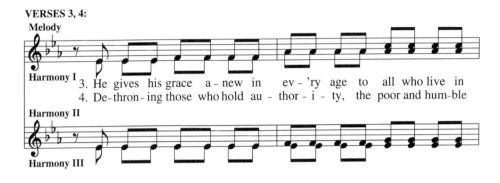

Harmony I

3. He gives his grace a - new in ev - 'ry age to all who live in
4. De - thron - ing those who hold au - thor - i - ty, the poor and hum-ble

Harmony II

Harmony III

3. rev-'rence ___ with him.   Grace is his strength, but he un -
4. peo - ple he makes great.   He gives in great a - bun-dance

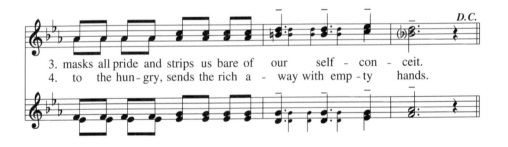

3. masks all pride and strips us bare of our self - con - ceit.
4. to the hun - gry, sends the rich a - way with emp - ty hands.

May God Bless and Keep You

RESPONSE: 1st time: Leader; 2nd time: All ($\bd = 60$)

May God bless and keep you, may God's face shine on you:

May God be kind to you and give you peace.

Text: Based on Numbers 6:22–27; Christopher Walker, b. 1947.
Music: Christopher Walker.
Text and music ©1988, 1989, Christopher Walker. Published by OCP Publications.

May God Bless You

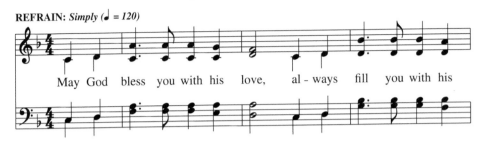

May God bless you with his love, al-ways fill you with his

love; may he hold you in the hol-low of his hand.

his

For the Lord is with you in good-ness and

hand.

love; may his light shine out in your heart.

Text: George Van Grieken, FSC, b. 1952.
Music: George Van Grieken, FSC; choral arr. by Randall DeBruyn, b. 1947.
Text and music ©1984, OCP Publications.

VERSES:

Melody

Harmony

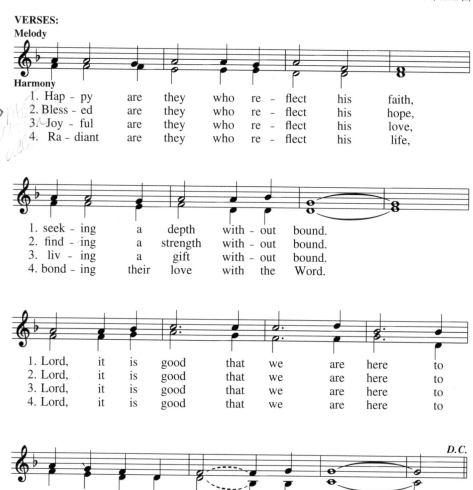

1. Hap - py are they who re - flect his faith,
2. Bless - ed are they who re - flect his hope,
3. Joy - ful are they who re - flect his love,
4. Ra - diant are they who re - flect his life,

1. seek - ing a depth with - out bound.
2. find - ing a strength with - out bound.
3. liv - ing a gift with - out bound.
4. bond - ing their love with the Word.

1. Lord, it is good that we are here to
2. Lord, it is good that we are here to
3. Lord, it is good that we are here to
4. Lord, it is good that we are here to

D.C.

1. see that faith which oth - ers have found.
2. see that hope which oth - ers have found.
3. see that love which oth - ers have found.
4. share that life with one _____ ac - cord.

May We Praise You

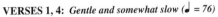

VERSES 1, 4: *Gentle and somewhat slow (♩ = 76)*

1. May we praise you, O Lord, with heart and hand and
4. To the Fa - ther be praise; to Son and Spir - it,

1. voice. And since life it-self is your gift to us, then may
4. praise. Un - to God the one let all praise be done, till the

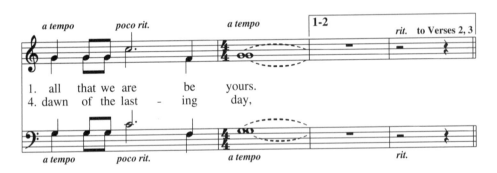

1. all that we are be yours.
4. dawn of the last - ing day,

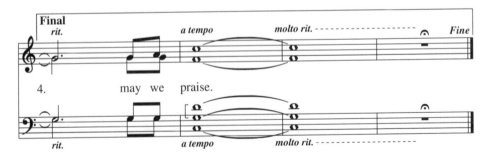

4. may we praise.

Text: Verse 1 based on Office prayer; verses 2–4, John Foley, SJ, b. 1939.
Music: John Foley, SJ.
Text and music ©1981, John B. Foley, SJ and New Dawn Music.

VERSES 2, 3: *a tempo*

2. May our liv - ing be true. May
3. Let your step guide our path. Let

2. May our liv - ing be true, true. May
3. Let your step guide our path, path. Let

*2. May our liv - ing be true. May
3. Let your step guide our path. Let

2. all re - turn to you. And when
3. shades of dark not last. May the

2. all re - turn to you. And when
3. shades of dark not last. May the

2. all re - turn to you. And when
3. shades of dark not last. May the

poco rit.

2. life is done let our pass - ing be like a
3. sun of jus - tice re - turn on high, and your

poco rit.

a tempo   *poco rit.*   *a tempo*   *rit.* **to Verses 3, 4**

2. birth in - to light of day.
3. love be our road and guide.

a tempo   *poco rit.*   *a tempo*   *rit.*

*Verse 2: Basses and tenors sing melody until 3rd line.

307

Mine Eyes Have Seen the Glory

VERSES:

1. Mine __ eyes have seen the glo - ry of the com - ing of the Lord;
2. I have seen him in the watch-fires of a hun - dred cir - cling camps;
3. He has sound - ed forth the trum - pet that shall nev - er call re - treat;
4. In the beau - ty of the lil - ies Christ was born a - cross the sea,

1. He is tram - pling out the vin - tage where the grapes of wrath are stored;
2. They have build - ed him an al - tar in the eve - ning dews and damps;
3. He is sift - ing out the hearts of all be - fore his judg - ment seat;
4. With a glo - ry in his bos - om that trans - fig - ures you and me;

1. He hath loosed the fate - ful light - ning of his ter - ri - ble swift
2. I can read his right - eous sen - tence by the dim and flar - ing
3. O be swift, my soul, to an - swer him; be ju - bi - lant, my
4. As he died to make us ho - ly, let us die that all be

REFRAIN:

1. sword: His truth is march - ing on.
2. lamps; His day is march - ing on.
3. feet! Our God is march - ing on.
4. free! While God is march - ing on.

Glo - ry! Glo - ry! Hal - le-

Text: Julia W. Howe, 1819–1910.
Music: American campmeeting tune, 19th cent.; attr. to William Steffe, ca. 1820–1911.

-lu - jah! Glo - ry! Glo - ry! Hal - le - lu - jah! Glo - ry!

Glo - ry! Hal - le - lu - jah! His truth is march - ing on.

Morning Has Broken

1. Morn-ing has bro - ken Like the first morn - ing,
2. Sweet the rain's new fall, Sun - lit from heav - en,
3. Mine is the sun - light! Mine is the morn - ing

1. Black-bird has spo - ken Like the first bird.
2. Like the first dew - fall On the first grass.
3. Born of the one light E - den saw play!

1. Praise for the sing - ing! Praise for the morn - ing!
2. Praise for the sweet - ness Of the wet gar - den,
3. Praise with e - la - tion, Praise ev - 'ry morn - ing,

1. Praise for them spring - ing Fresh from the Word!
2. Sprung in com - plete - ness Where his feet pass.
3. God's re - cre - a - tion Of the new day!

Text: 55 54 D; Eleanor Farjeon, 1881–1965 ©1957, Eleanor Farjeon. Reprinted by permission of Harold Ober Assoc., Inc.
Music: BUNESSAN; Trad. Gaelic Melody; choral arr. by Randall DeBruyn, b. 1947 ©1990, OCP Publications.

My Soul Rejoices

REFRAIN: (♩ = 100)

Descant

Melody

My soul re - joic - es in God, my
My soul re - joic - es

in the Lord! In God, my
Sav - ior. My spir - it finds its joy in God, the liv - ing

1-5 to Verses | Final | Fine
God. God.

1-5 to Verses | Final | Fine
God. God.

VERSES:

Descant

Melody

1. My soul pro - claims your might - y deeds. My
2. Your mer - cy flows through - out the land and
3. You cast the might - y from their thrones and
4. You fill the hun - gry with good things. With
5. Just as you prom - ised A - bra - ham, you

D.C.

1. spir - it sings the great - ness of your name.
2. ev - 'ry gen - er - a - tion knows your love.
3. raise the poor and low - ly to new life.
4. emp - ty hands you send the rich a - way.
5. come to free your peo - ple, Is - ra - el.

Text: Based on Luke 1:46–55; Owen Alstott, b. 1947.
Music: Owen Alstott.
Text and music ©1984, 1991, OCP Publications.

Now Thank We All Our God

1. Now thank we all our God, With heart, and hands, and voic - es,
2. O may this gra - cious God Through all our life be near us!
3. All praise and thanks to God The Fa - ther now be giv - en,

1. Who won - drous things hath done, In whom his world re - joic - es;
2. With ev - er - joy - ful hearts And bless - ed peace to cheer us;
3. The Son and Spir - it blest, Who reigns in high - est heav - en,

1. Who from our moth - er's arms Hath blessed us on our way
2. Pre - serve us in his grace, And guide us in dis - tress,
3. E - ter - nal, Tri - une God, Whom earth and heav'n a - dore;

1. With count - less gifts of love, And still is ours to - day.
2. And free us from all sin, Till heav - en we pos - sess.
3. For thus it was, is now, And shall be, ev - er - more.

Text: 67 67 66 66; *Sirach* 50:22–24; Martin Rinkart, 1586–1649; tr. by Catherine Winkworth, 1827–1878, alt.
Music: NUN DANKET; Johann Crüger, 1598–1662; adapt. by William H. Monk, 1823–1889, fr. Felix Mendelssohn, 1809–1847.

Now the Green Blade Rises

1. Now the green blade ris - es from the bur-ied grain,
2. In the grave they laid him, love by ha-tred slain,
3. Forth he came at Eas - ter, like the ris - en grain,
4. When our hearts are win - try, griev-ing, or in pain,

1. Wheat that in dark earth man - y days has lain;
2. Think - ing that he would nev - er wake a - gain,
3. He that for three days in the grave had lain,
4. Your touch can call us back to life a - gain,

1. Love lives a - gain, that with the dead has been;
2. Laid in the earth like grain that sleeps un - seen;
3. Raised from the dead, my liv - ing Lord is seen;
4. Fields of our hearts that dead and bare have been;

1-4. Love is come a - gain like wheat a - ris - ing green.

Text: 11 10 10 11; John M. C. Crum, 1872–1958; *Oxford Book of Carols* ©1964, Oxford University Press.
Music: NOËL NOUVELET; French Trad. Carol; choral arr. by Randall DeBruyn, b. 1947 ©1992, OCP Publications.

Now We Remain

REFRAIN: *With reverence* (♩ = 92)

Soprano/Melody
Alto

We hold the death of the Lord deep in our hearts.

Baritone

Liv - ing, now we re - main with

Je - sus, the Christ.

1-4   2 *to Vss*   Final 3 *Fine*

verse 2 next page

VERSES 1, 3, 4:

one phrase

1. Once we were peo - ple a - fraid, lost in the night.
3. He chose to give of him - self, be - came our bread.
4. We are the pres - ence of God; this is our call.

(Vs 3 *rit.*)

1. Then by your cross we were saved; dead be - came liv - ing,
3. Bro - ken that we might live. Love be - yond love,
4. Now to be - come bread and wine: food for the hun - gry,

Text: 1 Corinthians, 1 John, 2 Timothy; David Haas, b. 1957.
Music: David Haas.
Text and music ©1983, G.I.A. Publications, Inc.

314

(Vs 3 a tempo) | 1-2 *D.C.* | 3

1. life from your giv - ing.
3. pain for our pain.
4. life for the wea - ry,

4. for to live with the

broaden

D.C. al fine

4. Lord, we must die with the Lord.

VERSE 2:

Melody

Harmony

2. Some-thing which we have known, some-thing we've touched,

2. what we have seen with our eyes:

D.C.

2. this we have heard; life - giv - ing Word.

315

O Bless the Lord

REFRAIN: *Brightly!* (♩ = ca. 96)

O bless the Lord!

O bless the Lord, the God of our sal - va - tion,

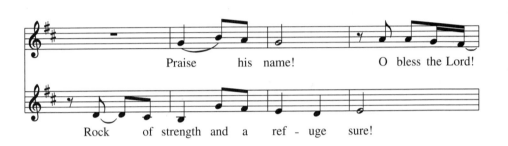

Praise his name! O bless the Lord!

Rock of strength and a ref - uge sure!

O bless the Lord!

O bless the Lord, the God of ev - 'ry na - tion

o - ver all the earth!

o - ver all the earth!

Text: Based on Psalm 148; John Michaels, b. 1947.
Music: John Michaels.
Text and music ©1984, OCP Publications.

VERSES:

Soprano/Alto

1. O bless the Lord, high - est heav - ens a- bove!
2. Let all the earth sing with joy to the Lord,
3. Let all the na - tions on earth bless the Lord,
4. Let all the peo - ple on earth bless the Lord!

Tenor/Bass

1. Bless the Lord! Glo - ri - fy his name!
2. all the seas, crea-tures of the deep!
3. for the Lord gov - erns all the world!
4. Young and old, glo - ri - fy his name!

1. Sun in the day, moon and stars in the night,
2. Moun-tains and hills, birds and beasts in the fields,
3. Let all the rul - ers on earth bless the Lord!
4. Let ev - 'ry voice sing with joy to the Lord:

D.C.

1. wor - ship and praise!
2. wor - ship and praise!
3. Wor - ship and praise!
4. "Glo - ry and praise!"

O Bless the Lord, My Soul

1. O bless the Lord, my soul! His grace to thee pro-claim! And
2. O bless the Lord, my soul! His mer-cies bear in mind! For-
3. He clothes us with his love; Up-holds us with his truth; He
4. Then bless his ho-ly name, Whose grace hath made us whole, Whose

1. all that is with-in me join To bless his ho-ly name!
2. get not all his ben-e-fits! The Lord to thee is kind.
3. heals all our in-fir-mi-ties And ran-soms us from death.
4. lov-ing kind-ness crowns our days! O bless the Lord, my soul!

Text: SM; para. of Psalm 103:1–5; James Montgomery, 1771–1854, alt.
Music: ST. THOMAS (WILLIAMS); *New Universal Psalmodist*, 1770; Aaron Williams, 1731–1776, alt.

O Come, All Ye Faithful

VERSES:

1. O come, all ye faith-ful, joy-ful and tri-um-phant, O come ye, O
2. Sing, choirs of an-gels, sing in ex-ul-ta-tion, Sing, all ye
3. Yea, Lord, we greet thee, born this hap-py morn-ing, Je-sus, to
4. Ad-é-ste fi-dé-les, lae-ti tri-um-phán-tes, Ve-ní-te, ve-

1. come ye to Beth - le-hem; Come, and be-hold him, born the
2. cit-i-zens of heav'n a-bove! Glo-ry to God, all glo-ry
3. thee be all glo - ry giv'n; Word of the Fa-ther, now in
4. ní - te in Béth - le-hem: Na-tum vi-dé-te Re-gem

REFRAIN:

1. King of an - gels;
2. in the high - est;
3. flesh ap-pear - ing;
4. An-ge-ló - rum:

O come, let us a-dore him, O come, let us a-
Ve-ní-te, a-do-ré-mus, ve-ní-te, a-do-

dore him, O come, let us a-dore him, Christ, the Lord!
ré-mus, ve-ní-te, a-do-ré-mus Dó-mi-num.

Text: Irregular with refrain; John F. Wade, 1711–1786; tr. by Frederick Oakeley, 1802–1880, alt.
Music: ADESTE FIDELES; melody attr. to John F. Wade; harm. *The English Hymnal*, 1906, alt.

319

O Come, Divine Messiah

Text: 78 76 with refrain; Abbé Simon-Joseph Pellegrin, 1663–1745; tr. by S. Mary of St. Philip, 1825–1904.
Music: VENEZ, DIVIN MESSIE; French Nöel, 16th cent.; choral arr. by Randall DeBruyn, b. 1947 ©1990, OCP Publications.

earth. Dis-pel the night and show your face, and bid us

hail the dawn of grace. O come, di - vine Mes -

si - ah; the world in si - lence waits the day when hope shall

sing its tri - umph and sad - ness flee a - way.

O Come, O Come, Emmanuel

1. O come, O come, Emmanuel,
2. O come, Thou Wisdom from on high,
3. O come, O come, Thou Lord of might,
4. O come, Thou Rod of Jesse's stem,
5. O come, Thou Key of David, come,
6. O come, Thou Dayspring from on high
7. O come, Desire of nations, bind

1. And ransom captive Israel,
2. Who or-d'rest all things mightily;
3. Who to thy tribes on Sinai's height
4. From ev-'ry foe deliver them
5. And open wide our heav'nly home;
6. And cheer us by thy drawing nigh;
7. In one the hearts of all human-kind;

1. That mourns in lonely exile here
2. To us the path of knowledge show,
3. In ancient times didst give the law,
4. That trust thy mighty pow'r to save,
5. Make safe the way that leads on high,
6. Disperse the gloomy clouds of night,
7. Bid thou our sad divisions cease,

Text: LM with refrain; Latin, 9th cent.; verses 1, 3, 4, 5, and 6, para. in *Psalteriolum Cantionum Catholicarum*, Cologne, 1710; tr. by John M. Neale, 1818–1866; verses 2 and 7, tr. *Hymnal 1940*, alt.
Music: VENI, VENI, EMMANUEL; Mode I; *Processionale*, 15th cent. French; adapt. by Thomas Helmore, 1811–1890.

1. Un - til the Son of God ap - pear.
2. And teach us in her ways to go.
3. In cloud and maj - es - ty and awe.
4. And give them vic - t'ry o'er the grave.
5. And close the path to mis - er - y.
6. And death's dark shad - ow put to flight.
7. And be thy - self our Prince of Peace.

REFRAIN:

Re - joice! Re - joice! Em - man - u - el

Shall come to thee, O Is - ra - el!

O Come, Little Children

1. O come, lit-tle chil-dren, come one and come all; O
2. O see in the man-ger so meek and so mild, O
3. His bed, lit-tle chil-dren, a man-ger with hay; His

1. come to the man-ger in Beth-le-hem's stall, And
2. see in the soft light the heav-en-ly Child, In
3. Moth-er and Jo-seph in ec-sta-sy pray; The

1. see what our Fa-ther in Heav-en a-bove Has
2. swad-dling clothes fold-ed, his beau-ty more sweet Than
3. shep-herds in won-der their glad wor-ship bring, While

1. sent to us all on this earth with his love.
2. an-gels, whose voic-es his low-ly birth greet.
3. cho-rus of an-gels sweet Glo-ri-as sing.

Text: 11 11 11 11; Johann C. von Schmid, 1768–1854; tr. by Melanie Schute, 1885–1922.
Music: IHR KINDERLEIN, KOMMET; Johann A. P. Schulz, 1747–1800; choral arr. by Elaine Rendler ©1988, OCP Publications.

O God, Hear Us

REFRAIN: *Reverently* (♩ = 108)

Descant

O God, hear

1st time Cantor, All repeat:
Soprano
(a tempo)

Alto

O God, hear us; hear

Tenor

Bass *(a tempo)*

1,2 2nd time to Verses | **Final**

5 *Fine*

us; hear our prayer. prayer.

1,2 2nd time to Verses | **Final**

5 *Fine*

our prayer.

5

VERSES:

1. You who chose the low — ly to con - found the
2. May we be your jus - tice; may we be your
3. On - ly earth - en ves - sels are __ we who

1. proud __ of heart, give us the heart __ of Ma - ry.
2. kind- ness and truth; ♩ may we be __ your mer - cy.
3. gath - er to - day. ♩ Make us ves-sels of glo - ry.

rit. *D.C.*

1-3. Hear us, O God.

Text: Bob Hurd, b. 1950.
Music: Bob Hurd; choral arr. by Craig S. Kingsbury, b. 1952.
Text and music ©1984, Bob Hurd. Published by OCP Publications.

O God, Our Help in Ages Past

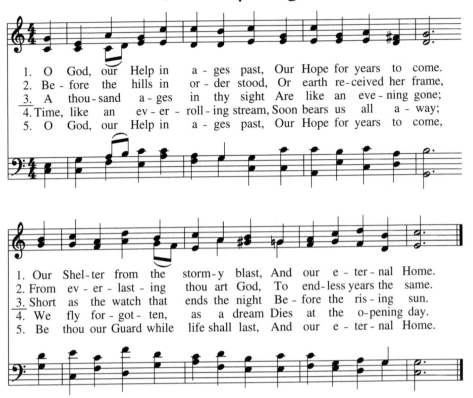

1. O God, our Help in a-ges past, Our Hope for years to come.
2. Be - fore the hills in or - der stood, Or earth re-ceived her frame,
3. A thou-sand a-ges in thy sight Are like an eve-ning gone;
4. Time, like an ev - er - roll - ing stream, Soon bears us all a - way;
5. O God, our Help in a-ges past, Our Hope for years to come,

1. Our Shel-ter from the storm-y blast, And our e - ter - nal Home.
2. From ev - er - last - ing thou art God, To end-less years the same.
3. Short as the watch that ends the night Be - fore the ris - ing sun.
4. We fly for - got - ten, as a dream Dies at the o-pening day.
5. Be thou our Guard while life shall last, And our e - ter - nal Home.

Text: CM; Based on Psalm 90; Isaac Watts, 1674–1748, alt.
Music: ST. ANNE; attr. to William Croft, 1678–1727.

O God, You Search Me

1. O God, you search me and you know me.
2. You know my rest-ing and my ris - ing.
3. Be - fore a word is on my tongue, Lord,
4. Al - though your Spir - it is up - on me,
5. For you cre - at - ed me and shaped me,

1. All my thoughts lie o - pen to your gaze.
2. You dis - cern my pur-pose from a - far,
3. You have known its mean-ing through and through.
4. Still I search for shel - ter from your light.
5. Gave me life with - in my moth-er's womb.

1. When I walk or lie down you are be - fore me:
2. And with love ev - er - last - ing you be - siege me:
3. You are with me be-yond my un - der - stand - ing:
4. There is no - where on earth I can es - cape you:
5. For the won - der of who I am I praise you:

1. Ev - er the mak - er and keep - er of my days.
2. In ev - 'ry mo - ment of life or death, you are.
3. God of my pres - ent, my past and fu - ture, too.
4. E - ven the dark - ness is ra - di - ant in your sight.
5. Safe in your hands, all cre - a - tion is made new.

Text: Psalm 139; Bernadette Farrell, b. 1957.
Music: Bernadette Farrell.
Text and music ©1992, Bernadette Farrell. Published by OCP Publications.

O Holy Mary

REFRAIN: (♩ = 54)

Descant

O ho - ly Dwell-ing Place of

Melody

O ho - ly Dwell-ing Place of God. O

God. O ho - ly!

ho - ly Tem - ple of the Word. O

div. *Fine*

Ho - ly Ma - ry, ho - ly Moth - er of God.

Fine

ho - ly Ma - ry, ho - ly Moth - er of God.

VERSES: *Freely*

1. O ra - diant star of heav - en, il - lu - min - ing the night;
2. O blest be - yond all oth - ers, of ev - 'ry land and race,
3. From heav'n the an - gel Ga - bri - el an - nounced the an - cient plan
4. With joy be - yond all meas - ure you cared for God's own son
5. Ex - qui - site was your sor - row, un - e - qualed was the loss
6. All praise and ad - o - ra - tion we sing now to your son

D.C.

1. re - flec - tion of the Son, __ our source of life and light.
2. pos - sess - ing in your soul __ the full - ness of God's grace.
3. and hum - bly you ac - cept - ed to bear the God - made - man.
4. and pon - dered in your heart __ the new age now be - gun.
5. you suf - fered when your son __ was raised up - on the cross.
6. who reigns in high - est heav - en and has the vic - t'ry won.

Text: Owen Alstott, b. 1947.
Music: Owen Alstott.
Text and music ©1985, OCP Publications.

O Little Town of Bethlehem

1. O lit-tle town of Beth-le-hem, How still we see thee lie!
2. For Christ is born of Ma - ry, And gath-ered all a - bove,
3. How si - lent-ly, how si - lent-ly, The won-drous gift is giv'n!
4. O ho - ly Child of Beth-le-hem! De-scend to us, we pray;

1. A - bove thy deep and dream-less sleep The si - lent stars go by;
2. While mor-tals sleep, the an - gels keep Their watch of won-d'ring love.
3. So God im-parts to hu - man hearts The bless-ings of his heav'n.
4. Cast out our sin and en - ter in; Be born in us to - day.

1. Yet in thy dark streets shin - eth The ev - er - last-ing Light:
2. O morn-ing stars, to - geth - er Pro - claim the ho - ly birth!
3. No ear may hear his com - ing, But in this world of sin,
4. We hear the Christ-mas an - gels The great glad tid-ings tell;

1. The hopes and fears of all the years Are met in thee to-night.
2. And prais - es sing to God the King, And peace to all on earth.
3. Where meek souls will re - ceive him, still The dear Christ en - ters in.
4. O come to us, a - bide with us, Our Lord Em - man - u - el!

Text: 86 86 76 86; Phillips Brooks, 1835–1893.
Music: ST. LOUIS; Lewis H. Redner, 1831–1908.

Of the Father's Love Begotten

Descant

4. O heav'n a - dore him; An - gel
5. Glo - ry to the Fa - ther, Glo - ry

Melody

1. Of the Fa - ther's love be - got - ten, Ere the worlds be -
2. Bless - ed was the day for ev - er When the Vir - gin,
3. This is he whom seers in old time Chant - ed of with
4. O ye heights of heav'n, a - dore him; An - gel hosts, his
5. Glo - ry be to God the Fa - ther, Glo - ry be to

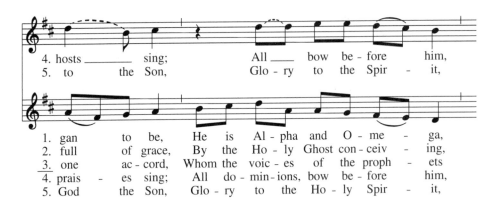

4. hosts sing; All bow be - fore him,
5. to the Son, Glo - ry to the Spir - it,

1. gan to be, He is Al - pha and O - me - ga,
2. full of grace, By the Ho - ly Ghost con - ceiv - ing,
3. one ac - cord, Whom the voic - es of the proph - ets
4. prais - es sing; All do - min - ions, bow be - fore him,
5. God the Son, Glo - ry to the Ho - ly Spir - it,

4. And ex - tol our King; Let none be
5. God, three in one. From all cre -

1. He the source, the end - ing he, Of the things that are, that
2. Bore the Sav - ior of our race, And the child, the world's Re -
3. Prom - ised in their faith - ful word; Now he shines, the long ex -
4. And ex - tol our God and King; Let no tongue on earth be
5. Per - sons three, yet God - head one. Glo - ry be from all cre -

Text: 87 87 87 7; *Corde Natus Ex Parentis*; Marcus Aurelius Clemens Prudentius, ca. 348–413; tr. by John M. Neale, 1818–1866 and
Henry W. Baker, 1821–1877, alt.; verse 5, Horatius Bonar, 1808–1889.
Music: DIVINUM MYSTERIUM; Sanctus trope; ca. 11th cent., Mode V; adapt. fr. *Piae Cantiones*, 1582; descant by Randall DeBruyn,
b. 1947 ©1990, OCP Publications.

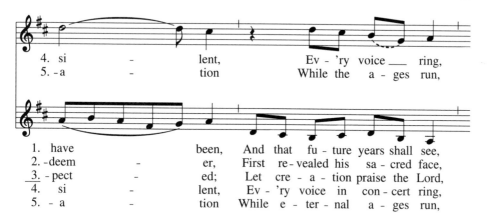

4. si - lent,   Ev - 'ry voice ___ ring,
5. -a - tion   While the a - ges run,

1. have   been, And that fu - ture years shall see,
2. -deem - er,   First re - vealed his sa - cred face,
3. - pect - ed;   Let cre - a - tion praise the Lord,
4. si - lent,   Ev - 'ry voice in con - cert ring,
5. - a - tion   While e - ter - nal a - ges run,

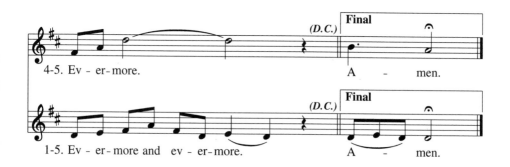

4-5. Ev - er - more.   A - men.

1-5. Ev - er - more and ev - er - more.   A - men.

On Eagle's Wings

Text: Adapt. fr. Psalm 91; Michael Joncas, b. 1951.
Music: Michael Joncas.
Text and music ©1979, New Dawn Music.

O Sacred Head, Surrounded

1. O Sa-cred Head, sur - round - ed By crown of pierc - ing thorn!
2. O Love, all love tran - scend - ing, O Wis - dom from on high!
3. O Je - sus, we a - dore thee, Up - on the cross our King!

1. O bleed - ing Head, so wound - ed, Re - viled and put to scorn!
2. O Truth, un - changed, un - chang - ing, Sur - ren - dered up to die!
3. We hum - bly bow be - fore thee, And of thy vic - t'ry sing!

1. No come - li - ness or beau - ty Thy wound - ed face be - trays,
2. Was e'er a love so won - drous! That from his heav'n - ly throne
3. Thy cross is our sal - va - tion, Our hope from day to day,

1. Yet an - gel hosts a - dore thee And trem - ble as they gaze.
2. God should de - scend a - mong us To suf - fer for his own.
3. Our peace and con - so - la - tion When life shall fade a - way.

Text: 76 76 D; Verse 1 ascr. to Bernard of Clairvaux, 1091−1153, alt.; verse 2, Owen Alstott, b. 1947; verse 3, Owen Alstott, composite. Verses 2-3 ©1977, OCP Publications.
Music: PASSION CHORALE; Hans L. Hassler, 1564−1612; adapt. and harm. by Johann S. Bach, 1685−1750.

On Jordan's Bank

1. On Jor - dan's bank the Bap - tist's cry An -
2. Then cleansed be ev - 'ry soul from sin; Make
3. For thou art our sal - va - tion, Lord, Our
4. All praise, e - ter - nal Son, to thee, Whose

1. nounc - es that the Lord is nigh; A - wake and heark - en,
2. straight the way of God with - in, Pre - pare we in our
3. ref - uge and our sure re - ward; Shine forth, and let thy
4. ad - vent set thy peo - ple free; Whom with the Fa - ther

1. for he brings Glad tid - ings of the King of kings.
2. hearts a home Where such a might - y guest may come.
3. light re - store Our souls to heav'n - ly grace once more.
4. we a - dore And Ho - ly Spir - it ev - er - more.

Text: LM; Charles Coffin, 1676–1749; tr. by John Chandler, 1806–1876, alt.
Music: WINCHESTER NEW; melody fr. *Musikalisch Hand-Buch,* Hamburg, 1690; harm. by William H. Monk, 1823–1889.

On This Day, the First of Days

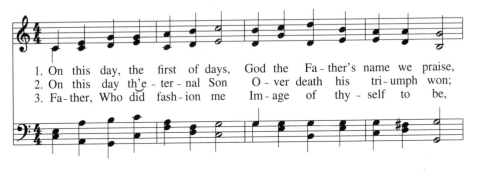

1. On this day, the first of days, God the Fa-ther's name we praise,
2. On this day th'e-ter-nal Son O-ver death his tri-umph won;
3. Fa-ther, Who did fash-ion me Im-age of thy-self to be,

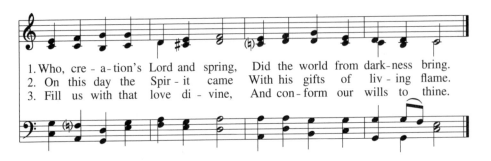

1. Who, cre-a-tion's Lord and spring, Did the world from dark-ness bring.
2. On this day the Spir-it came With his gifts of liv-ing flame.
3. Fill us with that love di-vine, And con-form our wills to thine.

Text: 77 77; *Die parente temporum; Carcassion Breviary,* 1748; tr. by Henry W. Baker, 1821–1877, alt.
Music: LÜBECK; Freylinghausen's *Geistreiches Gesangbuch,* 1704; adapt. and harm. by William H. Havergal, 1793–1870.

One Bread, One Body

Text: Based on 1 Corinthians 10 and 12, Galatians 3, *Didache* 9; John Foley, SJ, b. 1939.
Music: John Foley, SJ.
Text and music ©1978, John B. Foley and New Dawn Music.

One Spirit, One Church

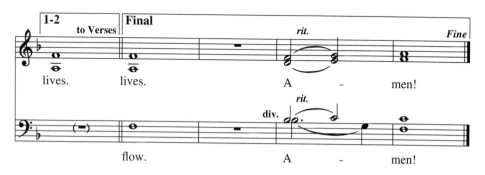

1-2 to Verses | **Final** | *rit.* *Fine*

lives.   lives.   A - men!

div. *rit.*

flow.   A - men!

VERSES: *Tenderly*

1. Come, Ho - ly Ghost,   Cre - a - tor blest,   and   in our hearts   take
2. O   Com-fort - er,   to   thee we cry,   thou   gift of God   sent

1. up   thy   rest;   come   with thy grace   and   heav'n-ly
2. from   on   high.   Thou   font of life   and   fire of

D.C.

1. aid   to   fill   the   hearts which   thou   hast   made.
2. love,   the   soul's a - noint - ing   from   a - bove.

Only a Shadow

1. The love we have for you, O Lord, is —
2. The bread we take and eat, O Lord, is —
3. Our own be - lief in you, O Lord, ⁊ is
4. The dreams we share to - day, O Lord, ⁊ are
5. The joy we share to - day, O Lord, ⁊ is

Soprano/Tenor

Alto/Bass

1. on - ly a— shad - ow of your love for us;
2. your bod - y bro - ken and shared with us;
3. on - ly— a shad - ow of your faith in us;
4. on - ly— a shad - ow of your dreams for us;
5. on - ly— a shad - ow of your joys for us;

1. on - ly a shad - ow of your love for us; your
2. your bod - y bro - ken and shared with us; the
3. on - ly a shad - ow of your faith in us; your
4. on - ly a shad - ow of your dreams for us, if
5. on - ly a shad - ow of your joys for us, when

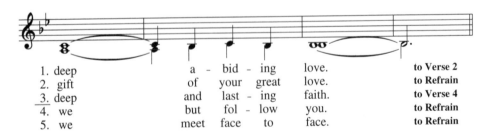

1. deep a - bid - ing love. **to Verse 2**
2. gift of your great love. **to Refrain**
3. deep and last - ing faith. **to Verse 4**
4. we but fol - low you. **to Refrain**
5. we meet face to face. **to Refrain**

Text: Carey Landry, b. 1944.
Music: Carey Landry; choral arr. by Louise Anderson.
Text and music ©1971, 1975, Carey Landry and North American Liturgy Resources (N.A.L.R.).

REFRAIN:

Our lives are in your hands, our lives

are in your hands. Our love for you will

grow, O Lord; your light in us will shine.

Only in God

Text: Based on Psalm 62; John Michael Talbot, b. 1954.
Music: John Michael Talbot; choral arr. by Phil Perkins, b.1948 and Rick Modlin, b.1966.
Text and music ©1980, 1995, BMG Songs, Inc. (ASCAP) and Birdwing Music (ASCAP).

not be a-fraid at all. My strong-hold, my

D.C.
(Final time to Coda) ✛

Sav - ior, I shall not be moved.

✛ **CODA**
Cantor or unison Choir

On - ly in God is my soul at rest, in him comes my sal - va - tion.

Our Blessing Cup

Text: Based on 1 Corinthians 10, Psalm 116; Bob Hurd, b. 1950.
Music: Bob Hurd; choral arr. by Craig S. Kingsbury, b. 1952.
Text and music ©1988, Bob Hurd. Published by OCP Publications.

1-2. mi - se - re - re,   mi - se - re - re,   mi - se - re - re
3-4. do - na no - bis,   do - na no - bis,   do - na no - bis

bread we break, it is a shar - ing in the bod - y of the

bread we break is a shar - ing in the bod - y of the

1. We will take the cup of life, and ___ call up - on God's
2. We ___ are your ser - vants, for ___ you have set us
3. with ___ all your peo - ple, praise and glo - ry to your
4. Though _ death sur-round-ed me, you ___ heard and an-swered

1-3 D.C. | **Final** | 2

1-2. no - bis.
3-4. pa - cem. ___

***1** | **Final** | 2

Lord.

2

D.C.

(=)

1. name.   (*D.C.* **to Refrain with Descant**)
2. free.   (*D.C.* **to Verse 3**)
3. name.   (*D.C.* **to Verse 4**)
4. me.   (*D.C.* **to Refrain and Final**
          Ending with Descant)

*Repeat Refrain 1st time only (or ostinato as desired)

Our Blessing Cup

REFRAIN: 1st time: Cantor, All repeat; Each time thereafter: All

Lyric and sustained (♩ = 76)

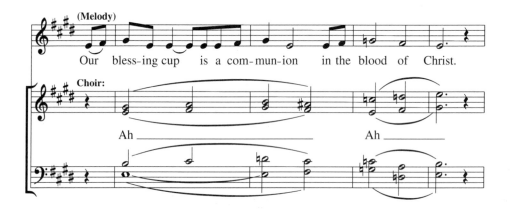

Our bless-ing cup is a com-mun-ion in the blood of Christ.

(Melody)

Our bless-ing cup is a com-mun-ion in the blood of Christ.

Choir:

Ah _____ Ah _____

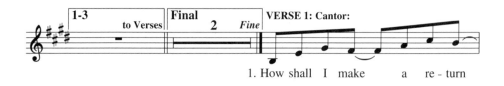

| 1-3 | Final | | VERSE 1: Cantor: |
| to Verses | 2 *Fine* | |

1. How shall I make a re-turn

1. to the Lord for all the good he has done for me? The

1. cup of sal-va - tion I will take up, and I will

D.C.

1. call up-on the name of the Lord.

Text: Based on 1 Corinthians 10:16, Psalm 116:12–13, Psalm 34:9a, 1 Corinthians 11:26; Michael Joncas, b. 1951.
Music: Michael Joncas.
Text and music ©1979, New Dawn Music.

VERSE 2: Cantor:

2. Taste and see, taste and

2. see the sweet - ness of the Lord, the

2. good - ness of the Lord.

VERSE 3: Cantor:

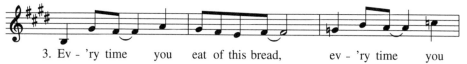

3. Ev - 'ry time you eat of this bread, ev - 'ry time you

3. drink of this cup you pro - claim the

3. death of the Lord un - til he comes.

347

Out of Darkness

Text: Christopher Walker, b. 1947.
Music: Christopher Walker.
Text and music ©1989, Christopher Walker. Published by OCP Publications.

VERSES:

1. Let us take the words you give. Strong and
2. Let us take the Christ you give. Bro - ken
3. Let us take the love you give, that the

1. faith - ful words to live. Words that in our
2. Bod - y, Christ we live. Christ the ris - en
3. way of love we live. Love to bring your

1. hearts are sown; words that bind us as your own.
2. from the tomb; Christ who calls us as your own.
3. peo - ple home; love to make us all your own.

rall. **D.C.**

rall.

Pan de Vida

*Bread of Life, body of the Lord,
**Power is for service, because God is love.

Text: Based on John 13:1–15; Galatians 3:28–29; Bob Hurd, b. 1950 and Pia Moriarty, b. 1948.
Music: Bob Hurd; choral arr. by Craig S. Kingsbury, b. 1952.
Text and music ©1988, Bob Hurd. Published by OCP Publications.

VERSES:

Melody

Harmony

1. We are the dwell-ing of God, fra - gile and
2. Us - te - des me lla - man "Se - ñor", me in - cli - no a la -
*2. You call me Teach-er and Lord, I who have
3. There is no Jew ___ or Greek; there is no

1. wound - ed and weak. We are the bod - y of Christ,
2. var - les los pies: Ha - gan lo mis - mo, hu - mil -
2. washed ___ your feet. So you must do as I do,
3. slave ___ or free; there is no wom - an or man;

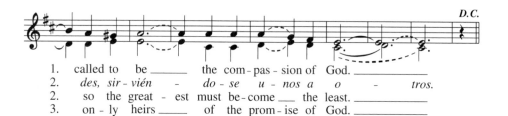

1. called to be ___ the com - pas - sion of God. _____
2. des, sir - vién - do - se u - nos a o - tros.
2. so the great - est must be - come ___ the least. _____
3. on - ly heirs ___ of the prom - ise of God. _____

*Verse 2 in English.

351

Pange Lingua Gloriosi/
Sing, My Tongue, the Savior's Glory
(Holy Thursday–English Setting)

1. Sing, my tongue, the Sav-ior's glo-ry, Of his flesh the mys-t'ry sing;
2. Of a pure and spot-less vir-gin Born for us on earth be-low,
3. On the night of that last sup-per Seat-ed with his cho-sen band,
4. Word made flesh, the bread of na-ture By his word to Flesh he turns;
5. *Down in ad-o-ra-tion fall-ing, This great sac-ra-ment we hail;*
6. To the ev-er-last-ing Fa-ther, And the Son who made us free,

1. Of the Blood all price ex-ceed-ing, Shed by our im-mor-tal king.
2. He, as man, with us con-vers-ing, Stayed, the seeds of truth to sow:
3. He, the Pas-chal vic-tim eat-ing, First ful-fills the Law's com-mand;
4. Wine in-to his Blood he chang-es, What though sense no change dis-cerns?
5. *O-ver an-cient forms of wor-ship New-er rites of grace pre-vail;*
6. And the Spir-it, God pro-ceed-ing From them Each e-ter-nal-ly,

1. Des-tined for the world's re-demp-tion, From a no-ble womb to spring.
2. Then he closed in sol-emn or-der Won-drous-ly his life of woe.
3. Then as food to the dis-ci-ples Gives him-self with his own hand.
4. On-ly be the heart in ear-nest, Faith its les-son quick-ly learns.
5. *Faith will tell us Christ is pres-ent, When our hu-man sens-es fail.*
6. Be sal-va-tion, hon-or, bless-ing, Might and end-less maj-es-ty.

Text: 87 87 87; St. Thomas Aquinas, 1227–1274; tr. by Edward Caswall, 1814–1878.
Music: ST. THOMAS; *Tantum Ergo*; John F. Wade, 1711–1786.

Pange Lingua Gloriosi/
Sing, My Tongue, the Savior's Glory
(Holy Thursday–Latin Setting)

1. Pan-ge lin-gua glo-ri-ó-si, Cór-po-ris my-sté-ri-um,
2. No-bis da-tus, no-bis na-tus Ex in-tá-cta Vír-gi-ne,
3. In su-pré-mae no-cte coe-nae, Ré-cum-bens cum frá-tri-bus,
4. Ver-bum ca-ro, pa-nem ve-rum Ver-bo car-nem éf-fi-cit:
5. *Tan-tum er-go Sa-cra-mén-tum Ve-ne-ré-mur cér-nu-i:*
6. *Ge-ni-tó-ri, Ge-ni-tó-que Laus et ju-bi-lá-ti-o,*

1. San-gui-nís-que pre-ti-ó-si, Quem in mun-di pré-ti-um
2. Et in mun-do con-ver-sá-tus, Spar-so ver-bi sé-mi-ne,
3. Ob-ser-vá-ta le-ge ple-ne Ci-bis in le-gá-li-bus,
4. Fit-que san-guis Chri-sti me-rum, Et si sen-sus dé-fi-cit,
5. *Et an-tí-quum do-cu-mén-tum No-vo ce-dat rí-tu-i;*
6. *Sa-lus, ho-nor, vir-tus quo-que Sit et be-ne-dí-cti-o:*

1. Fruc-tus ven-tris ge-ne-ró-si Rex ef-fú-dit gén-ti-um.
2. Su-i mo-ras in-co-lá-tus Mi-ro clau-sit ór-di-ne.
3. Ci-bum tur-bae du-o-dé-nae Se dat su-is má-ni-bus.
4. Ad fir-mán-dum cor sin-cé-rum So-la fi-des súf-fi-cit.
5. *Prae-stet fi-des sup-ple-mén-tum Sén-su-um de-fé-ctu-i.*
6. *Pro-ce-dén-ti ab u-tró-que Com-par sit lau-dá-ti-o.*

Text: 87 87 87; St. Thomas Aquinas, 1227–1274.
Music: ST. THOMAS; *Tantum Ergo*; John F. Wade, 1711–1786.

Parce Domine/Spare Your People, Lord

REFRAIN:

Par - ce Dó - mi - ne, par - ce pó - pu - lo ___ tu - o: ___
Spare your peo-ple, Lord, spare your peo - ple in your lov-ing kind - ness!

Fine

Ne in ae - tér - num i - ra - scá - ris no - bis.
Show us your mer - cy; we have sinned a - gainst you, Lord.

VERSES: Unison Choir or solo

1. Have mercy on me, God, in your good - ness;
2. For I know my of - fense; _____
3. A clean heart create for me, _____ God;
4. Restore my joy in your sal - va - tion;
5. For you do not de - sire sac - ri - fice;

1. In your abundant compassion blot out my of - fense. _____
2. My sin is always be - fore _____ me.
3. Renew in me a stead - fast spir - it.
4. Sustain in me a will - ing spir - it.
5. A burnt offering you would not ac - cept. _____

Text: Irregular; Refrain from Joel 2:17; English tr. by Owen Alstott, b. 1947 ©1973, OCP Publications. Verses from Psalm 51 ©1991,
Confraternity of Christian Doctrine, Inc. Used with permission. All rights reserved.
Music: PARCE DOMINE; Refrain, Mode I; verses by Randall DeBruyn, b. 1947 ©1982, OCP Publications.

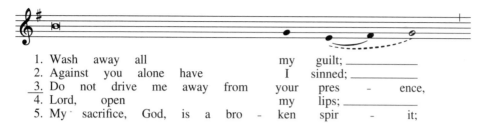

1. Wash away all my guilt; _____
2. Against you alone have I sinned; _____
3. Do not drive me away from your pres - ence,
4. Lord, open my lips; _____
5. My sacrifice, God, is a bro - ken spir - it;

D.C.

1. From my sin cleanse me. _____
2. I have done such evil in your sight. _____
3. Nor take from me your Ho - ly Spir - it. _____
4. My mouth will proclaim your praise. _____
5. God, do not spurn a broken, hum - bled heart. _____

Patience, People

REFRAIN, part I: *Not too fast (♩ = 72)*

Descant *(a tempo)*

Pa - tience, peo - ple,

Soprano (Melody) *(a tempo)*

Alto

Pa - tience, peo - ple,

Tenor

Bass *(a tempo)*

poco rit.

till the Lord is come.

poco rit.

till the Lord is come.

poco rit.

VERSES: *Slightly faster, with expression (♩ = 76)*

1. See _____ the farm - er a - wait the yield of the
2. You _____ have seen _____ the pur - pose of the
3. Stead - y your hearts; for the Lord is close at

1. soil. He watch - es it in
2. Lord. You know of his com -
3. hand. And do not grum - ble,

Text: Based on James 5:7–9, 11; John Foley, SJ, b. 1939.
Music: John Foley, SJ.
Text and music ©1977, 1979, John B. Foley, SJ and New Dawn Music.

356

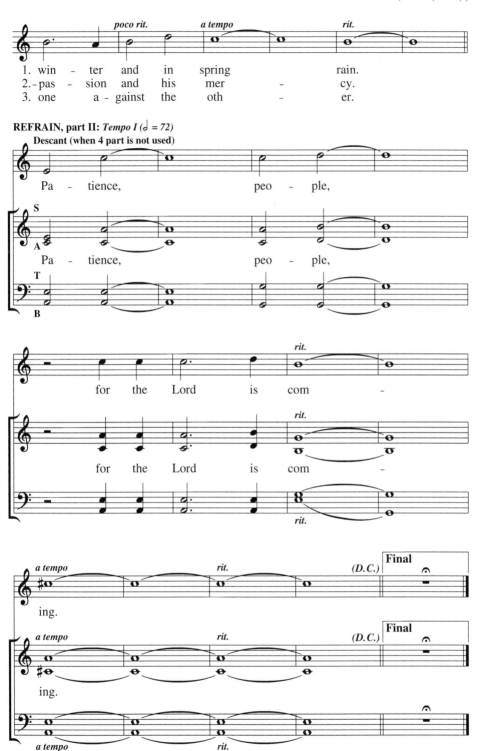

REFRAIN, part II: *Tempo I (♩ = 72)*

Descant (when 4 part is not used)

1. win - ter and in spring rain.
2.-pas - sion and his mer - cy.
3. one a - gainst the oth - er.

Pa - tience, peo - ple,

Pa - tience, peo - ple,

for the Lord is com -

for the Lord is com -

ing.

ing.

Peace

REFRAIN: *Moderately*

Peace I leave with you, my friends, peace the

world can-not give. Peace I leave with you, my

1-7   to Verses

friends, so that your joy be ev – er full.

Final

full. Peace I leave with you, my

Text: Based on John 14:27 et al.; Weston Priory, Gregory Norbet, OSB, b. 1940.
Music: Weston Priory, Gregory Norbet, OSB; choral arr. by Craig S. Kingsbury, b. 1952.
Text and music ©1971, 1986, from the recording *Locusts And Wild Honey*, The Benedictine Foundation of the State of Vermont, Inc., Weston, VT.

Fine

friends, so that your joy be ev - er full.

VERSES:

1. The Fa - ther's love I came to give,
2. Take ____ his gift and be at peace;
3. By ____ this love which you should have,
4. Take ____ my words of life to heart,
5. All ____ I have I give to you;
6. I came so that you may have life,
7. If ____ you love me keep my word,

D.C.

1. to be the hope for all who live.
2. the Spir - it of our love I bring.
3. all ____ will know you are my friends.
4. and you will live with hope and joy.
5. I share with you the Fa - ther's love.
6. and have it to ____ the full.
7. and ____ our home we'll make with you.

Peace Is Flowing Like a River

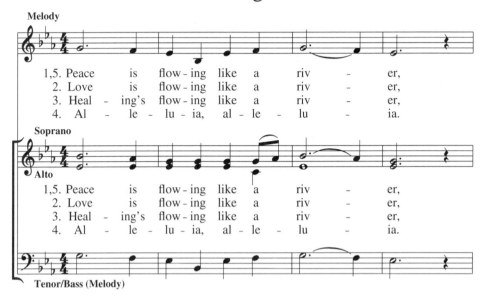

Melody

1,5. Peace is flow-ing like a riv - er,
2. Love is flow-ing like a riv - er,
3. Heal - ing's flow-ing like a riv - er,
4. Al - le - lu - ia, al - le - lu - ia.

Soprano
Alto

1,5. Peace is flow-ing like a riv - er,
2. Love is flow-ing like a riv - er,
3. Heal - ing's flow-ing like a riv - er,
4. Al - le - lu - ia, al - le - lu - ia.

Tenor/Bass (Melody)

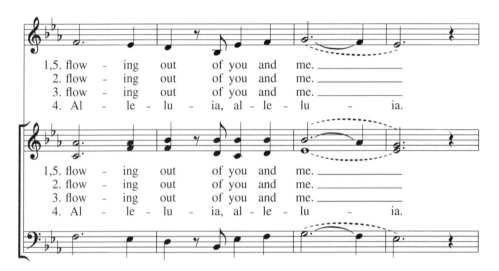

1,5. flow - ing out of you and me. _____
2. flow - ing out of you and me. _____
3. flow - ing out of you and me. _____
4. Al - le - lu - ia, al - le - lu - ia.

1,5. flow - ing out of you and me. _____
2. flow - ing out of you and me. _____
3. flow - ing out of you and me. _____
4. Al - le - lu - ia, al - le - lu - ia.

Text: Traditional; based on Psalm 107; adapt. by Carey Landry, b. 1944.
Music: Traditional; adapt. by Carey Landry; choral arr. by Louise Anderson.
Text and music ©1975, North American Liturgy Resources (N.A.L.R.).

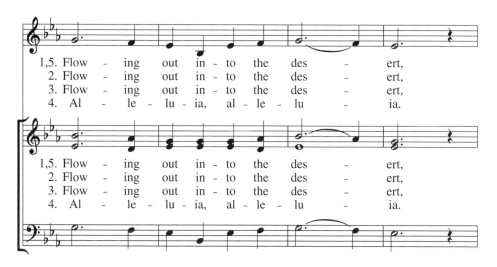

1,5. Flow - ing out in - to the des - ert,
2. Flow - ing out in - to the des - ert,
3. Flow - ing out in - to the des - ert,
4. Al - le - lu - ia, al - le - lu - ia.

1,5. Flow - ing out in - to the des - ert,
2. Flow - ing out in - to the des - ert,
3. Flow - ing out in - to the des - ert,
4. Al - le - lu - ia, al - le - lu - ia.

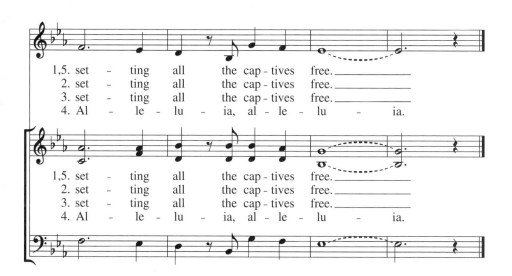

1,5. set - ting all the cap - tives free.
2. set - ting all the cap - tives free.
3. set - ting all the cap - tives free.
4. Al - le - lu - ia, al - le - lu - ia.

1,5. set - ting all the cap - tives free.
2. set - ting all the cap - tives free.
3. set - ting all the cap - tives free.
4. Al - le - lu - ia, al - le - lu - ia.

Panis Angelicus/Jesus, Our Living Bread

1. Pa - nis an - gé - li - cus fit pa - nis hó - mi-num;
2. Te tri - na Dé - i - tas ú - na-que pó - sci-mus,
1. Je - sus, our liv - ing bread, great gift from heav - en sent,
2. O bless - ed Trin - i - ty, we praise and wor - ship you;

1. Dat pa - nis cáe - li-cus fi - gú - ris tér - mi-num:
2. Sic nos tu ví - si - ta, sic - ut te có - li - mus;
1. Ful - fill the signs of old, and be our nour - ish-ment.
2. Strength-en our u - ni-ty, our faith and trust re - new.

1. O res mi - rá - bi - lis! mán - du - cat Dó - mi-num
2. Per tu - as sé - mi - tas duc nos quo tén - di-mus,
1. We hum - ble peo - ple come to eat your sa - cred food,
2. Lord, lead us all our days to heav'n - ly peace and light;

1. Pau - per, ser - vus, et hú - mi - lis.
2. Ad lu - cem quam in - há - bi - tas.
1. In peace, joy, love and grat - i - tude.
2. Grant us rest, there, be - fore your sight.

Text: 12 12 12 8; St. Thomas Aquinas, 1227–1274; tr. by Jerome Siwek, b. 1930 ©1986, Jerome Siwek.
Music: SACRIS SOLEMNIIS; Louis Lambillotte, SJ, 1796–1855.

People, Look East

1. Peo - ple, look East. The time is near Of the
2. Fur - rows, be glad, though earth is bare. One more
3. Stars, keep the watch when night is dim. One more
4. An - gels, an - nounce on this great feast Him who

1. crown - ing of the year. Make your house fair as you are
2. seed is plant - ed there. Give up your strength the seed to
3. light the bowl shall brim. Shin - ing be - yond the frost - y
4. com - eth from the East. Set ev - 'ry peak and val - ley

1. a - ble. Trim the hearth and set the ta - ble. Peo - ple, look
2. nour - ish, That in course the flow'r may flour - ish. Peo - ple, look
3. weath - er, Bright as sun and moon to - geth - er. Peo - ple, look
4. hum - ming With the word, the Lord is com - ing. Peo - ple, look

1. East and sing to - day: Love, the Guest, is on the way.
2. East and sing to - day: Love, the Rose, is on the way.
3. East and sing to - day: Love, the Star, is on the way.
4. East and sing to - day: Love, the Lord, is on the way.

Text: 87 98 87; Eleanor Farjeon, 1881–1965 ©1957, Eleanor Farjeon; reprinted by permission of Harold Ober Assoc., Inc.
Music: BESANÇON; French Trad. Carol; choral arr. by Randall DeBruyn, b. 1947 ©1990, OCP Publications.

Praise God from Whom All Blessings Flow

1. Praise God from whom all bless - ings flow; Praise him, all
2. From all that dwell be - low the skies Let the Cre -
3. E - ter - nal are thy mer - cies Lord And truth e -
4. Praise God from whom all bless - ings flow; Praise him, all

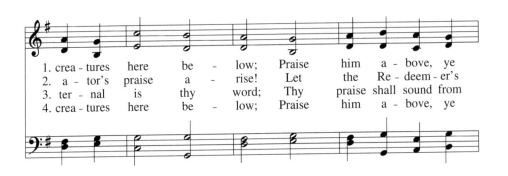

1. crea - tures here be - low; Praise him a - bove, ye
2. a - tor's praise a - rise! Let the Re - deem - er's
3. ter - nal is thy word; Thy praise shall sound from
4. crea - tures here be - low; Praise him a - bove, ye

1. heav'n - ly host; Praise Fa - ther, Son and Ho - ly Ghost.
2. name be sung Through ev - 'ry land by ev - 'ry one.
3. shore to shore Till suns shall rise and set no more.
4. heav'n - ly host; Praise Fa - ther, Son and Ho - ly Ghost.

Text: LM; Verses 1 and 4, Thomas Ken, 1637–1711; verses 2 and 3, Isaac Watts, 1674–1748.
Music: OLD HUNDREDTH; melody fr. *Pseaumes octante trois de David*, 1551; harm. attr. to Louis Bourgeois, ca. 1510–1561.

Praise His Name

REFRAIN: *Fast; with driving power (♩. = 63)*

Melody

Fine

Al - le-lu - ia! Al-le-lu-ia! Al - le-lu - ia!

Harmony I

Harmony II

Al - le-lu - ia! Al-le-lu-ia! Al - le-lu - ia!

VERSES:

1. You ser-vants of the Lord, _____ bless _____ the _ Lord: _____
2. ⁊ High a-bove the na-tions the _ Lord _ is _ God; _____
3. ⁊ Rais-ing up the low - ly and the poor from the _ dust, he
4. ⁊ Glo - ry to the Fa - ther and _ glo - ry to the Son; _____

(Vs 3 cue)

1. Bless-ed be his name _ for - ev - er! From east to west, _
2. high a-bove the heav-ens his glo-ry! Who is like him, en-
3. gives them a home with his peo-ple: bless-ing the bar - ren,
4. glo - ry to the Ho - ly Spir-it: glo - ry and hon - or,

D.C.

1. praised be the name of the Lord _ our God!
2. throned on the stars a - bove earth and sky?
3. giv - ing them chil - dren sing-ing for joy!
4. wis - dom and pow-er for - ev - er - more!

GOSPEL VERSE:

Melody

Harmony

Send forth your Spir- it, O Lord, and o - pen our

D.C.

hearts to your Word; and you will re-new the earth!

Text: Based on Psalm 113; Michael Joncas, b. 1951.
Music: Michael Joncas.
Text and music ©1979, New Dawn Music.

Praise, My Soul, the King of Heaven

1. Praise, my soul, the King of heav - en; To his
2. Praise him for his grace and fa - vor To his
3. Fa - ther - like he tends and spares us; Well our
4. An - gels, help us to a - dore him; You be -

1. feet thy tri - bute bring; Ran - somed, healed, re - stored, for -
2. chil - dren in dis - tress; Praise him still the same as
3. fee - ble frame he knows; In his hand he gen - tly
4. hold him face to face; Sun and moon bow down be -

1. giv - en, Ev - er - more his prais - es sing:
2. ev - er, Slow to chide and swift to bless:
3. bears us, Res - cues us from all our foes.
4. fore him, In his ho - ly dwell - ing place.

Al - le -

1-4. lu - ia, Al - le - lu - ia,

Praise the ev - er - last - ing King.
Glo - rious in his faith - ful - ness.
Wide - ly yet his mer - cy flows.
Praise with us the God of grace.

Text: 87 87 87; Based on Psalm 103; Henry F. Lyte, 1793 –1847, alt.
Music: LAUDA ANIMA; John Goss, 1800 –1880.

Praise the Lord, Ye Heavens

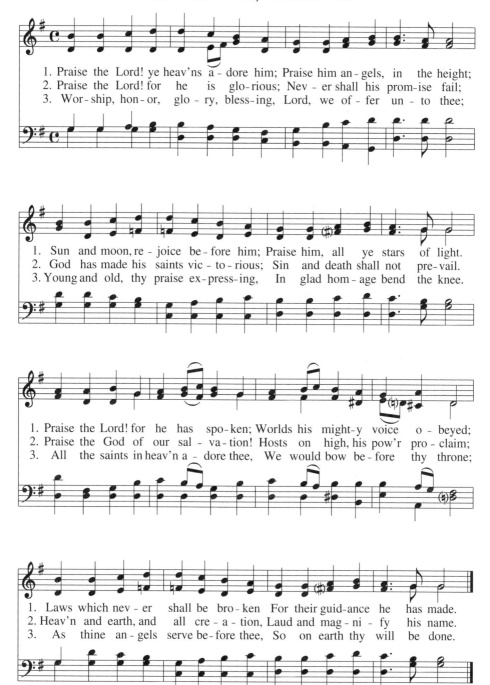

1. Praise the Lord! ye heav'ns a - dore him; Praise him an - gels, in the height;
2. Praise the Lord! for he is glo - rious; Nev - er shall his prom - ise fail;
3. Wor - ship, hon - or, glo - ry, bless - ing, Lord, we of - fer un - to thee;

1. Sun and moon, re - joice be - fore him; Praise him, all ye stars of light.
2. God has made his saints vic - to - rious; Sin and death shall not pre - vail.
3. Young and old, thy praise ex - press - ing, In glad hom - age bend the knee.

1. Praise the Lord! for he has spo - ken; Worlds his might - y voice o - beyed;
2. Praise the God of our sal - va - tion! Hosts on high, his pow'r pro - claim;
3. All the saints in heav'n a - dore thee, We would bow be - fore thy throne;

1. Laws which nev - er shall be bro - ken For their guid - ance he has made.
2. Heav'n and earth, and all cre - a - tion, Laud and mag - ni - fy his name.
3. As thine an - gels serve be - fore thee, So on earth thy will be done.

Text: 87 87 D; Psalm 148; verses 1–2, *Foundling Hospital Psalms, Hymns and Anthems...*, 1796, alt.; verse 3, Edward Osler, 1798–1863.
Music: HYMN TO JOY; Ludwig van Beethoven, 1770–1827; adapt. by Edward Hodges, 1796–1867.

Prayer of St. Francis

VERSES:

unison

1. Make me a chan-nel of your peace. Where
2. Make me a chan-nel of your peace. Where
3. Make me a chan-nel of your peace. It

1. there is ha-tred, let me bring your love. _____ Where
2. there's de-spair in life, let me bring hope. _____ Where
3. is in par-don-ing that we are par-doned, _____ In

1. there is in-ju-ry, your par-don, Lord, And
2. there is dark-ness _____ on-ly light, And
3. giv-ing of our-selves that we re-ceive, And in

1, Final   D.C. to Vs 2 |**2**
                  (Fine)

1. where there's doubt, true faith in you.
2. where there's sad-ness   ev-er joy.
3. dy-ing that we're born to e-ter-nal life.

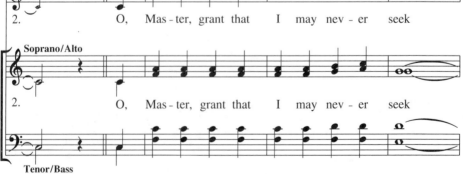

REFRAIN:

Optional Descant

2. O, Mas-ter, grant that I may nev-er seek

Soprano/Alto

2. O, Mas-ter, grant that I may nev-er seek

Tenor/Bass

Text: Sebastian Temple, b. 1928.
Music: Sebastian Temple.
Text and music ©1967, OCP Publications.

Praise to the Lord

1. Praise to the Lord, the Al-might-y, the king of cre-a-tion;
2. Praise to the Lord, who shall pros-per our work and de-fend
3. Praise to the Lord! O let all that is in us a-dore

1. O my soul, praise him, for he is your health and sal-va-tion.
2. us; Sure-ly his good-ness and mer-cy shall dai-ly at-tend
3. him! All that has life and breath come now with prais-es be-fore

1. Come all who hear: Now to his al-tar draw near,
2. us. Pon-der a-new what the Al-might-y can do,
3. him! Let the "A-men" sound from his peo-ple a-gain,

1. Join-ing in glad ad-o-ra-tion.
2. Who with his love will be-friend us.
3. Now as we wor-ship be-fore him.

Text: 14 14 47 8; Joachim Neander, 1650–1680; tr. by Catherine Winkworth, 1827–1878, alt.
Music: LOBE DEN HERREN; *Erneuerten Gesangbuch*, Stralsund, 1665; choral arr. fr. *The Chorale Book for England*, 1863.

Precious Lord, Take My Hand

1. Pre - cious Lord, take my hand, Lead me on, let me
2. When my way grows drear, Pre - cious Lord, lin - ger
3. When the dark - ness ap - pears And the night draws

1. stand, I am tired, I am weak, I am worn;
2. near, When my life is al - most gone;
3. near, And the day is past and gone,

1. Through the storm, through the night, Lead me on to the
2. Hear my cry, hear my call, Hold my hand lest I
3. At the riv - er I stand, Guide my feet, hold my

1. light:
2. fall: } Take my hand, pre - cious Lord, lead me home.
3. hand:

Text: 66 9 D; Thomas A. Dorsey, 1899–1993.
Music: PRECIOUS LORD; Thomas A. Dorsey.

Psalm 42
(As the Deer Longs)

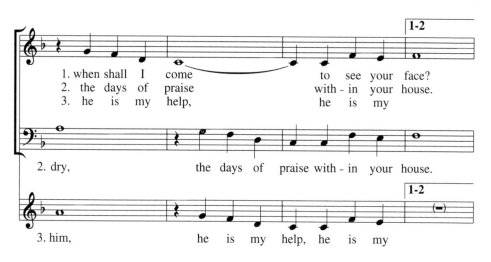

1-2

1. when shall I come to see your face?
2. the days of praise with-in your house.
3. he is my help, he is my

2. dry, the days of praise with-in your house.

1-2

3. him, he is my help, he is my

D.S. **Final**

2. My tears have 3. God.
3. Why do I

2. My tears have

Final

3. God.

3. He is my God.

3. He is my God.

Ready the Way

*VERSES: (♩. = 63)

1. "Read - y the way of the Lord!" Read - y the
2. "Let ev - 'ry val - ley be filled. Let ev - 'ry
3. Des - ert and waste-land will bloom. Des - ert and
4. Those who are blind will then see. Those who are
5. Strength-en the ones who are weak. Strength-en the

1. way of the Lord!" A voice___ cries out in the
2. val - ley be filled. Let ev - 'ry moun - tain be
3. waste-land will bloom. Glo - ry and splen - dor will
4. deaf will then hear. Those who are lame will then
5. ones who are weak. Say to the fright-ened: "Have

1. wil - der - ness: "Read - y the way of the
2. hum - bled; let ev - 'ry val - ley be
3. fill the land. Des - ert and waste - land will
4. leap for joy. Those who are mute will then
5. cour - age." Strength - en the ones who are

REFRAIN:

1. Lord!" (to Verse 2)
2. filled." (to Refrain)
3. bloom. (to Verse 4) Here is your God,
4. sing. (to Refrain)
5. weak. (to Refrain)

*Complete score with modulation is available from the publisher.

Text: Based on Isaiah 35, 40, Ezekiel 11; Bob Hurd, b. 1950.
Music: Bob Hurd; choral arr. by Craig S. Kingsbury, b. 1952.
Text and music ©1986, 1987, Bob Hurd. Published by OCP Publications.

374

coming with your vindication. Look
and behold the saving power of

1 *D.C. to Verses 3, 5* | **Final**
2

God. The

saving power of God.

Rejoice, the Lord Is King

1. Re - joice, the Lord is King: Your Lord and King a -
2. Our Lord and Sav - ior reigns, The God of truth and
3. His king - dom can - not fail, He rules o'er earth and
4. Re - joice in glo - rious hope! Our Lord and judge shall

1. dore! Re - joice, give thanks and sing, And tri - umph
2. love; When he has purged our stains, He took his
3. heav'n; The keys of death and hell Are to our
4. come And take his ser - vants up To their e -

1. ev - er - more:
2. seat a - bove:
3. Je - sus giv'n:
4. ter - nal home:

Lift up your heart, lift

1-4. up your voice! Re - joice, a - gain I say, re - joice!

Text: 66 66 88; Charles Wesley, 1707–1788, alt.
Music: DARWALL'S 148th; John Darwall, 1731–1789; harm. by William H. Monk, 1823–1889, alt.

Remember Your Love

REFRAIN:
Descant

Melody

Re - mem - ber your love and your faith - ful - ness, O

Lord. Re - mem - ber your peo - ple and have mer - cy on us,

1-5 to Verses | **Final** 4 *Fine* | **VERSES:**

Lord. Lord.

1. The Lord is my light and my sal-
2. If you dwelt,___ O Lord, up - on our
3. O Lord, hear the sound ___ of my
4. As sen - ti - nels wait up - on the
5. Be - fore all the moun-tains were be-

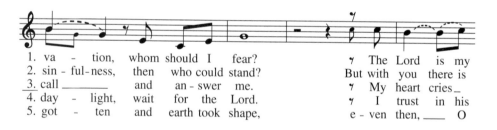

1. va - tion, whom should I fear? The Lord is my
2. sin - ful-ness, then who could stand? But with you there is
3. call ___ and an - swer me. My heart cries_
4. day - light, wait for the Lord. I trust in his
5. got - ten and earth took shape, e - ven then, ___ O

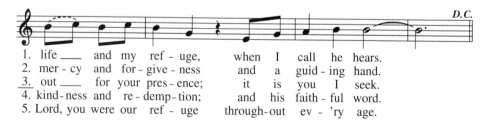

D.C.

1. life ___ and my ref - uge, when I call he hears.
2. mer - cy and for - give - ness and a guid - ing hand.
3. out ___ for your pres - ence; it is you I seek.
4. kind - ness and re - demp - tion; and his faith - ful word.
5. Lord, you were our ref - uge through-out ev - 'ry age.

Text: Based on Psalms 5, 27, 90, 130; Mike Balhoff, b. 1946.
Music: Darryl Ducote, b. 1945 and Gary Daigle, b. 1957.
Text and music ©1978, Damean Music.

Resucitó/He Is Risen

ESTRIBILLO/REFRAIN:

Re - su - ci - tó, re - su - ci - tó, re - su - ci -
ya, a - le - lu - ya, a - le - lu -

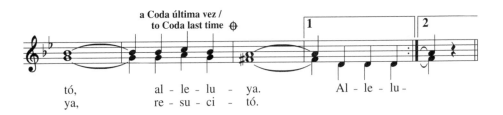

a Coda última vez /
to Coda last time

tó, al - le - lu - ya. **1** Al - le - lu - **2**
ya, re - su - ci - tó.

ESTROFAS/VERSES:

1. La muer - te ¿dón - de es - tá la muer - te?
2. Gra - cias se - an da - das al Pa - dre
3. A - le - grí - a, a - le - grí - a her - ma - nos,
4. Si con El mo - ri - mos, y con El vi - vi - mos,

1. *And death now, van - ished is the fear now,*
2. *The king - dom, praise to God, the king - dom!*
3. *Our glad - ness, bless - ful in our glad - ness,*
4. *With him then, die and live with him then,*

1. ¿Dón - de es - tá mi muer - te?
2. que nos pa - só a su rei - no
3. que si hoy nos que - re - mos
4. y con El can - ta - mos.

1. *ban - ished are my tears now,*
2. *Raised up to the king - dom,*
3. *this will be our glad - ness,*
4. *rise and sing our hymn then,*

Text: Spanish by Kiko Argüello ©1972, Francisco Gómez Argüello and Ediciones Musical PAX. Sole U.S. Agent: OCP Publications.
  English by Robert C. Trupia ©1988, OCP Publications.
Music: Kiko Argüello; arr. by Mary Frances Reza ©1972, Francisco Gómez Argüello and Ediciones Musical PAX. Sole U.S. Agent: OCP
  Publications.

al %

1. ¿Dón-de su vic - to - ria? _____
2. don - de se vi - ve de a - mor. _____
3. 7 es que re - su - ci - tó. _____
4. 7 A - le - lu - ya. _____

} Re - su - ci -

1. *death has passed a - way.* _____
2. *we shall live in love.* _____
3. *that he is a - live.* _____
4. *sing al - le - lu - ia.* _____

} Re - su - ci -

CODA

Melodía/
Melody

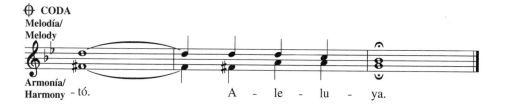

Armonía/
Harmony - tó. A - le - lu - ya.

379

River of Glory

Text: Dan Schutte, b. 1947.
Music: Dan Schutte.
Text and music ©1991, Daniel L. Schutte. Published by OCP Publications.

VERSES:

Descant (Vss 3 and 4)

3. Ah. _____ God will pro - vide. Ah. _____
4. Ah. _____ Night turned a - way. Ah. _____

Soprano/Melody

Alto

1. Foun - tain of mer - cy, grace flow - ing free, streams of sal -
2. Here there is ha - ven, heal - ing and health, joy for the
3. Bread for our jour - ney God will pro - vide. Hope for all
4. Dark - ness is ban - ished, night turned a - way. Christ is our

Tenor

Bass

poco rit.   *rit.*   *accel.*   **D.C.**

3. __ Je - sus, com - pan - ion and guide!
4. __ Lift - ing and lead - ing our way.

poco rit.   *rit.*   *accel.*   **D.C.**

1. va - tion, spill - ing with love from a tree!
2. ask - ing, love in a - bun - dance of wealth!
3. a - ges, Je - sus, com - pan - ion and guide!
4. sun - light, lift - ing and lead - ing our way!

poco rit.   *rit.*   *accel.*

Save Us, O Lord

REFRAIN: *Yearning, insistent (♩ = ca. 152)*

Descant (after Vss 2, 3)

Save   us,   heal   us;   hear   our

Melody   *(a tempo)*

Save us, O Lord;   car - ry us back.   Rouse your pow - er and

prayer.   Show   your   glo - ry.   Bring   us

come.   Res-cue your peo-ple; show us your face.   Bring   us

1-3   to Verses   Final   *rit.*   Fine

back.   back.

1-3   to Verses   Final   *rit.*   Fine

back.   back.

VERSE 1: *Slightly faster (♩ = 156 - 160)*

1. O Shep - herd of Is - ra - el, hear us.   Re - turn and we shall be

Text: Based on Psalm 80; Bob Dufford, SJ, b. 1943.
Music: Bob Dufford, SJ.
Text and music ©1981, 1983, Robert J. Dufford, SJ and New Dawn Music.

1. saved.　A - rise,　O Lord; hear our cries. O Lord;　bring　us　back!

VERSE 2: *Calming*

2. How　long　will you　hide from your

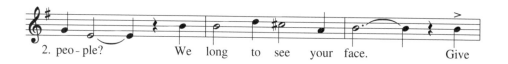

2. peo - ple?　We　long　to　see　your　face.　　Give

2. ear　to　us.　Draw near　to　us,　　Lord　God　of　hosts!

VERSE 3:

3. Turn　　a- gain;　　care　for　your vine;　pro - tect what your

3. right hand has　plant- ed.　　Your　vine- yards are tram- pled, up -

3. root- ed,　and burned.　Come　to　us,　Fa - ther　of　might!

See amid the Winter's Snow

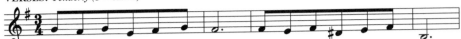

VERSES: *Tenderly (♩ = ca. 76)*

1. See a - mid the win-ter's snow, born for us on earth be - low,
2. Say, you ho - ly shep-herds, say, tell your joy - ful news to - day.

poco rit.

1. see, the gen - tle lamb ap - pears, prom-ised from e - ter - nal years.
2. Why have you now left your sheep on the lone - ly moun-tain steep?

Descant *a tempo*

1. Oo _____
2. Al - le - lu - ia,

Melody *a tempo*

1. There with - in a man-ger lies he who built the star - ry skies;
2. "As we watched at dead of night, there ap-peared a won-drous light;

D.C.

1. ah ____

1. he, who throned in heights sub-lime, sits a-mid the cher-u - bim.

Text: Edward Caswall, 1814–1878.
Music: Kevin Keil, b. 1956 ©1992, Kevin Keil. Published by OCP Publications.

Final

2. Christ   is   born   in   Beth -

Final

2. an - gels sing - ing 'Peace on earth'   told   us   of   the

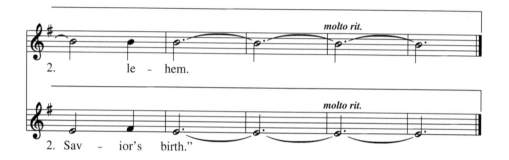

molto rit.

2.   le - hem.

molto rit.

2. Sav - ior's   birth."

Seed, Scattered and Sown

REFRAIN: (♩ = 104)

Seed, scat-tered and sown, wheat, gath-ered and grown,
(Seed) (wheat)

bread, bro-ken and shared as one, the liv-ing bread of God.

Vine, fruit of the land, wine, work of our hands,
(Vine) (wine)

one cup that is shared by all; the liv-ing cup, the liv-ing bread of

Text: Based on *Didache* 9, 1 Corinthians 10:16–17, Mark 4:3–6; Dan Feiten.
Music: Dan Feiten.
Text and music ©1987, Ekklesia Music, Inc.

VERSES:

1. Is not the bread we break, a
2. The seed which falls on rock will
3. As wheat up-on the hills was

1. shar - ing in our Lord? Is not the
2. with - er and will die. The seed with -
3. gath - ered and was grown, so may the

1. cup we bless, the blood of Christ out - poured?
2. in good ground will flow - er and have life.
3. church of God be gath - ered in - to one.

Seek the Lord

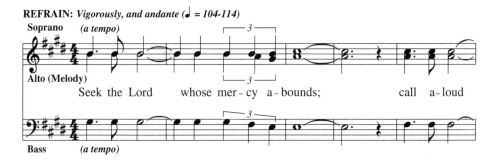

REFRAIN: *Vigorously, and andante* (♩ = 104-114)

Soprano *(a tempo)*

Alto (Melody)

Seek the Lord whose mer-cy a-bounds; call a-loud

Bass *(a tempo)*

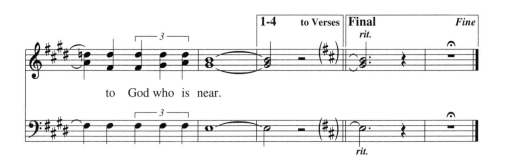

1-4 to Verses | Final | *Fine*
rit.

to God who is near.

rit.

VERSES 1, 2:

Melody

Harmony

1. To - day is the day and now the prop - er hour to for-
2. As high as the sky is a - bove the earth, so

rit. D.C.

1. sake our sin - ful lives and turn to the Lord.
2. high a - bove our ways, the ways of the Lord.

Text: Isaiah 55:6–9; Roc O'Connor, SJ, b. 1949.
Music: Roc O'Connor, SJ.
Text and music ©1975, Robert F. O'Connor, SJ and New Dawn Music.

VERSE 3:

3. O-pen your heart   to hear the voice of God,   whose

3. words, whose ways   lead us to life.

VERSE 4:

4. Some - day we'll live   in the house of God;

4. hearts full of praise   for God's gra - cious love.

See Us, Lord, about Your Altar

1. See us, Lord, about your altar,
2. Hear our prayers, O loving Father,
3. Once were seen the blood and water,
4. Wheat and grape contain the meaning:
5. Hear us yet: so much is needful
6. Members of his Mystic Body,

1. Tho' so many, we are one; Many souls by
2. Hear in them your Son, our Lord; Hear him speak our
3. Now is seen but bread and wine; Once in human
4. Food and drink he is to all; One in him we
5. In our frail, disordered life; Stay with us and
6. Now we know our prayer is heard, Heard by you be-

1. love united In the heart of Christ, your Son.
2. love and worship As we sing with one accord.
3. form he suffered, Now his form is but a sign.
4. kneel adoring, Gathered by his loving call.
5. tend our weakness Till that day of no more strife.
6. cause your children Have received the 'ternal Word.

Text: 87 87; John Greally, b. 1934, alt.
Music: DRAKES BOUGHTON; Edward Elgar, 1857–1934.
Text and music ©Burns & Oates, Ltd., England.

Seek Ye First

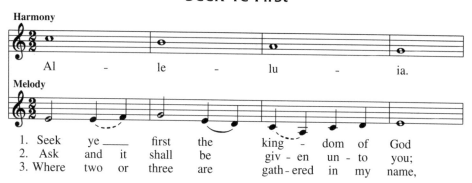

Harmony

Al - le - lu - ia.

Melody

1. Seek ye ___ first the king - dom of God
2. Ask and it shall be giv - en un - to you;
3. Where two or three are gath - ered in my name,

Al - le - lu - ia.

1. and his right - eous - ness,
2. seek and ye shall ___ find;
3. there am I in their midst;

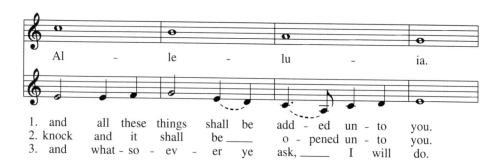

Al - le - lu - ia.

1. and all these things shall be add - ed un - to you.
2. knock and it shall be ___ o - pened un - to you.
3. and what - so - ev - er ye ask, ___ I will do.

Al - le - lu - ia.

1. Al - le - lu, al - le - lu - ia.
2. Al - le - lu, al - le - lu - ia.
3. Al - le - lu, al - le - lu - ia.

Send Out Your Spirit

REFRAIN: (♩ = 138)

Descant
Melody
Lord, send out your Spir - it; re -

new the face of the earth.

face of the earth.

VERSES:

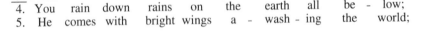

1. You set the earth on its foun - da - tion firm,
2. You sprang up springs run - ning down to the streams,
3. From sea to shore how your won - ders are seen,
4. You rain down rains on the earth all be - low;
5. He comes with bright wings a - wash - ing the world;

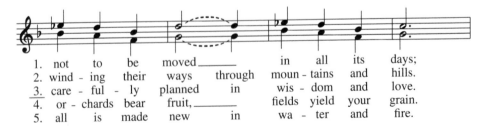

1. not to be moved _____ in all its days;
2. wind - ing their ways through moun - tains and hills.
3. care - ful - ly planned in wis - dom and love.
4. or - chards bear fruit, _____ fields yield your grain.
5. all is made new in wa - ter and fire.

Text: Tim Schoenbachler.
Music: Tim Schoenbachler.
Text and music ©1979, OCP Publications.

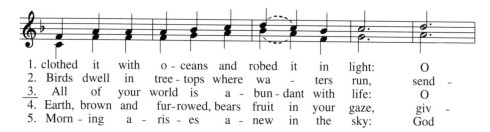

1. clothed it with o - ceans and robed it in light: O
2. Birds dwell in tree - tops where wa - ters run, send -
3. All of your world is a - bun - dant with life: O
4. Earth, brown and fur-rowed, bears fruit in your gaze, giv -
5. Morn - ing a - ris - es a - new in the sky: God

2 *D.C.*

1. bless the Lord, all you his works.
2. ing their song in - to the world.
3. my soul, bless you the Lord.
4. ing us bread, giv - ing us life.
5. re - cre - ates in a new day.

Send Us Your Spirit

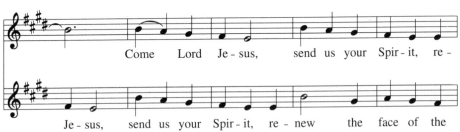

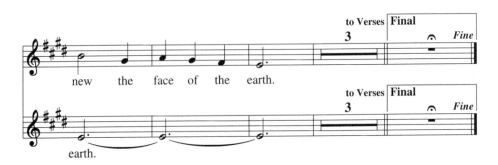

Text: David Haas, b. 1957.
Music: David Haas.
Text and music ©1981, 1982, G.I.A. Publications, Inc.

VERSES:

1. Come _____ to us, Spir - it of God, breathe in us
2. Fill us with __ the fire of your love, burn in us
3. Send __ us __ the wings of new birth, fill all the

1. now, _____ we sing to - geth - er.
2. now, _____ bring us to - geth - er.
3. earth with the love you have taught us. Let

1. Spir - it of hope and of light, fill ____ our lives,
2. Come to us, dwell in us, change our lives, ____ O Lord,
3. all ____ cre - a - tion now be shak - en with love,

1-3. come to us, Spir - it of God.

395

Send Us Your Spirit

1. Send us your Spir - it, O Lord.
2. Hold us with mer - cy, O Lord.
3. Teach us your wis - dom, O Lord.
4. Send us good sum - mer, O Lord.

1. Eve - ning en - folds us and holds us too near.
2. Sor - row has spo - ken, has bro - ken our hearts.
3. Shad - ows have cloud - ed, have crowd - ed our sight.
4. Win - ters have chilled us, and stilled us too long.

1. Wake the morn - ing light. Make our liv - ing bright.
2. Clothe us in your care. Be the life we bear.
3. Give us hearts that see. Set our lov - ing free.
4. Give us love's own fire. Be our true de - sire.

1. Shine on our dark - ness, O Lord.
2. Feed us and fill us, O Lord.
3. Hear us and help us, O Lord.
4. Send us your Spir - it, O Lord.

Text: Inspired by *Veni, Sancte Spiritus*; Dan Schutte, b. 1947.
Music: Dan Schutte.
Text and music ©1985, Daniel L. Schutte and New Dawn Music.

Shelter Me, O God

Text: Based on Psalms 16 and 61, Luke 13; Bob Hurd, b. 1950.
Music: Bob Hurd; choral arr. by Craig S. Kingsbury, b. 1952.
Text and music ©1984, Bob Hurd. Published by OCP Publications.

Servant Song

Text: Donna Marie McGargill, OSM, b. 1944.
Music: Donna Marie McGargill, OSM; choral arr. by Dennis Richardson, b. 1947.
Text and music ©1984, OCP Publications.

1. I _____ am _____ your song.
2. Sing _____ your songs _____ in me.
3. Fire _____ my life with your love.
4. Come, _____ see _____ for me.
5. "Let it be done _____ to me."

Oooh _____

REFRAIN:

Harmony

Melody

1. Je - sus, Je - sus, you _____
2. Je - sus, Je - sus, you _____
3. Je - sus, Je - sus, be _____ the
4. Je - sus, Je - sus, you _____
5. Je - sus, Je - sus, "Let it be

1. are _____ the Lord.
2. are _____ my Lord.
3. warmth of my heart.
4. are _____ my Light.
5. done _____ to me."

Je - sus,

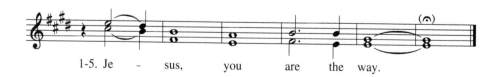

1-5. Je - sus, you are the way.

Shepherd Me, O God

*REFRAIN: *Gentle and tranquil* (♩ = 54-58)

Shep-herd me, O God, be-yond my wants, be-

Harmony (tacet Final Refrain)

Shep-herd me be-yond my wants, be-

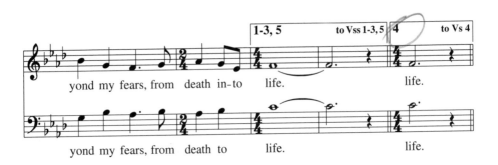

1-3, 5   to Vss 1-3, 5   **4**   to Vs 4

yond my fears, from death in-to life.   life.

yond my fears, from death to life.   life.

Final   *rit.*   Fine   **VERSES 1-3:**

life.

1. God is my shep-herd, so
2. Gen-tly you raise me and
3. Though I should wan-der the

1. noth-ing shall I want, I rest in the mead-ows of
2. heal my wea-ry soul, you lead me by path-ways of
3. val - ley of death, I fear no e-vil, for

1. faith-ful-ness and love, I walk by the qui - et
2. right-eous-ness and truth, my spir - it shall sing the
3. you are at my side, your rod and your staff, my

*Final Refrain a bit slower.

Text: Based on Psalm 23; Marty Haugen, b. 1950.
Music: Marty Haugen.
Text and music ©1987, G.I.A. Publications, Inc.

1. wa - ters of peace.
2. mu - sic of your Name.
3. com - fort and my hope.

VERSE 4:

Melody

Harmony

women 4. You have set me a ban - quet of love

unison

4. in the face of ha - tred, *—3 beats* crown-ing me with

poco rit. *rit.* *D.C.*

4. love be - yond my pow'r to hold.

VERSE 5:

All 5. Sure - ly your kind-ness and mer - cy fol - low me

poco rit. *a tempo*

5. all the days of my life; I will dwell in the

D.C. al fine

5. house of my God for - ev - er - more.

Shepherd of Souls

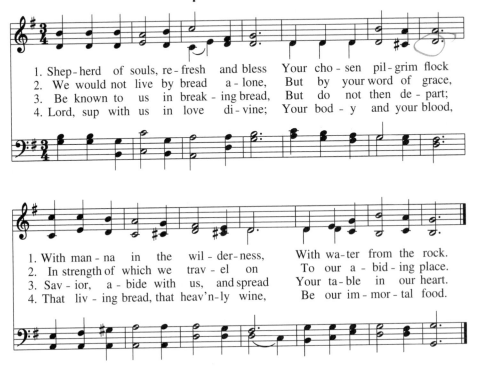

1. Shep-herd of souls, re-fresh and bless Your cho-sen pil-grim flock
2. We would not live by bread a-lone, But by your word of grace,
3. Be known to us in break-ing bread, But do not then de-part;
4. Lord, sup with us in love di-vine; Your bod-y and your blood,

1. With man-na in the wil-der-ness, With wa-ter from the rock.
2. In strength of which we trav-el on To our a-bid-ing place.
3. Sav-ior, a-bide with us, and spread Your ta-ble in our heart.
4. That liv-ing bread, that heav'n-ly wine, Be our im-mor-tal food.

Text: CM; verses 1–2, James Montgomery, 1771–1854; verses 3–4, anon.
Music: ST. AGNES; John B. Dykes, 1823–1876.

Silent Night, Holy Night

1. Si - lent night! Ho - ly night! All is calm,
2. Si - lent night! Ho - ly night! Shep - herds quake
3. Si - lent night! Ho - ly night! Son of God,

OOH

1. all is bright Round yon Vir - gin Moth - er and child!
2. at the sight; Glo - ries stream from heav - en a - far;
3. love's pure light Ra - diant beams from thy ho - ly face,

1. Ho - ly in - fant so ten - der and mild, Sleep in
2. Heav'n - ly hosts sing "Al - le - lu - ia! Christ the
3. With the dawn of re - deem - ing grace, Je - sus,

1. heav - en - ly peace, Sleep in heav - en - ly peace.
2. Sav - ior is born, Christ the Sav - ior is born."
3. Lord, at thy birth, Je - sus, Lord, at thy birth.

Text: 66 89 66; Joseph Mohr, 1792–1848; tr. by John F. Young, 1820–1885.
Music: STILLE NACHT; Franz X. Gruber, 1787–1863; harm. by Carl H. Reinecke, 1824–1910.

403

Sing a Joyful Song

Text: Based on Psalm 145; Jim Farrell, b. 1947.
Music: Jim Farrell.
Text and music ©1984, OCP Publications.

VERSES:

1. The heav-ens pro-claim God's name, and
2. Our God is a might-y God, un-
3. Sing praise, O Je-ru-sa-lem! Sing
4. Sing praise to the God of gods, the

1. earth in re-ply ech-oes back with
2. e-qualed in pow'r, yet with gen-tle
3. praise to your King, rul-ing earth with
4. An-cient of Days! Ho-ly, ho-ly,

1. joy-ful songs of praise!
2. mer-cy cov-ers the earth.
3. jus-tice age af-ter age.
4. ho-ly Lord of all!

D.C.

Sing a New Church

VERSES:

1. Sum-moned by the God who made us Rich in
2. Ra-diant ris - en from the wa - ter; Robed in
3. Trust the good - ness of cre - a - tion; Trust the
4. Bring the hopes of ev - 'ry na - tion; Bring the
5. Draw to - geth - er at one ta - ble All the

1. our di - ver - si - ty, Gath-ered in the name of
2. ho - li - ness and light, Male and fe - male in God's
3. Spir - it strong with - in. Dare to dream the vi - sion
4. art of ev - 'ry race. Weave a song of peace and
5. hu - man fam - i - ly; Shape a cir - cle ev - er

1. Je - sus, Rich - er still in u - ni - ty:
2. im - age, Male and fe - male, God's de - light:
3. prom - ised Sprung from seed of what has been.
4. jus - tice; Let it sound through time and space.
5. wid - er And a peo - ple ev - er free.

Text: 87 87 D; Delores Dufner, OSB ©1991, The Sisters of St. Benedict. Published by OCP Publications.
Music: NETTLETON; J. Wyeth's *Repository of Sacred Music, Pt. II,* 1813; choral arr. by Randall DeBruyn, b. 1947 ©1992, OCP Publications.

REFRAIN:

Let us bring the gifts that dif - fer And, in

splen - did, var - ied ways, Sing a new church in - to

be - ing One in faith and love and praise.

Sing a New Song

ANTIPHON: *Joyfully, with spirit (♩ = ca. 144)*

Descant: Sing a new song; sing

Melody: Sing a new song un-to the Lord; let your song be

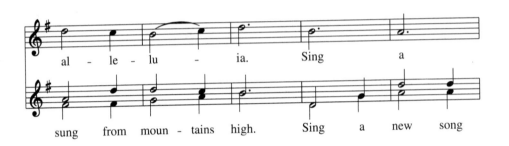

al - le - lu - ia. Sing a

sung from moun - tains high. Sing a new song

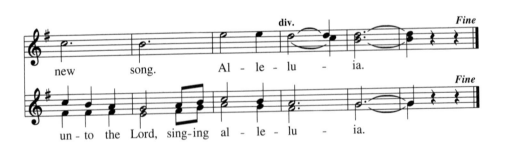

new song. Al - le - lu - ia. *Fine*

un - to the Lord, sing-ing al - le - lu - ia. *Fine*

VERSES:

1. Yah - weh's peo - ple dance for joy. O come be - fore the
2. Rise, O chil - dren, from your sleep; your Sav - ior now has
3. Glad my soul for I have seen the glo - ry of the

Text: Based on Psalm 98; Dan Schutte, b. 1947.
Music: Dan Schutte.
Text and music ©1972, Daniel L. Schutte. Administered by New Dawn Music.

1. Lord.   And play for him on glad tam - bou -
2. come.   He has turned your sor - row to
3. Lord.   The trum - pet sounds; the dead shall be

1. rines, and let your trum - pet sound.
2. joy, and filled your soul with song.
3. raised. I know my Sav - ior lives.

Sing a New Song

REFRAIN:

Sing a new song to the Lord. Praise him in the as-sem-bly of his church.

Fine

Sing a new song to the Lord. Praise him, all you peo-ple of God.

VERSES:

1. Be glad,___ O___ Is - ra-el, be-cause ___ of your cre - a - tor; re-
2. Praise his name with danc - ing, play drums and harp ___ in praise, ___ for
3. Let God's peo-ple cel - e-brate the tri - umph of ___ their king. ___

D.C.

1. joice, ___ O ___ Zi - on, be-cause ___ of ___ your king.
2. God de - lights in his peo - ple, and lifts his chil-dren on high.
3. Let them shout ___ and praise his name, while sing-ing all the night long.

Text: Grayson Warren Brown, b. 1948.
Music: Grayson Warren Brown; arr. by Grayson Warren Brown, Val Parker, and Larry Adams.
Text and music ©1992, Grayson Warren Brown. Published by OCP Publications.

Sing Out, Earth and Skies

VERSES: *Light and dancing (♩ = 80)*

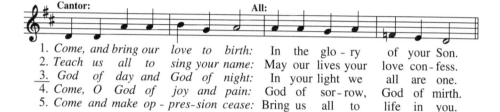

Cantor: ... **All:**

1. Come, O God of all the earth: Come to us, O Right-eous One;
2. Come, O God of wind and flame: Fill the earth with right-eous-ness;
3. Come, O God of flash-ing light: Twink-ling star and burn-ing sun;
4. Come, O God of snow and rain: Show-er down up-on the earth;
5. Come, O Jus-tice, Come, O Peace: Come and shape our hearts a-new;

Cantor: ... **All:**

1. Come, and bring our love to birth: In the glo-ry of your Son.
2. Teach us all to sing your name: May our lives your love con-fess.
3. God of day and God of night: In your light we all are one.
4. Come, O God of joy and pain: God of sor-row, God of mirth.
5. Come and make op-pres-sion cease: Bring us all to life in you.

REFRAIN:

Melody

Sing out, earth and skies! Sing of the God who loves you!

Descant (Tenor)

Harmony (Alto)

Sing out, earth and skies! Sing of the God who

Raise your joy-ful cries! Dance to the life a-round you!

loves you! Raise your dance to the life a-round you!

Text: Marty Haugen, b. 1950.
Music: Marty Haugen.
Text and music ©1985, G.I.A. Publications, Inc.

Sing Alleluia, Sing

Sing al-le-lu - ia, sing al - le-lu-ia, sing al - le-lu-ia to the Lord!

Sing his praise, sing his praise!

Sing al - le-lu-ia to the Lord!

VERSES:

1. Let my soul re - joice in the King, as to him our
2. When his chil - dren lived in fear, God as - sured them

1-2. Oo

Text: Gary Ault, b. 1944.
Music: Gary Ault.
Text and music ©1973, 1978, Damean Music.

1. prais-es we bring, sing-ing of his might-y deeds a-mong
2. he was near, lead-ing them in - to the prom-ised

1-2. Oo

1. all.
2. land.
He is Lord, he is Lord and by

1-2. He is Lord, he is Lord and by

1-2. all cre-a - tion a - dored. He chose us as a

D.C.

1-2. peo-ple all his own.

Sing, My Tongue, the Savior's Glory
(for Passion Sunday, Good Friday)

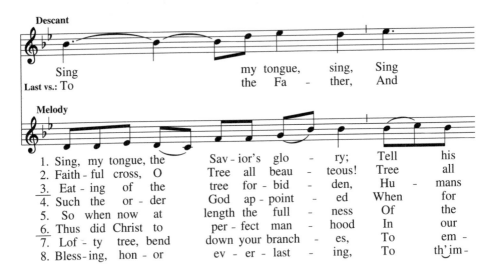

Descant

Sing my tongue, sing, Sing

Last vs.: To the Fa - ther, And

Melody

1. Sing, my tongue, the Sav-ior's glo - ry; Tell his
2. Faith - ful cross, O Tree all beau - teous! Tree all
3. Eat - ing of the tree for - bid - den, Hu - mans
4. Such the or - der God ap - point - ed When for
5. So when now at length the full - ness Of the
6. Thus did Christ to per - fect man - hood In our
7. Lof - ty tree, bend down your branch - es, To em -
8. Bless - ing, hon - or ev - er - last - ing, To th' im -

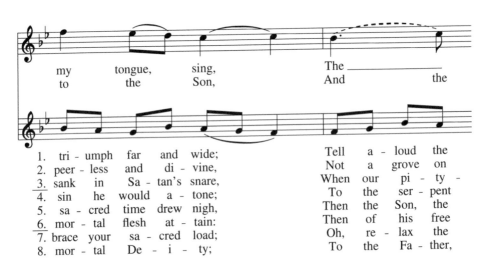

my tongue, sing, The _____

to the Son, And the

1. tri - umph far and wide; Tell a - loud the
2. peer - less and di - vine, Not a grove on
3. sank in Sa - tan's snare, When our pi - ty -
4. sin he would a - tone; To the ser - pent
5. sa - cred time drew nigh, Then the Son, the
6. mor - tal flesh at - tain: Then of his free
7. brace your sa - cred load; Oh, re - lax the
8. mor - tal De - i - ty; To the Fa - ther,

Text: 87 87 87; Venantius H. Fortunatus, 530–609; tr. by John M. Neale, 1818–1866.
Music: PANGE LINGUA GLORIOSI; chant, Mode III; descant by Randall DeBruyn, b. 1947 ©1990, OCP Publications.

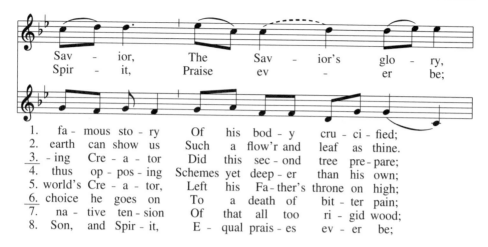

Sav - ior, The Sav - ior's glo - ry,
Spir - it, Praise ev - er be;

1. fa - mous sto - ry Of his bod - y cru - ci - fied;
2. earth can show us Such a flow'r and leaf as thine.
3. - ing Cre - a - tor Did this sec - ond tree pre - pare;
4. thus op - pos - ing Schemes yet deep - er than his own;
5. world's Cre - a - tor, Left his Fa - ther's throne on high;
6. choice he goes on To a death of bit - ter pain;
7. na - tive ten - sion Of that all too ri - gid wood;
8. Son, and Spir - it, E - qual prais - es ev - er be;

The Sav - ior's glo - ry,
Glo - ry in heav - en

1. How up - on the cross a vic - tim,
2. Sweet the nails, and sweet the wood, _____
3. Des - tined, man - y a - ges la - ter,
4. Thence the rem - e - dy pro - cur - ing,
5. From a vir - gin's womb ap - pear - ing,
6. And as lamb up - on the al - tar
7. Gent - ly, gent - ly bear the mem - bers
8. Glo - ry through the earth and heav - en,

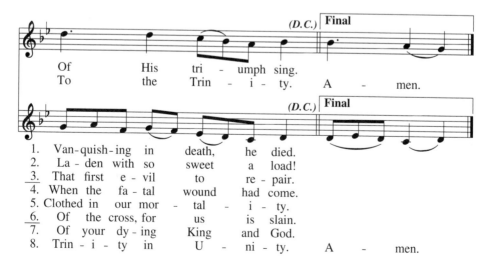

(D.C.) | **Final**

Of His tri - umph sing.
To the Trin - i - ty. A - men.

1. Van - quish - ing in death, he died.
2. La - den with so sweet a load!
3. That first e - vil to re - pair.
4. When the fa - tal wound had come.
5. Clothed in our mor - tal - i - ty.
6. Of the cross, for us is slain.
7. Of your dy - ing King and God.
8. Trin - i - ty in U - ni - ty. A - men.

Sing of Mary

1. Sing of Ma - ry, pure and low - ly, Vir - gin
2. Sing of Je - sus, son of Ma - ry, In the
3. Glo - ry be to God the Fa - ther; Glo - ry

1. Moth - er un - de - filed; Sing of God's own
2. home at Naz - a - reth, Toil and la - bor
3. be to God the Son; Glo - ry be to

1. Son most ho - ly, Who be - came her lit - tle child.
2. can - not wea - ry Love en - dur - ing un - to death.
3. God the Spir - it; Glo - ry to the Three in One.

1. Fair - est child of fair - est moth - er, God the Lord who
2. Con - stant was the love he gave her, Though he went forth
3. From the heart of bless - ed Ma - ry, From all saints the

Text: 87 87 D; Roland F. Palmer, 1891–1985 © Estate of Roland F. Palmer.
Music: PLEADING SAVIOR; *Christian Lyre,* 1830.

1. came to earth, Word made flesh, our
2. from her side, Forth to preach and
3. song as - cends, And the Church the

1. ver - y broth - er, Takes our na - ture by his birth.
2. heal and suf - fer, Till on Cal - va - ry he died.
3. strain re - ech - oes Un - to earth's re - mot - est ends.

Sing of the Lord's Goodness

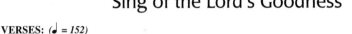

VERSES: (♩ = 152)

1. Sing of the Lord's good-ness, Fa-ther of all wis-dom,
2. Pow-er he has wield-ed, hon-or is his gar-ment,
3. Cour-age in our dark-ness, com-fort in our sor-row,
4. Praise him with your sing-ing, praise him with the trum-pet,

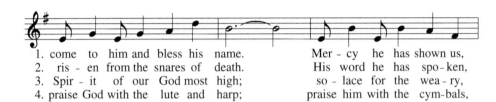

1. come to him and bless his name. Mer-cy he has shown us,
2. ris-en from the snares of death. His word he has spo-ken,
3. Spir-it of our God most high; so-lace for the wea-ry,
4. praise God with the lute and harp; praise him with the cym-bals,

1. his love is for-ev-er, faith-ful to the end of
2. one bread he has bro-ken, new life he now gives to
3. par-don for the sin-ner, splen-dor of the liv-ing
4. praise him with your danc-ing, praise God till the end of

REFRAIN:

Descant

You peo-ple come   sing

(Melody)

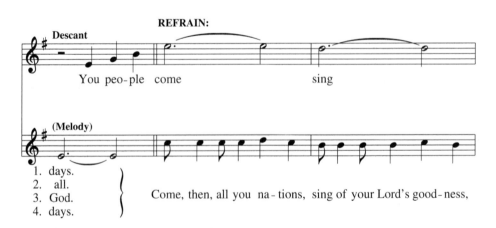

1. days.
2. all.
3. God.
4. days.

Come, then, all you na-tions, sing of your Lord's good-ness,

Text: Ernest Sands, b. 1949.
Music: Ernest Sands; descant by Christopher Walker, b. 1947.
Text and music ©1981, 1984, Ernest Sands. Published by OCP Publications.

praise, sing praise to God. Come and ring out the

mel - o - dies of praise and thanks to God. Ring out the

Lord's glo - ry, praise him with your mu - sic, wor - ship him and bless his

Lord's glo - ry, praise him with your mu - sic, wor - ship him and bless his

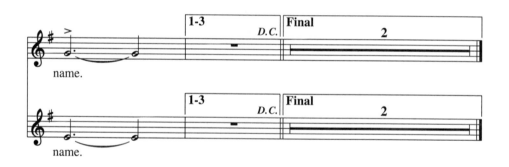

name.

name.

Sing to the Mountains

ANTIPHON: *Lightly (♩ = 176)*

Descant

Melody

Sing to the moun-tains, sing to the sea. Raise your

voic - es, lift your hearts. This is the day the Lord has

made. Let all the earth re - joice. [1-3] to Verses

Final joice. Let all the earth re - joice. *Fine*

VERSE 1:

1. I will give thanks to you, my Lord. You have

1. an-swered my plea. You have saved my soul from

1. death. You are my strength and my song. *D.C.*

Text: Based on Psalm 118; Bob Dufford, SJ, b. 1943.
Music: Bob Dufford, SJ; verse 2 arr. by Randall DeBruyn, b. 1947.
Text and music ©1975, 1979, Robert J. Dufford, SJ and New Dawn Music.

VERSE 2:

Soprano
Alto

2. Ho - ly, ho - ly, ho - ly Lord.

Tenor
Bass

D.C.

2. Heav - en and earth are full of your glo - ry.

VERSE 3:

Descant
Melody

3. This is the day that the Lord has made. Let us be

3. glad and re - joice. Death has lost and

D.C.

3. all is life. Sing of the glo - ry of God.

Somos el Cuerpo de Cristo/
We Are the Body of Christ

ESTRIBILLO/REFRAIN: Todos/All (♩ = *ca. 112*)

So - mos el cuer - po de Cris - to.
So - mos el cuer - po de Cris - to.

We are the
We are the

bod - y of Christ.
bod - y of Christ.

He - mos o - í - do el lla -
Tra - e - mos su san - to men -

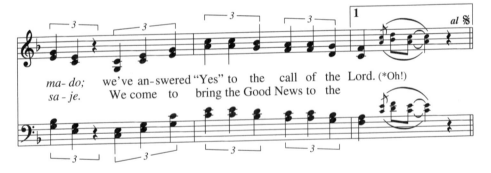

ma - do; we've an-swered "Yes" to the call of the Lord. (*Oh!)
sa - je. We come to bring the Good News to the

1 al %

2 a las Estrofas/to Verses
Solista/Cantor:

Final *Fine*

world. (3a. *Que*) world. (*Oh!)

*Add after Verse 2 (optional).

Text: Jaime Cortez.
Music: Jaime Cortez.
Text and music ©1994, Jaime Cortez. Published by OCP Publications.

ESTROFAS/VERSES 1, 2:

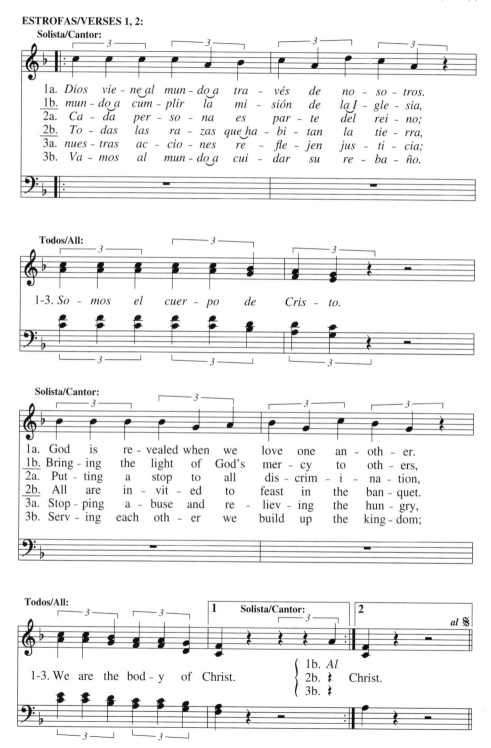

Solista/Cantor:

1a. *Dios vie - ne al mun - do a tra - vés de no - so - tros.*
1b. *mun - do a cum - plir la mi - sión de la I - gle - sia,*
2a. *Ca - da per - so - na es par - te del rei - no;*
2b. *To - das las ra - zas que ha - bi - tan la tie - rra,*
3a. *nues - tras ac - cio - nes re - fle - jen jus - ti - cia;*
3b. *Va - mos al mun - do a cui - dar su re - ba - ño.*

Todos/All:

1-3. *So - mos el cuer - po de Cris - to.*

Solista/Cantor:

1a. God is re - vealed when we love one an - oth - er.
1b. Bring - ing the light of God's mer - cy to oth - ers,
2a. Put - ting a stop to all dis - crim - i - na - tion,
2b. All are in - vit - ed to feast in the ban - quet.
3a. Stop - ping a - buse and re - liev - ing the hun - gry,
3b. Serv - ing each oth - er we build up the king - dom;

Todos/All:

1-3. We are the bod - y of Christ.

1 Solista/Cantor:

{ 1b. *Al*
2b. 𝄾 Christ.
3b. 𝄾

2

al 𝄋

Song of the Body of Christ

REFRAIN: *Gently (♩ = 80-84)*

We come to share our sto - ry, we come to break the

bread, we come to know our ris - ing from the dead.

VERSES:

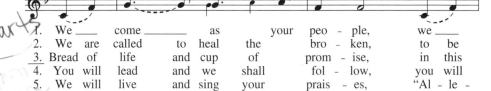

1. We ___ come ___ as your peo - ple, we ___
2. We are called to heal the bro - ken, to be
3. Bread of life and cup of prom - ise, in this
4. You will lead and we shall fol - low, you will
5. We will live and sing your prais - es, "Al - le -

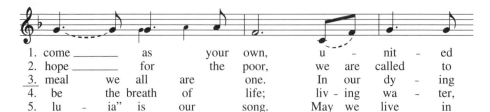

1. come ___ as your own, u - nit - ed
2. hope ___ for the poor, we are called to
3. meal we all are one. In our dy - ing
4. be the breath of life; liv - ing wa - ter,
5. lu - ia" is our song. May we live in

1. with each oth - er, love ___ finds a home.
2. feed the hun - gry at ___ our ___ door.
3. and our ris - ing, may your king-dom come.
4. we are thirst - ing for ___ your ___ light.
5. love and peace our whole ___ life ___ long.

Text: David Haas, b. 1957.
Music: NO KE ANO' AHI' AHI; Trad. Hawaiian Song; adapt. by David Haas.
Text and music ©1989, G.I.A. Publications, Inc.

Songs of Thankfulness and Praise

1. Songs of thank-ful-ness and praise, Je-sus, Lord, to thee we raise,
2. Man-i-fest at Jor-dan's stream, Proph-et, Priest, and King su-preme;
3. Grant us grace to see thee, Lord, Mir-rored in thy ho-ly Word;

1. Man-i-fest-ed by the star To the sag-es from a-far;
2. And at Ca-na, wed-ding guest, In thy God-head man-i-fest;
3. May we im-i-tate thee now, And be pure, as pure art thou;

1. Branch of roy-al Da-vid's stem In thy birth at Beth-le-lem;
2. Man-i-fest in pow'r di-vine, Chang-ing wa-ter in-to wine;
3. That we like to thee may be At thy great E-pi-pha-ny;

1. Prais-es be to thee ad-dressed,
2. Prais-es be to thee ad-dressed, } God in flesh made man-i-fest.
3. And may praise thee, ev-er-blessed,

Text: 77 77 D; Christopher Wordsworth, 1807–1885.
Music: SALZBURG; Jakob Hintze, 1622–1702; arr. by Johann S. Bach, 1685–1750.

Soon and Very Soon

1. Soon and ver - y soon, We are going to see the King;
2. No more cry - ing there, We are going to see the King;
3. No more dy - ing there, We are going to see the King;

1. Soon and ver - y soon, We are going to see the King;
2. No more cry - ing there, We are going to see the King;
3. No more dy - ing there, We are going to see the King;

1. Soon and ver - y soon, We are going to see the King; Hal - le -
2. No more cry - ing there, We are going to see the King;
3. No more dy - ing there, We are going to see the King;

1-3. lu - jah! Hal - le - lu - jah! We're going to see the King.

Text: 57 57 57 with refrain; Andrae Crouch, b. 1945.
Music: SOON AND VERY SOON; Andrae Crouch; adapt. by William F. Smith, b. 1941.
Text and music ©1976, Bud John Songs, Inc./Crouch Music. Admin. by EMI Christian Music Publishing. All rights reserved. Used by per-
mission.

Soul of My Savior

1. Soul of my Sav - ior, sanc - ti - fy my breast;
2. Strength and pro - tec - tion may thy Pas - sion be;
3. Hear me, Lord Je - sus, lis - ten as I pray:

1. Bod - y of Christ, be thou my sav - ing guest;
2. O Bless-ed Je - sus, hear and an - swer me;
3. "Lead me from night to nev - er end - ing day.

1. Blood of my Sav - ior, bathe me in thy tide;
2. Deep in thy wounds, Lord, hide and shel - ter me;
3. Fill all the world with love and grace di - vine,

1. Wash me with wa - ter flow-ing from his side.
2. So shall I nev - er, nev - er part from thee.
3. And glo - ry, laud, and praise be ev - er thine."

Text: 10 10 10 10; Verses 1-2 attr. to Pope John XXII, 1249–1334; tr. by Edward Caswall, 1814–1878, alt.; verse 3, composite, based on *God of Our Fathers*; Daniel C. Roberts, 1841–1907.
Music: ANIMA CHRISTI; W.J. Maher, 1823–1877, alt.

Spirit, Come

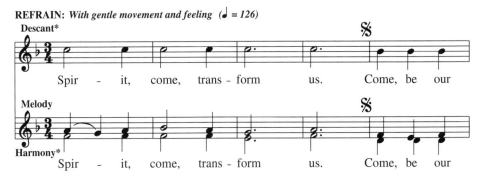

REFRAIN: *With gentle movement and feeling* ($\quad$ = 126)

Descant*

Spir - it, come, trans - form us. Come, be our

Melody

Harmony*

Spir - it, come, trans - form us. Come, be our

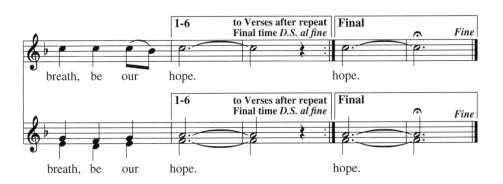

1-6 / to Verses after repeat / Final time D.S. *al fine*   Final   *Fine*

breath, be our hope.   hope.

1-6 / to Verses after repeat / Final time D.S. *al fine*   Final   *Fine*

breath, be our hope.   hope.

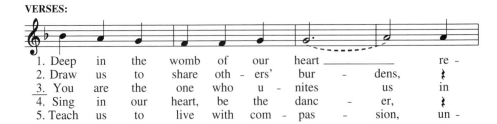

VERSES:

1. Deep in the womb of our heart _____ re -
2. Draw us to share oth - ers' bur - dens,
3. You are the one who u - nites us in
4. Sing in our heart, be the danc - er,
5. Teach us to live with com - pas - sion, un -

D.C.

1. veal ___ your pres - ence, O God.
2. heal - ing and lov - ing with truth.
3. striv - ing for jus - tice, for peace.
4. birth - ing our love as we grow.
5. fold - ing cre - a - tor's love.

*Descant and harmony sung only on repeat.

Text: Gregory Norbet, b. 1940.
Music: Gregory Norbet.
Text and music ©1988, Gregory Norbet. Published by OCP Publications.

Take Up Your Cross

1. Take up your cross, the Sav - ior said, If you would
2. Take up your cross, be not a - shamed! Let not dis -
3. Take up your cross, which gives you strength, Which makes your
4. Take up your cross, and fol - low Christ, Nor think till

1. my dis - ci - ple be; De - ny your - self, the
2. grace your spir - it fill! For God him - self en -
3. trem - bling spir - it brave: 'Twill guide you to a
4. death to lay it down; For on - ly they who

1. world for - sake, And hum - bly fol - low af - ter me.
2. dured to die Up - on a cross, on Cal - vary's hill.
3. bet - ter home And lead to vic - t'ry o'er the grave.
4. bear the cross May hope to wear the glo - rious crown.

Text: LM; Based on text by Charles W. Everest, 1814–1877 ©1977, OCP Publications.
Music: ERHALT UNS, HERR; melody fr. J. Klug's *Geistliche Lieder*, 1543; harm. by Johann S. Bach, 1685–1750, alt.

Table of Plenty

REFRAIN: *Lively* (♩ = ca. 152)

Descant: Let us come to the feast! O

Melody: Come to the feast of heav-en and earth! come to the ta - ble, ta - ble of plen-ty, where God will pro - vide what we need, here at the ta - ble of plen - ty.

Come to the ta - ble of plen - ty! God will pro - vide for all that we need, here at the ta - ble of plen - ty.

VERSES:

1-4. Ah, ____

1. O, come and sit at my ta - ble
2. O, come and eat with - out mon - ey;
3. My bread will ev - er sus - tain you
4. Your fields will flow - er in full - ness;

Text: Dan Schutte, b. 1947.
Music: Dan Schutte.
Text and music ©1992, Daniel L. Schutte. Published by OCP Publications.

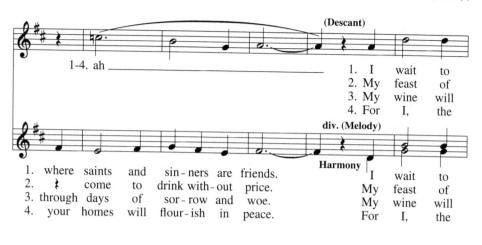

(Descant)

1-4. ah

1. I wait to
2. My feast of
3. My wine will
4. For I, the

div. (Melody)

1. where saints and sin-ners are friends.
2.   come to drink with-out price.
3. through days of sor-row and woe.
4. your homes will flour-ish in peace.

Harmony

1. I wait to
2. My feast of
3. My wine will
4. For I, the

1. wel - come the lost and lone - ly to share the
2. glad - ness will feed your spir - it with faith and
3. flow like a sea of glad - ness to flood the
4. giv - er of home and har - vest, will send my

1. wel - come the lost and lone - ly to share the
2. glad - ness will feed your spir - it with faith and
3. flow like a sea of glad - ness to flood the
4. giv - er of home and har - vest, will send my

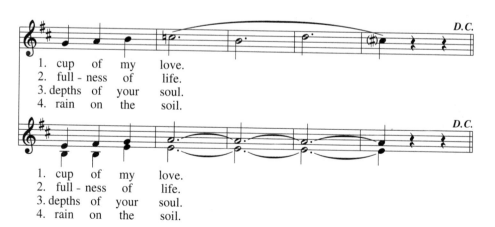

D.C.

1. cup of my love.
2. full - ness of life.
3. depths of your soul.
4. rain on the soil.

D.C.

1. cup of my love.
2. full - ness of life.
3. depths of your soul.
4. rain on the soil.

431

Take Christ to the World

REFRAIN: *Strong and vigorous (♩ = ca. 56-66)* **1st time Cantor(s), All repeat; thereafter: All**

Take Christ to the world, cel-e-brate our faith, man-i-fest his *DED-I-CATE OUR

love to all: take Christ to the world, show that we are
LIVES TO HIM:

| 1,7 | 2-6 | Final |
| D.C. | to Verses | Fine |

his in the way we live.   live.   live.

VERSES 1-3: Cantor(s)

Melody

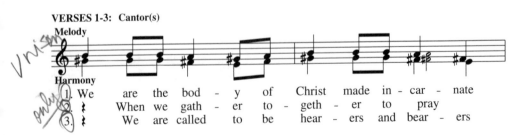

Harmony

1. We are the bod - y of Christ made in - car - nate
2. When we gath - er to - geth - er to pray
3. We are called to be hear - ers and bear - ers

*Final Refrain.

Text: Paul Inwood, b. 1947.
Music: Paul Inwood.
Text and music ©1987, 1989, 1991, Paul Inwood. Published by OCP Publications.

432

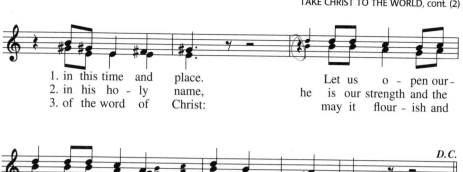

1. in this time and place.
2. in his ho - ly name,
3. of the word of Christ:

Let us o - pen our-
he is our strength and the
may it flour - ish and

D.C.

1. selves to be tru - ly path - ways of his grace.
2. song on our lips, he is pres - ent in our midst.
3. grow in our hearts, bring-ing oth - ers to his light.

VERSE 4 & 5: Cantor(s)

4. When we of - fer our - selves ___ to join more com -
5. Go - ing forth, we can be for the world liv - ing

4. plete - ly in his life, we are the al - tar,
5. wit - ness - es of love in our ser - vice to

D.C.

4. we are the meal, we be - come his sac - ri - fice.
5. all those we meet as we jour - ney on in faith.

433

Taste and See

REFRAIN: (♩ = 72)

Taste and see, taste and see that the Lord is good, the Lord is good. (4. The) good.

1-7 to Verses | **Final** *Fine*

VERSES:

1. I will bless the Lord at all _____ times, his
2. Glo - ri - fy the Lord _____ with _____ me, to -
3. Look up - on the Lord _____ and be ra - diant;
4. an - gel of the Lord is with his peo - ple to
5. Saints _____ of the Lord, _____ re - vere him;
6. Chil - dren of the Lord _____ come and hear, and
7. Keep _____ e - vil words _____ from your tongue, your

1. praise _____ al - ways on my lips. The
2. geth - er let us praise his name. I
3. hide not your face _____ from the Lord. He
4. res - cue those who trust in him. _____
5. those _____ who fear _____ him lack noth - ing.
6. learn _____ the fear _____ of the Lord. _____
7. lips _____ from speak - ing de - ceit. _____

Text: Based on Psalm 34; Stephen Dean.
Music: Stephen Dean.
Text and music ©1981, Stephen Dean. Published by OCP Publications.

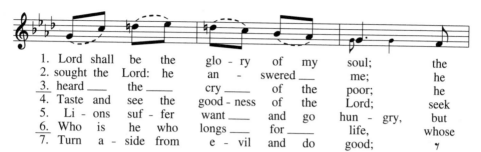

1. Lord shall be the glo - ry of my soul; the
2. sought the Lord: he an - swered __ me; he
3. heard __ the __ cry __ of the poor; he
4. Taste and see the good - ness of the Lord; seek
5. Li - ons suf - fer want __ and go hun - gry, but
6. Who is he who longs __ for __ life, whose
7. Turn a - side from e - vil and do good; ⸠

1. hum - ble shall hear __ and be glad.
2. set __ me free from all my fear.
3. res - cued them from all their woes.
4. ref - uge in him __ and be glad.
5. those __ who seek him lack no bless-ing.
6. on - ly love is for his wealth?
7. seek __ and strive __ af - ter peace.

435

Taste and See

*Complete score with modulation is available from the publisher.

Text: Based on Psalm 34, 136, *The Magnificat;* Bob Hurd, b. 1950.
Music: Bob Hurd; choral arr. by Craig S. Kingsbury, b. 1952.
Text and music ©1988, Bob Hurd. Published by OCP Publications.

VERSE 3:

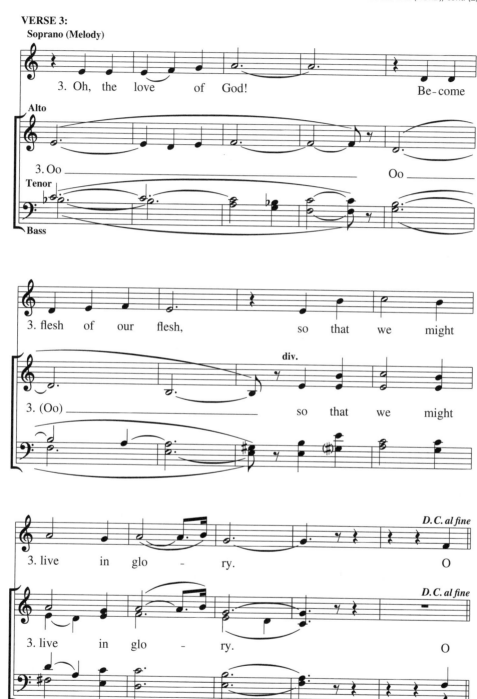

Soprano (Melody): 3. Oh, the love of God! Be-come

Alto: 3. Oo _____ Oo _____

Tenor / Bass

3. flesh of our flesh, so that we might

div.

3. (Oo) _____ so that we might

3. live in glo - ry. O

D.C. al fine

3. live in glo - ry. O

D.C. al fine

437

Taste and See

ANTIPHON: (♩ = ca. 112)

Fine

Taste and see the good-ness of the Lord, let us taste the good-ness of the Lord.

VERSE 1:

Melody

Harmony

1. I will bless the Lord, his praise be ev-er in my mouth. Let my

D.C.

1. soul glo-ry in the Lord; the low - ly will hear and be glad.

VERSE 2:

Melody

Harmony

2. Glo - ri-fy the Lord with me; to - geth-er we'll praise his name. I

D.C.

2. sought the Lord, and he an-swered me, de - liv-ered me from all my fears.

Text: Based on Psalm 34:2-9; John Michael Talbot, b. 1954
Music: John Michael Talbot; choral arr. by Rick Modlin, b. 1966.
Text and music ©1985, 1995, Birdwing Music. Administered by EMI Christian Music Publishing. All rights reserved. Used by permission.

VERSE 3:

Melody

Harmony

3. Look to him and be ra-diant with joy, and your face will not blush with shame. Af -

D.C. al fine

3. flic-ted ones call out to him; from all their dis-tress they are saved.

That There May Be Bread

REFRAIN:

That there may be bread, that there may be joy for all hu-man-i-ty to share with gra-ti-tude: let this be our prayer and may each child of earth long for a free-dom that will flour-ish in all lands.

Fine

Text: Weston Priory, Gregory Norbet, OSB, b. 1940.
Music: Weston Priory, Gregory Norbet, OSB; choral arr. by Craig S. Kingsbury, b. 1952.
Text and music ©1979, 1986, from the recording *That There May Be Bread*, The Benedictine Foundation of the State of Vermont, Inc., Weston, VT.

VERSES:

Melody

Harmony

1. Sim - ple   is   the   truth _____   that   our   love   can -
2. Still,   the   long   night   falls,   and   yet   for   some,   deep
3. Lord,   what   should   I   do _____   to _____   have   e -
4. Lord,   who   is   my   neigh -   bor?   The   one   whose
5. Grate - ful   for   our   life,   can   we   be   free   to
6. At   this   ta - ble   of _____   thanks -   giv - ing
7. Sign   of   God's   deep   love _____   is   this   ban - quet

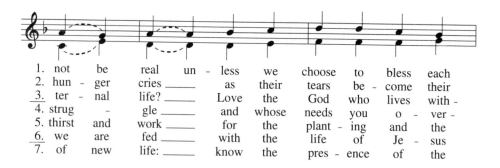

1. not   be   real   un - less   we   choose   to   bless   each
2. hun - ger   cries _____   as   their   tears   be - come   their
3. ter - nal   life? _____   Love   the   God   who   lives   with -
4. strug -   gle _____   and   whose   needs   you   o - ver -
5. thirst   and   work _____   for   the   plant - ing   and   the
6. we   are   fed _____   with   the   life   of   Je - sus
7. of   new   life: _____   know   the   pres - ence   of   the

_D.C._

1. oth -   er,   as   bless - ing   we   have   known.
2. bread _____   ⸯ   their   hope   too   soon   may   die.
3. in   you   and   your   neigh - bor   as   your - self.
4. look,   while   your   own   com - fort   you   se - cure.
5. har -   vest   of   King - dom's   life   in   all?
6. Ri -   sen,   in   whom   our   hope   is   born.
7. Ho -   ly,   in   spir - it   and   in   truth.

441

Thanks Be to God

*1. Thanks be to God whose love has gath - ered us this day;
2. Thanks be to God for all the gifts of life and light;
3. Thanks be to God who knows our se - cret joys and fears;
4. Thanks be to God who nev - er turns his face a - way;
5. Thanks be to God who made our world and all we see;

1. thanks be to God who helps and guides us on our way.
2. thanks be to God whose care pro - tects us day and night.
3. thanks be to God who when we call him al - ways hears.
4. thanks be to God who heals and par - dons all who stray.
5. thanks be to God who gave his Son to set us free.

1. Thanks be to God who gives us voice that we may thank him:
2. Thanks be to God who keeps in mind us who for - get him:
3. Thanks be to God our rock and strength ev - er sus - tain - ing:
4. Thanks be to God who wel - comes us in - to the king - dom:
5. Thanks be to God whose Spir - it brings warmth and re - joic - ing:

1-5. De - o gra - ti - as, De - o gra - ti - as, thanks be to God most high.

Verse 1: Unison Choir.

Text: Stephen Dean.
Music: CHARIS; Stephen Dean.
Text and music ©1994, Stephen Dean. Published by OCP Publications.

The Advent of Our King

1. The advent of our King
   Our thoughts must now employ;
   Then let us meet him on the road
   With songs of holy joy.

2. The co-eternal Son
   A maiden's offspring see;
   A servant's form Christ putteth on,
   To set his people free.

3. In glory from his throne
   Again will Christ descend,
   And summon all who are his own
   To joys that never end.

4. Our joyful praises sing
   To Christ, who set us free;
   Like tribute to the Father bring,
   And Holy Ghost, to thee.

Text: SM; Robert Campbell, 1814–1868, alt.
Music: ST. THOMAS (WILLIAMS); Aaron Williams, 1731–1776.

The Church's One Foundation

1. The Church's one foun - da - tion Is Je - sus Christ her Lord;
2. E - lect from ev - 'ry na - tion, Yet one o'er all the earth,
3. 'Mid toil and trib - u - la - tion, And tu - mult of her war
4. Yet she on earth hath un - ion With God, the Three in One,

1. She is his new cre - a - tion By wa - ter and the word:
2. Her char - ter of sal - va - tion, One Lord, one faith, one birth;
3. She waits the con - sum - ma - tion Of peace for ev - er - more;
4. And with the saints, com - mun - ion With those whose rest is won.

1. From heav'n he came and sought her To be his ho - ly bride;
2. One ho - ly Name she bless - es, Par - takes one ho - ly food,
3. Till with the vi - sion glo - rious Her long - ing eyes are blest,
4. O hap - py ones and ho - ly! Lord, give us grace that we

1. With his own blood he bought her, And for her life he died.
2. And to one hope she press - es, With ev - 'ry grace en - dued.
3. And the great Church vic - to - rious Shall be the Church at rest.
4. Like them, the meek and low - ly, On high may dwell with thee.

Text: 76 76 D; Samuel J. Stone, 1839–1900.
Music: AURELIA; Samuel S. Wesley, 1810–1876.

The Coming of Our God

1. The com-ing of our God Our thoughts must now em - ploy; Then
2. The co - e - ter - nal Son A maid - en's off - spring see; A
3. Daugh-ter of Si - on rise To greet thine in - fant King; Nor
4. In glo - ry from his throne A - gain will Christ de - scend, And
5. Let deeds of dark-ness fly Be - fore the ap - proach-ing morn, For
6. Our joy - ful prais - es sing To Christ, who set us free; Like

1. let us meet him on the road With songs of ho - ly joy.
2. ser-vant's form Christ put - teth on, To set his peo - ple free.
3. let thy stub - born heart de - spise The par - don he doth bring.
4. sum-mon all who are his own To joys that nev - er end.
5. un - to sin 'tis ours to die And serve the Vir - gin born.
6. tri - bute to the Fa - ther bring, And Ho - ly Ghost, to thee.

Text: SM; Charles Coffin, 1676–1749; tr. by Robert Campbell, 1814–1868.
Music: OPTATUS VOTIS OMNIUM; anon.; choral arr. by Randall DeBruyn, b. 1947 ©1985, OCP Publications.

The Cup We Bless

REFRAIN: 1st time: Choir or Cantor; Each time thereafter: All

Text: Refrain based on 1 Corinthians 10:16, verses based on Psalm 116; Christopher Willcock, b. 1947.
Music: Christopher Willcock.
Text and music ©1983, 1990, Christopher Willcock, SJ. Published by OCP Publications.

VERSES: Cantor

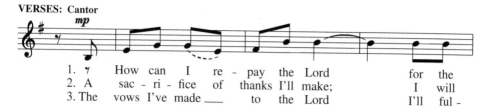

1. How can I re - pay the Lord for the
2. A sac - ri - fice of thanks I'll make; I will
3. The vows I've made ___ to the Lord I'll ful -

1. good-ness I've re - ceived? ___ The cup of bless-ing
2. call ___ on the Lord's name. I'll walk ___ in the
3. fill be - fore the peo - ple, with - in the house ___

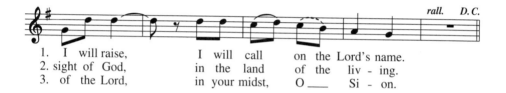

1. I will raise, I will call on the Lord's name.
2. sight of God, in the land of the liv - ing.
3. of the Lord, in your midst, O ___ Si - on.

The Cry of the Poor

REFRAIN: *Moderate tempo* (♩ = 66)

Descant *(a tempo)*

The Lord hears the cry of the poor.

Soprano *(a tempo)*

The Lord hears the cry of the poor.

Alto

Tenor

Bass *(a tempo)*

Bless - ed be the Lord. *Fine*

Bless - ed be the Lord. *Fine*

be the Lord.

VERSES: *Slightly faster* (♩ = 76)

1. I will bless the Lord at all times, with praise
2. Let the low - ly hear and be glad: the Lord
3. Ev - 'ry spir - it crushed God will save; will be
4. We pro - claim your great - ness, O God, your praise

1. ev - er in my mouth. Let my soul glo - ry in the
2. lis - tens to their pleas; and to hearts bro - ken God is
3. ran - som for their lives; will be safe shel - ter for their
4. ev - er in our mouth; ev - 'ry face bright-ened in your

rit. *D.C.*

1. Lord, who will hear the cry of the poor.
2. near, who will hear the cry of the poor.
3. fears, and will hear the cry of the poor.
4. light, for you hear the cry of the poor.

Text: Based on Psalm 34:1–2, 17–19, 22; John Foley, SJ, b. 1939.
Music: John Foley, SJ.
Text and music ©1978, 1991, John B. Foley, SJ and New Dawn Music.

The Glory of these Forty Days

1. The glory of these forty days We celebrate with songs of praise; For Christ, by whom all things were made, Himself has fasted and has prayed.
2. Alone and fasting Moses saw The loving God who gave the law; And to Elijah, fasting, came The steeds and chariots of flame.
3. So Daniel trained his mystic sight, Deliver'd from the lion's might; And John, the Bridegroom's friend, became The herald of Messiah's name.
4. Then grant us, Lord, like them to be Full oft' in fast and prayer with thee; Our spirits strengthen with thy grace, And give us joy to see thy face.
5. O Father, Son, and Spirit blest, To thee be ev'ry prayer adrest; Who art in threefold Name adored, From age to age, the only Lord.

Text: LM; *Clarum decus jejunii*; Gregory the Great, ca. 540–604; tr. by Maurice F. Bell, 1862–1947 © Oxford University Press, London.
Music: ERHALT UNS, HERR; melody from J. Klug's *Geistliche Lieder*, 1543; harm. by Johann S. Bach, 1685–1750, alt.

The First Noel

Text: Irregular with refrain; Trad. English Carol, 17th cent.
Music: THE FIRST NOEL; Trad. English Carol, 17th cent.; harm. by John Stainer, 1840–1901.

1. cold win-ter's night ____ that was ____ so deep.
2. so it con-tin-ued both day ____ and night.
3. fol-low the star ____ wher-ev-er it went.
4. o-ver the place ____ where Je-sus lay.
5. gold ____ and myrrh ____ and frank-in-cense.

REFRAIN:

No-el, No-el, No-el, No-el,

Born is the King of Is-ra-el.

The Goodness of the Lord

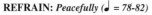

REFRAIN: *Peacefully (♩ = 78-82)*

I be-lieve, I be-lieve I shall see the good-ness of the Lord in the

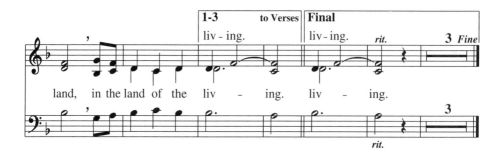

land, in the land of the liv - ing. liv - ing.

VERSES 1, 2:

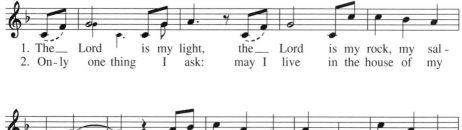

1. The__ Lord is my light, the__ Lord is my rock, my sal-
2. On-ly one thing I ask: may I live in the house of my

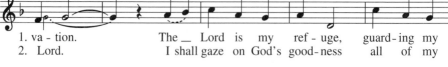

1. va - tion. The __ Lord is my ref - uge, guard-ing my
2. Lord. I shall gaze on God's good-ness all of my

1. life; of whom should I be a - fraid?
2. days; I shall live in the shel - ter of God.

VERSE 3: *Slightly faster (♩ = ca. 88)*

3. I be-lieve I shall see the good-ness of God in the land

rit. ***D.C. al fine***

3. of the liv-ing. Be strong, wait for the Lord.

The King of Glory

REFRAIN:

The King of glo - ry comes, the na - tion re - joic - es.

Fine

O - pen the gates be - fore him, lift up your voic - es.

VERSES:

Descant

1. Who is the King of glo - ry; how shall we call him?
2. In all of Gal - i - lee, in cit - y or vil - lage,
3. Sing then of Da - vid's Son, our Sav - ior and broth - er;
4. He gave his life for us, the pledge of sal - va - tion,
5. He con - quered sin and death; he tru - ly has ris - en,

Melody

D.C.

1. He is Em - man - u - el, the prom - ised of a - ges.
2. He goes a - mong his peo - ple cur - ing their ill - ness.
3. In all of Gal - i - lee was nev - er an - oth - er.
4. He took up - on him - self the sins of the na - tion.
5. And he will share with us his heav - en - ly vi - sion.

Text: Willard F. Jabusch, b. 1930 ©Willard F. Jabusch. Administered by OCP Publications.
Music: Trad. Israeli Folk Song; choral arr. by Randall DeBruyn, b. 1947 ©1983, OCP Publications.

The King of Kings, Christ Jesus Reigns

VERSES:

1. The King of Kings, Christ Je-sus reigns The Lord of ev-'ry na-
2. E-ter-nal King, Christ is God's Word From end-less a-ges spo-
3. O ris-en King, you light the way To heav-en's glo-rious por-

1. tion; In lov-ing wis-dom he or-dains The course of all cre-
2. ken; En-fleshed on earth, his voice was heard And Sa-tan's might was
3. tal; If in our hearts your truth has sway, We too have life im-

REFRAIN:

Christ, we a-dore you! Christ, we im-

1. a - tion!
2. bro - ken!
3. mor - tal!

Christ, we a-dore you! Christ, we im-

plore you: Christ, keep us ev - er be-fore you!

Christ, keep us be-fore you!

plore you:

Christ, keep us ev - er be-fore you!

Christ, keep us be-fore you!

Text: 87 87 with refrain; Melvin Farrel, SS, 1930−1986 ©1977, OCP Publications.
Music: ICH GLAUB AN GOTT; *Mainz Gesangbuch*, 1870; choral arr. by Randall DeBruyn, b. 1947 ©1990, OCP Publications.

The King of Love My Shepherd Is

1. The King of love my shep-herd is, Whose good-ness fails me nev - er; I noth-ing lack if I am his, And he is mine for - ev - er.
2. Where streams of liv - ing wa - ter flow With gen - tle care he leads me, And where the ver - dant pas - tures grow, With heav'n - ly food he feeds me.
3. Per - verse and fool - ish I have strayed, But yet in love he sought me, And on his shoul - der gent - ly laid, And home, re - joic - ing, brought me.
4. In death's dark vale I fear no ill, With you, dear Lord, be - side me, Your rod and staff my com - fort still, Your cross be - fore to guide me.
5. You spread a ta - ble in my sight, Your sav - ing grace be - stow - ing; And O what joy and true de - light From your pure chal - ice flow - ing!
6. And so through all the length of days, Your good - ness fails me nev - er, Good Shep - herd, may I sing your praise With - in your house for - ev - er.

Text: 87 87; Based on Psalm 23; Matthew 18; John 10; Henry W. Baker, 1821–1877.
Music: ST. COLUMBA; Trad. Irish Melody; adapt. by Randall DeBruyn, b. 1947 ©1990, OCP Publications.

The King Shall Come When Morning Dawns

1. The King shall come when morn-ing dawns And
2. Not, as of old, a lit-tle child, To
3. O bright-er than the ris-ing morn When
4. O bright-er than that glo-rious morn Shall
5. The King shall come when morn-ing dawns And

1. light tri-um-phant breaks, When beau-ty gilds the
2. bear and fight and die, But crowned with glo-ry
3. he, vic-to-rious rose And left the lone-some
4. this fair morn-ing be, When Christ, our King, in
5. light and beau-ty brings. Hail, Christ, the Lord! Thy

1. east-ern hills And life to joy a-wakes.
2. like the sun That lights the morn-ing sky.
3. place of death, De-spite the rage of foes.
4. beau-ty comes And we his face shall see!
5. peo-ple pray: Come quick-ly, King of kings.

Text: CM; Greek; tr. by John Brownlie, 1859–1925.
Music: MORNING SONG; *Sixteen Tune Settings*, Philadelphia, 1812; *Kentucky Harmony*, 1816; choral arr. by Randall DeBruyn, b. 1947
©1990, OCP Publications.

The Light of Christ

REFRAIN:

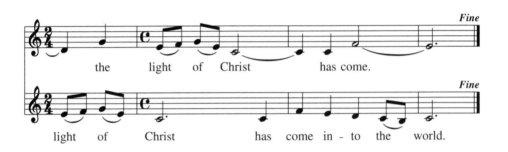

The light of Christ has come in-to the world,
The light of Christ has come in-to the world, the
the light of Christ has come.
light of Christ has come in-to the world.

VERSES:

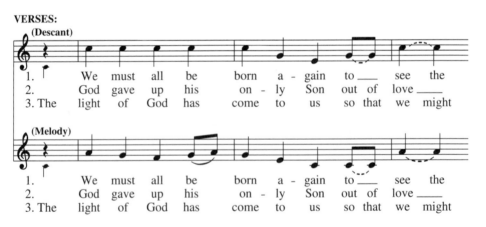

1. We must all be born a-gain to __ see the
2. God gave up his on-ly Son out of love __
3. The light of God has come to us so that we might

Text: Donald Fishel, b. 1950.
Music: Donald Fishel; verses descant by Randall DeBruyn, b. 1947.

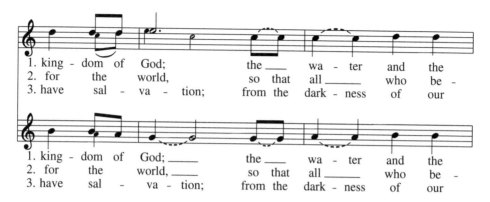

1. king - dom of God; the wa - ter and the
2. for the world, so that all who be -
3. have sal - va - tion; from the dark - ness of our

1. king - dom of God; the wa - ter and the
2. for the world, so that all who be -
3. have sal - va - tion; from the dark - ness of our

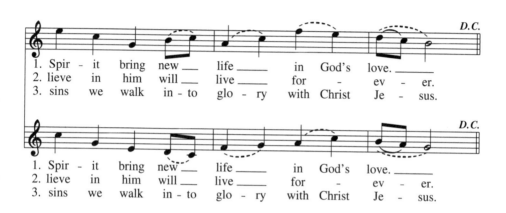

D.C.

1. Spir - it bring new life in God's love.
2. lieve in him will live for - ev - er.
3. sins we walk in - to glo - ry with Christ Je - sus.

D.C.

1. Spir - it bring new life in God's love.
2. lieve in him will live for - ev - er.
3. sins we walk in - to glo - ry with Christ Je - sus.

The Lord Is Near

REFRAIN: *Slow and lyric (♩ = 72)*

O the Lord is near to all who call on him; he is close to

O the Lord is near to all who call on him;

O the Lord is near to all who call on him; he is

all who seek his face, slow to an-ger and full of com-

he is close to all who seek his face, slow to

close to all who seek his face, slow to an-ger and

pas - sion and a - bound - ing in mer - ci - ful

an - ger and full of com - pas - sion and a -

full of com-pas - sion and a - bound - ing in

Text: Based on Psalm 27; Michael Joncas, b. 1951.
Music: Michael Joncas.
Text and music ©1979, New Dawn Music.

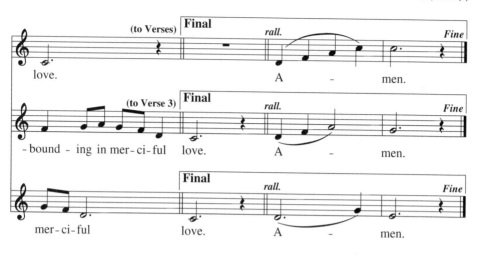

(to Verses) | **Final** rall. *Fine*

love.　　　　　　A　-　men.

(to Verse 3) | **Final** rall. *Fine*

-bound-ing in mer-ci-ful　love.　　A　-　men.

Final rall. *Fine*

mer-ci-ful　love.　　A　-　men.

VERSES: Cantor

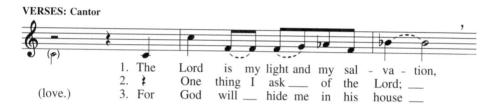

(♭)

(love.)

1. The　Lord　is　my light and my　sal - va - tion,
2. One　thing I　ask ___ of the　Lord; ___
3. For　God　will ___ hide me　in　his　house ___

3

1. there　is　noth - ing　　at　all ___　I
2. there　is　on - ly　one　thing ___　I
3. and　con - ceal　me　in　the　shel - ter　of　his

(’)

1. fear;　　　the　Lord　is　the　ref - uge　of　my
2. seek:　　　to　dwell　in　the　house ___　of　the
3. tent.　E - ven　now ___　my　head　is　held ___

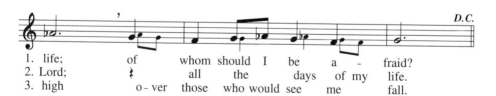

D.C.

1. life;　　of　whom should　I　be　a - fraid?
2. Lord;　　all　the　days　of my　life.
3. high　o - ver　those　who would see　me　fall.

461

The Snow Lay on the Ground

VERSES: *unison on verse*

1a. The snow lay on the ground, the stars shone
1b. *Ve - ní - te, a - do - ré - mus Dó - mi -*
2a. 'Twas Ma - ry, daugh - ter pure of ho - ly
2b. She laid him in a stall at Beth - le -
3a. Saint Jo - seph, too, was near to tend the
3b. The an - gels hov - er'd 'round, and sang this
4a. And thus that man - ger poor be - came a
4b. O come, then, let us join the heav'n - ly

1a. bright, When Christ our Lord was born on
1b. *num, Ve - ní - te, a - do - ré - mus*
2a. Anne, That brought in - to this world the
2b. hem; The ass and ox - en shared the
3a. child; To guard him and pro - tect his
3b. song: *Ve - ní - te, a - do - ré - mus*
4a. throne; For he whom Ma - ry bore was
4b. host, To praise the Fa - ther, Son, and

REFRAIN:

1a. Christ - mas night. *next verse*
1b. *Dó - mi - num.*
2a. God made man.
2b. roof with them.
3a. moth - er mild:
3b. *Dó - mi - num.*
4a. God the Son.
4b. Ho - ly Ghost.

Ve - ní - te, a - do -

Text: 10 10 10 10 with refrain; 19th cent.; anon.
Music: VENITE ADOREMUS; Old English Carol; melody adapt. by Charles W. Douglas, 1867–1944; choral arr. by Randall DeBruyn, b. 1947 ©1990, OCP Publications.

-ré - mus Dó - mi - num, Ve -

ní - te, a - do - ré - mus Dó - mi - num.

The Lord Jesus

REFRAIN: *Meditative, with movement*

The Lord Je - sus, af - ter eat - ing with his friends, washed their

feet and said to them: "Do you know what I, your Lord, have done to

you? I have giv - en you ex - am - ple that

1-4 *rit.* **to Verses** | **Final** *rit.* *Fine*

so you al - so should do." do."

VERSES:
Melody *a tempo*

Harmony
1. "You _____ are my friends: and you can have no great - er
2. "Peace I leave with you, and peace I give to all who
3. "I _____ am the vine and you, the branch: re - main in
4. "Those who come to me will nev - er thirst nor want for

rit. **D.C.**

1. love than to give your life _____ for _____ your _____ friends."
2. live with _____ sin - cere love for ev - 'ry _____ one."
3. me and _____ you will bear a - bun - dant _____ fruit."
4. food, and _____ I will raise them up on the last day."

Text: Weston Priory, Gregory Norbet, OSB, b. 1940.
Music: Weston Priory, Gregory Norbet, OSB.
Text and music ©1973, from the recording *Listen*, The Benedictine Foundation of the State of Vermont, Inc., Weston, VT.

The Spirit Is A-Movin'

REFRAIN:

Descant
Harmony

The Spir-it is a-mov-in' all o - ver,

Melody

The Spir - it is a-mov-in' all o - ver,

all o - ver this land. (Fine)

all o - ver this land. (Fine)

VERSES:

1. Peo-ple are gath - er-in', the church is born; _____ the
2. Old _____ ones _____ are _____ dream-ing dreams, _____ and
3. Old _____ walls _____ are _____ fall - ing down, _____ and
4. Filled _ with the Spir-it we are sent to serve. _ We are
5. The Spir - it fills _____ us _____ all with pow'r, _____ to

D.C.

1. Spir-it is a-blow-in' on a world _____ re - born. _____
2. young _ men and wom - en _____ see _____ the _____ light. _____
3. peo-ple all o - ver are _____ speak-ing with each oth - er. _____
4. called _ out to-geth-er, we are called _____ to _____ work. _____
5. be _ God's _ wit-ness-es to all _____ we _____ meet. _____

Text: Carey Landry, b. 1944.
Music: Carey Landry.
Text and music ©1969, 1979, 1996, Carey Landry and North American Liturgy Resources (N.A.L.R.).

The Strife Is O'er

REFRAIN:

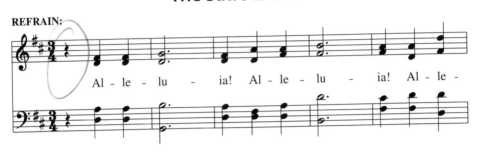

Al - le - lu - ia! Al - le - lu - ia! Al - le -

rit. *Fine* **VERSES:**

lu - ia!
1. The strife is o'er, the bat - tle
2. On the third morn he rose a -
3. O Ris - en Lord, all praise to

rit.

1. done; Now is the Vic - tor's tri - umph won; O let the
2. gain, Glo-rious in maj - es - ty to reign; O let us
3. thee, Who from our sin has set us free, That we may

D.C.

1. song of praise be sung: Al - le - lu - ia!
2. swell the joy - ful strain: Al - le - lu - ia!
3. live e - ter - nal - ly! Al - le - lu - ia!

Text: 888 with alleluias; *Finita iam sunt praelia;* Latin, 12th cent.; tr. by Francis Pott, 1832–1909, alt.
Music: VICTORY; Giovanni da Palestrina, 1525–1594; adapt. by William H. Monk, 1823–1889.

There Is a Balm in Gilead

REFRAIN: *1st time unison*

There is a balm in Gil-e-ad to make the wound-ed whole, there is a balm in Gil-e-ad to heal the sin-sick soul.

Fine

VERSES:

1. Some - times I feel dis - cour - aged, and __ think my work's in vain,
2. If you can - not preach like Pe - ter, if you can - not pray like Paul,
3. Don't __ ev - er feel dis - cour - aged, for __ Je - sus is your friend;

D.C.

1. but __ then the Ho - ly Spir - it re - vives my soul a - gain.
2. you can tell the love of Je - sus, and say, "He died for all."
3. and __ if you lack for knowl - edge he'll ne'er re - fuse to lend.

Text: Irregular; Jeremiah 8:22; Spiritual.
Music: BALM IN GILEAD; Spiritual.

The Supper of the Lord

REFRAIN: *Gently (♩ = 76-80)* **1st time: Cantor; Each time thereafter: All**

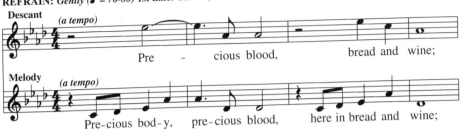

Descant (a tempo)
Pre - cious blood, bread and wine;

Melody (a tempo)
Pre-cious bod-y, pre-cious blood, here in bread and wine;

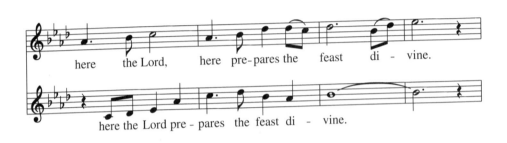

here the Lord, here pre-pares the feast di - vine.

here the Lord pre - pares the feast di - vine.

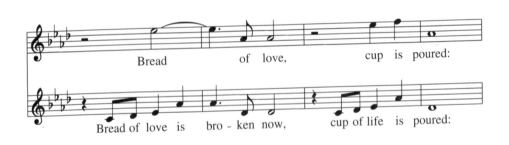

Bread of love, cup is poured:

Bread of love is bro - ken now, cup of life is poured:

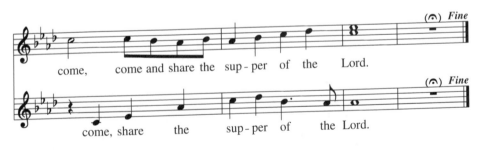

(⌒) *Fine*
come, come and share the sup-per of the Lord.

(⌒) *Fine*
come, share the sup-per of the Lord.

Text: Verses 1–4 based on John 4, 6; Laurence Rosania.
Music: Laurence Rosania.
Text and music ©1994, Laurence Rosania. Published by OCP Publications.

VERSES:

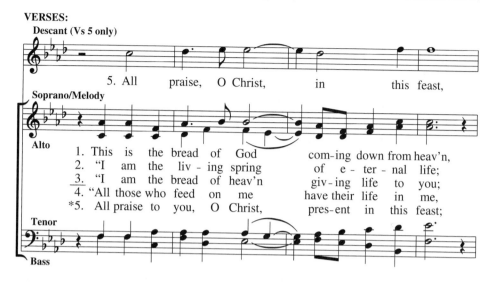

Descant (Vs 5 only)

5. All praise, O Christ, in this feast,

Soprano/Melody

Alto

1. This is the bread of God coming down from heav'n,
2. "I am the liv - ing spring of e - ter - nal life;
3. "I am the bread of heav'n giv-ing life to you;
4. "All those who feed on me have their life in me,
*5. All praise to you, O Christ, pres-ent in this feast;

Tenor

Bass

poco rit. **D.C.**

5. in this bread we share in one life, one Lord.

poco rit. **D.C.**

1. giv - ing life to us, ___ to all the world.
2. you that drink from me shall not thirst a - gain."
3. you that eat this bread ___ shall nev - er die."
4. as I have my life in the liv-ing God."
5. in this bread we share in one life, one Lord.

poco rit.

*Verse 5 unison with descant.

There Is a Longing

There is a long-ing in our hearts, O Lord, for you to re-

veal your-self to us. There is a long-ing in our

hearts for love we on-ly find in you, our God.

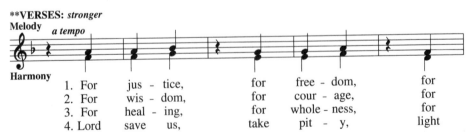

VERSES: *stronger*

Melody *a tempo*

Harmony

1. For jus - tice,	for free - dom,	for
2. For wis - dom,	for cour - age,	for
3. For heal - ing,	for whole - ness,	for
4. Lord save us,	take pit - y,	light

*Add SATB harmony after Verse 2.

**Add harmony to Verses 2 and 3; begin Verse 4 in unison,
and add harmony again with "We call you…"

Text: Anne Quigley.
Music: Anne Quigley.
Text and music ©1992, 1994, Anne Quigley. Published by OCP Publications.

1. mer - cy: hear our prayer. In sor - row,
2. com - fort: hear our prayer. In weak - ness,
3. new life: hear our prayer. In sick - ness,
4. in our dark - ness. We call you,

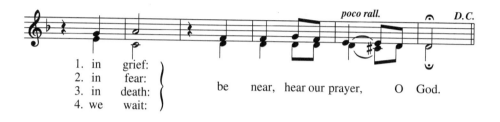

1. in grief: ⎫
2. in fear: ⎪ be near, hear our prayer, O God.
3. in death: ⎬
4. we wait: ⎭

There Is Nothing Told

VERSES: Cantor/Unison Choir *With steady, yet expressive, movement*

1-6. There is noth-ing told a-bout this wom-an, but that

1. she had once be-come en-gaged, and an an-gel ad-
2. she had brought in-to the world, in the land of Ju-
3. she had searched for three long days for her child who was
4. she at Ca-na was a guest, and that Je-sus changed
5. she was stand-ing by the cross when her son stretched his
6. she was one in prayer with those up-on whom tongues of

1. dressed her and said: "You are bless-ed a-mong all your kind."
2. de-a, her son; for some shep-herds have passed on this tale.
3. bus-y else-where, and her heart then did not un-der-stand.
4. wa-ter to wine, so that all might be-lieve who he was.
5. arms out on high, and met death with a thief on each side.
6. fire did de-scend, and the Spir-it bap-tized them with flame.

REFRAIN:

Soprano/Melody
Alto

On this day all earth and all par-a-dise join in nam-ing you hap-py and

Tenor
Bass

blessed; Vir-gin Ma-ry, bless-ed are you. Blest are you.

Text: *Une Femme dont on n'a rien dit*; Didier Rimaud, b. 1922; tr. by Christopher Willcock, b. 1947 ©1988, Christopher Willcock, SJ. Published by OCP Publications.
Music: Christopher Willcock ©1988, Christopher Willcock, SJ. Published by OCP Publications.

There's a Wideness in God's Mercy

1. There's a wide-ness in God's mer-cy Like the wide-ness of the sea;
2. For the love of God is broad-er Than the meas-ures of our mind,
3. Trou-bled souls, why will you scat-ter Like a crowd of fright-ened sheep?

1. There's a kind-ness in his jus-tice Which is more than lib-er-ty.
2. And the heart of the E-ter-nal Is most won-der-ful-ly kind.
3. Fool-ish hearts, why will you wan-der From a love so true and deep?

1. There is plen-ti-ful re-demp-tion In the blood that has been shed;
2. If our love were but more sim-ple We should take him at his word,
3. There is wel-come for the sin-ner And more grac-es for the good;

1. There is joy for all the mem-bers In the sor-rows of the Head.
2. And our lives would be thanks-giv-ing For the good-ness of our Lord.
3. There is mer-cy with the Sav-ior, There is heal-ing in his blood.

Text: 87 87 D; Frederick W. Faber, 1814–1863, alt.
Music: IN BABILONE; *Oude en Nieuwe Hollanste Boerenlities,* ca. 1710.

This Alone

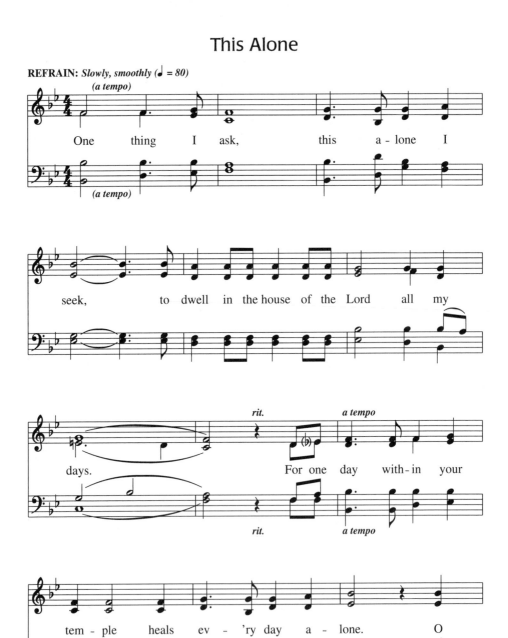

Text: Based on Psalm 27; Tim Manion.
Music: Tim Manion.
Text and music ©1981, 1983, Timothy J. Manion and New Dawn Music.

Lord, bring me to your dwell - ing.

VERSES 1, 3:

1. Hear,__ O__ Lord,__ the sound of my call - ing.
3. Wait on __ the Lord, and__ hope in his mer - cy.

rit. *D.C.*

1. Hear, __ O Lord, and show me your way.
3. Wait on __ the Lord, and live in his love.

VERSE 2:

2. The Lord is my light and hope of sal - va - tion. The

rit. *D.C.*

2. Lord is my ref - uge; whom should I fear?

They'll Know We Are Christians

VERSES:

Harmony / Melody

1. We are one in the Spir-it, we are one in the Lord,
2. We will walk with each oth-er, we will walk hand in hand,
3. We will work with each oth-er, we will work side by side,
4. All __ praise to the Fa-ther, from __ whom all things come,

1. We are one in the Spir-it, we are one in the
2. We will walk with each oth-er, we will walk hand in
3. We will work with each oth-er, we will work side by
4. And all praise to Christ Je-sus, his __ on - ly __

1. Lord, And we pray that all u - ni - ty may one day be re-stored.
2. hand, And to - geth - er we'll spread the news that God is in our land.
3. side, And we'll guard each one's dig - ni - ty and save __ each one's pride.
4. Son, And all praise to the Spir - it, who __ makes __ us __ one.

REFRAIN:

And they'll know we are Chris-tians by our love, by our

love, by our love.

love, Yes they'll know we are Chris-tians by our love.

Text: Peter Scholtes, b. 1938.
Music: Peter Scholtes; arr. by Dennis Fitzpatrick.
Text and music ©1966, F.E.L. Publications, Ltd., assigned 1991 to the Lorenz Corporation. Reproduced by permission. License no.
343138.

This Body

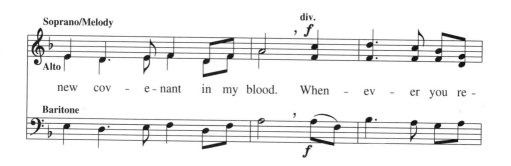

477

This Day Was Made by the Lord

Text: Based on Psalm 118; Christopher Walker, b. 1947.
Music: Christopher Walker.
Text and music ©1988, 1989, Christopher Walker. Published by OCP Publications.

VERSES:

Melody/Cantor:

```
* 1.  I       thank you, your   love      is      e  -  ter - nal,                    you  have
* 2. Your    hand raised me     up _____  in      tri - umph,                         you  have
* 3. The     stone which the    build - ers  re  -  ject - ed                          is   the
  4. You     o - pened the      gates _____ of     heav - en,                          you  have
  5. ⁊  You  are   my strength and  my      Sav - ior,                                 you  have
```

All: *Unison*

```
1. giv  -  en   me    life.   You    have   giv  -  en   me    life.
2. giv  -  en   me    life.   You    have   giv  -  en   me    life.
3. cor  -  ner-stone. _____   Is     the    cor  -  ner-stone. _____
4. giv  -  en   me    life.   You    have   giv  -  en   me    life.
5. giv  -  en   me    life.   You    have   giv  -  en   me    life.
```

Soprano

Alto

```
1. You    have   giv  -  en   me    life.
2. You    have   giv  -  en   me    life.
3. Is     the    cor  -  ner-stone. _____
4. You    have   giv  -  en   me    life.
5. You    have   giv  -  en   me    life.
```

Baritone

D.C.

```
1-5. I    will   pro - claim   the   won - ders   you   do!
```

D.C.

```
1-5. I    will   pro - claim   the   won - ders   you   do!
```

*For Easter Day and Easter Season.

479

This Is the Day

REFRAIN: *Rhythmic and joyful (♩. = ca. 160)*

Melody - 1st time Cantor/All repeat:

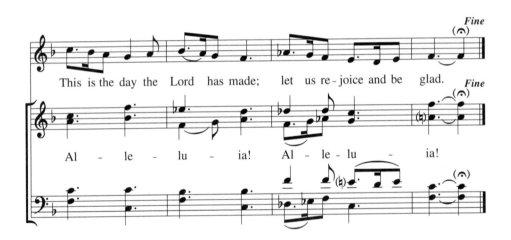

This is the day the Lord has made; let us re-joice and be glad.

Al - le - lu - ia! Al - le - lu - ia!

This is the day the Lord has made; let us re-joice and be glad. *Fine*

Al - le - lu - ia! Al - le - lu - ia!

VERSE 1: unison

1. Give thanks to the Lord for he is good, his mer-cy en-

1. dures for - ev - er; let the house of Is - ra - el

Text: Based on Psalm 118; Michael Joncas, b. 1951.
Music: Michael Joncas.
Text and music ©1981, 1982, Michael Joncas. Published by Cooperative Ministries, Inc. Exclusive agent: OCP Publications.

1. say: "His mer - cy en-dures for - ev - er."

VERSE 2: unison

2. The Lord's right hand has struck with pow'r, the Lord's right

2. hand is ex - alt - ed; I shall not die, but

2. live and de - clare the works of the Lord.

VERSE 3:

Melody

Harmony

3. The stone which the build-ers re - ject - ed has be - come the

3. cor - ner - stone. By the Lord has this been done;

3. it is won - der - ful in our eyes!

This Day God Gives Me

1. This day God gives me Strength of high heav - en,
2. This day God sends me Strength as my guard - ian,
3. God's way is my way, God's shield is 'round me,
4. Ris - ing I thank you, Might - y and Strong One,

1. Sun and moon shin - ing, Flame in my hearth,
2. Might to up - hold me, Wis - dom as guide.
3. God's host de - fends me, Sav - ing from ill.
4. King of Cre - a - tion, Giv - er of Rest,

1. Flash - ing of light - ning, Wind in its swift - ness,
2. Your eyes are watch - ful, Your ears are lis - t'ning,
3. An - gels of heav - en, Drive from me al - ways
4. Firm - ly con - fess - ing Three - ness of Per - sons,

1. Deeps of the o - cean, Firm - ness of earth.
2. Your lips are speak - ing, Friend at my side.
3. All that would harm me, Stand by me still.
4. One - ness of God - head, Tri - ni - ty blest.

Text: 55 54 D; ascr. to St. Patrick, 372–466; adapt. by James D. Quinn, SJ, b. 1919 ©1969, James D. Quinn, SJ. Reprinted by permission of Selah Publishing Co., Kingston, N.Y.
Music: BUNESSAN; Trad. Gaelic Melody; choral arr. by Randall DeBruyn, b. 1947 ©1990, OCP Publications.

Those Who See Light

Descant

Melody
1-3. Those who see light can walk in the dark.

1-3. Those who see love can see God.

1. Those who look up will dis - cov - er God's face,
2. Those who have wit - nessed the sun rise and set,
3. Those who see good in each per - son they meet,

1. those who look down will un - cov - er God's path,
2. those who have stud - ied a flow - er un - fold,
3. those who look af - ter their neigh - bors in need,

1. those who per - ceive God is here with us now will
2. those who have fo - cused on land, sea, and sky have
3. those who be - lieve God's now liv - ing in them will

1. see God's re - turn.
2. seen Je - sus Christ.
3. see God's re - turn.

Text: E. Donald Osuna, b. 1936.
Music: Nancy Elze; descant by John Strege ©1972, 1978, F.E.L. Publications, Ltd., assigned 1991 to the Lorenz Corporation.
Reproduced by permission. License no. 343138.

Those Who Sow in Tears

*REFRAIN: (♩ = 80-84) 1st time: Cantor; thereafter: All

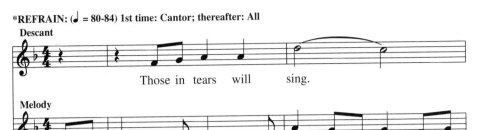

Descant

Those in tears will sing.

Melody

Those who sow in tears will sing when they reap. Those who

Those in tears will sing. Al - le -

sow in tears will sing when they reap: sing al - le -

1-5 to Verses | **Final** *Fine*

lu - ia! Al - le - lu - ia! ia!

1-5 to Verses | **Final** *Fine*

lu - ia! Al - le - lu - ia! ia!

VERSES:

1. When the Lord ___ gave back free - dom ___ to Zi - on it
2. Then they said a - mong the na - tions: ___ "See how the
3. Those who set out ___ in tears, ___ bear - ing the
4. Set us free, ___ O Lord, ___ like the wa - ter in

*Repeat refrain 1st time.

Text: Psalm 126; Bernadette Farrell, b. 1957.
Music: Bernadette Farrell.
Text and music ©1994, Bernadette Farrell. Published by OCP Publications.

484

1. seemed like a dream, and our mouth was filled with
2. Lord sets them free." Oh _____ yes, the Lord has
3. seed to be sown, will come home _____ re -
4. land that is dry! For the ones who sow in

D.C.

1. laugh - ter, our tongue with shouts of joy!
2. blessed us and done great things for us.
3. joic - ing, _____ car - ry - ing their sheaves.
4. tears will reap with shouts of joy!

Though the Mountains May Fall

ANTIPHON: *Spirited, allegro (♩ = 160)*

Soprano (Harmony)

Alto (Melody)
Though the moun - tains may fall and the hills turn to dust,

Tenor (Melody)

Bass (Harmony)

yet the love of the Lord will stand

as a shel - ter for all who will call on his name.

Fine

Sing the praise and the glo - ry of God.

Text: Based on Isaiah 54:6–10, 49:15, 40:31–32; Dan Schutte, b. 1947.
Music: Dan Schutte; choral arr. by Michael Pope, SJ.
Text and music ©1975, 1979, Daniel L. Schutte and New Dawn Music.

VERSES: *more gently*

1. Could the Lord ev - er leave you? Could the Lord for -
2. Should you turn and for - sake him, he will gent - ly
3. Go to him when you're wea - ry; he will give you
4. As he swore to your fa - thers, when the flood de -

1. get his love? Though a moth - er for -
2. call your name. Should you wan - der a -
3. ea - gle's wings. You will run, nev - er
4. stroyed the land. He will nev - er for -

1. sake her child, he will not a - ban - don you.
2. way from him, he will al - ways take you back.
3. tire, _____ for your God will be your strength.
4. sake you; _____ he will swear to you a - gain.

To Be Your Bread

Text: David Haas, b. 1957.
Music: David Haas; choral arr. by Marty Haugen, b. 1950.
Text and music ©1981, 1982, David Haas. Published by Cooperative Ministries, Inc. Exclusive agent: OCP Publications.

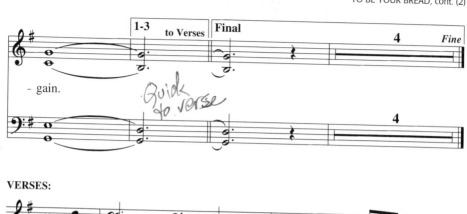

- gain.

Quick to verse

VERSES:

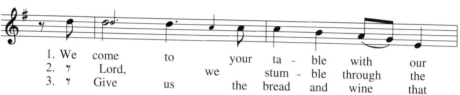

1. We come to your ta - ble with our
2. ⁊ Lord, we stum - ble through the
3. ⁊ Give us the bread and wine that

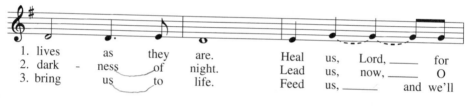

1. lives as they are. Heal us, Lord, _____ for
2. dark - ness of night. Lead us, now, _____ O
3. bring us to life. Feed us, _____ and we'll

rit.   *D.C.*

1. we are bro - ken; make us one a - gain.
2. Lord, we fol - low; bring us home to you.
3. nev - er hun - ger, nev - er thirst a - gain.

To You, O God, I Lift Up My Soul

REFRAIN: 1st time: Cantor; each time thereafter: All

Poco marcato - very rhythmic (♩ = 80)

To you, O God, I lift up my soul;

lift up my spir - it to my Lord.

1 D.C. **2-4** to Verses

To you I lift up my soul.

Final

To you I lift up my soul.

Text: Based on Psalm 25:1, 4–5, 8–9, 10, 14; Bob Hurd, b. 1950.
Music: Bob Hurd; choral arr. by Craig S. Kingsbury, b. 1952.
Text and music ©1991, 1992, Bob Hurd. Published by OCP Publications.

To you I lift up my soul.

VERSES:

1. Make me to know your ways, O God;
2. Good and up - right our gra - cious God,
3. Stead - fast and kind your ways, O God;

1.	teach me your paths,	guide me.
2.	show - ing the way,	guid - ing the
3.	all who re - vere your	cov - e - nant

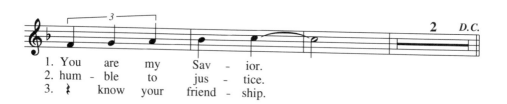

1. You are my Sav - ior.
2. hum - ble to jus - tice.
3. know your friend - ship.

To You, O Lord

Text: Based on Psalm 25 ©1969, 1981, I.C.E.L., Inc.
Music: Owen Alstott, b. 1947; choral arr. by Randall DeBruyn, b.1947 ©1985, OCP Publications.

VERSES:

1. I will fol - low your ways, O Lord;
2. Of my weak - ness and sin - ful - ness
3. Put an end to my suf - fer - ing;
4. I will place all my trust in you;

Oooh

1. I will walk in your paths, for you are my
2. be not mind - ful, O Lord. In your kind - ness,
3. bring me out of dis - tress and re - lieve the
4. I will not be a - shamed, for I know that

Oooh   Oooh

rit.   D.C.

1. Sav - ior and my God.
2. Lord, re - mem - ber me.
3. trou - bles of my heart.
4. you, O Lord, are near.

(Oooh)

rit.   D.C.

rit.

To You, O Lord

*Refrain may be sung twice through first time only: Cantor or Unison Choir; All repeat.**

Text: Based on Psalm 25; Scott Soper.
Music: Scott Soper.
Text and music ©1988, Scott Soper. Published by OCP Publications.

D.C.

1. God, _____ and for you I will wait.
2. hum - ble _____ to fol - low his ways.

VERSE 3:

3. Your way, O Lord, is kind - ness to those who are

3. true. Your friend-ship is with those who love you;

D.C. al fine

3. you re - veal to them your Word.

Turn to Me

REFRAIN: *Gently, Andante* (♩ = ca. 126)
(a tempo)

Turn to me, O turn, and be saved, says the Lord, for I am God; there is no oth-er, none be-side me.

2   **1-3** to Verses   **Final 3** *Fine*

I call your name.

VERSE 1:

1. I am God, who com-forts you; who are

slightly faster

1. you to be a-fraid of flesh that fades, is

rit. ⌒   *a tempo*   *rit. D.C.*

1. made like the grass of the field soon to with-er.

VERSE 2:
Harmony

Melody 2. Lis-ten to me, my peo-ple; give ear to me, my

slightly faster

2. na-tion: a law will go forth from me, and my

Text: Based on Isaiah 45, 51; John Foley, SJ, b. 1939.
Music: John Foley, SJ.
Text and music ©1975, 1978, 1979, John B. Foley, SJ and New Dawn Music.

2. jus-tice for a light to the peo-ple.

VERSE 3:
Harmony I

Melody

3. Lift up your eyes to the heav-ens, and look at the

Harmony II

3. earth down be - low. The heav-ens will van-ish like smoke, and the

3. earth will wear out like a gar-ment.

To Jesus Christ, Our Sovereign King

VERSES: *unison*

1. To Je-sus Christ, our sov-'reign king, Who is the world's sal-va-tion, All praise and hom-age do we bring And thanks and ad-o-ra-tion.
2. Thy reign ex-tend, O king be-nign, To ev-'ry land and na-tion; For in thy king-dom, Lord di-vine, A-lone we find sal-va-tion.
3. To thee and to thy church, great king, We pledge our hearts' ob-la-tion; Un-til be-fore thy throne we sing In end-less ju-bi-la-tion.

REFRAIN:

Christ Je-sus, vic-tor! Christ Je-sus, Christ Je-sus, Christ, vic-tor! Christ Je-sus, rul-er! Christ Je-sus, Lord and re-deem-er! Christ, Lord and re-deem-er! Christ Je-sus, Lord and re-deem-er! Christ Je-sus, Lord, re-deem-er!

Text: 87 87 with refrain; Martin B. Hellriegel, 1891–1981 ©1978, assigned to Mrs. Irene C. Mueller.
Music: ICH GLAUB AN GOTT; *Mainz Gesangbuch*, 1870; choral arr. by Randall DeBruyn, b. 1947 ©1990, OCP Publications.

498

Ubi Caritas

ANTIPHON: Repeat Antiphon final time   *Tranquil and flowing (♪ = ca. 120)*

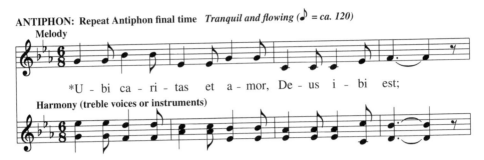

Melody

*U – bi ca – ri – tas   et a – mor, De – us i – bi   est;

Harmony (treble voices or instruments)

Fine

u – bi ca – ri – tas   et a – mor, De – us i – bi   est.

VERSES 1&3: Cantor/Choir

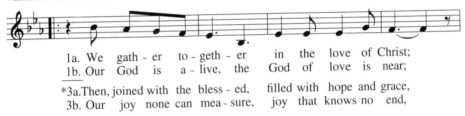

1a. We gath – er to – geth – er in the love of Christ;
1b. Our God is a – live, the God of love is near;

*3a. Then, joined with the bless – ed, filled with hope and grace,
3b. Our joy none can mea – sure, joy that knows no end,

2nd time: D.C.

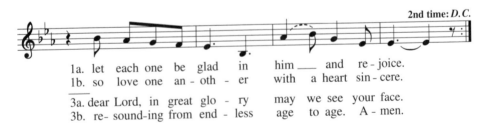

1a. let each one be glad in him ___ and re – joice.
1b. so love one an – oth – er with a heart sin – cere.

3a. dear Lord, in great glo – ry may we see your face.
3b. re – sound-ing from end – less age to age. A – men.

*During Vss 2 & 3, the Antiphon may be hummed or sung softly by a few singers or played by instruments.

Text: Adapt. fr. Holy Thursday Liturgy; Laurence Rosania.
Music: Laurence Rosania.
Text and music ©1992, Laurence Rosania. Published by OCP Publications.

*VERSE 2: Cantor/Choir

2a. We, the man - y, be - come one bod - y
2b. Let all quar - rels, all di - vi - sion,

2a. as the Spir - it binds, and we seek to be
2b. all our con - flict cease; then will Christ tru - ly

2nd time: D. C.

2a. one in Christ and one in heart and mind.
2b. dwell a - mong us as our Lord of Peace.

Unless a Grain of Wheat

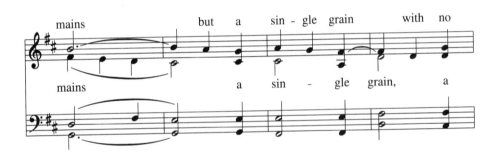

Text: Based on John 12, 14, 15, 2 Timothy 2; Bernadette Farrell, b. 1957.
Music: Bernadette Farrell.
Text and music ©1983, 1986, Bernadette Farrell. Published by OCP Publications.

VERSES:

1. If we have died with him then we shall live with him;
2. an - y one serves ___ me then they must fol - low me;
3. Make your home in me as I make mine in you;
4. If you re - main in me and my word lives in you,
5. Those who love me are loved by my Fa - ther;
6. Peace I leave with you, my peace I give to you;

1. if we hold firm we shall reign with him. ___
2. where - ev - er I am my ser - vants will be.
3. those who re - main in me bear much fruit. ___
4. then you will be my dis - ci - ples. ___
5. we shall be with them and dwell in them. ___
6. peace which the world can - not give is my gift.

OPTIONAL SATB VERSES 3 AND 5

VERSES:

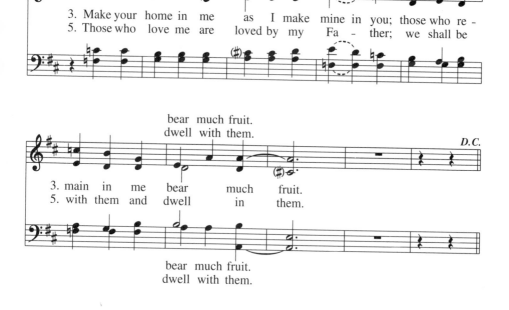

3. Make your home in me as I make mine in you; those who re -
5. Those who love me are loved by my Fa - ther; we shall be

bear much fruit.
dwell with them.

3. main in me bear much fruit.
5. with them and dwell in them.

bear much fruit.
dwell with them.

Unless a Grain of Wheat

REFRAIN: (♩ = 116)

Un-less a grain of wheat fall to the ground and

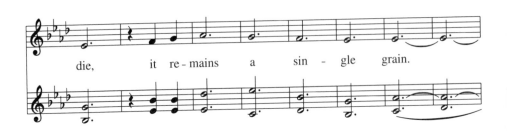

die, it re-mains a sin - gle grain.

But if it die it will yield a rich

har - vest. *Fine* **VERSES:**
1. In his own bod - y, by his own
2. Do not draw back now, do not be

2. Oo _____ Oo _____

Text: Based on John 12:24 and George Herbert's *Love Bade Me Welcome*; adapt. by Bob Hurd, b. 1950.
Music: Bob Hurd; choral arr. by Craig S. Kingsbury, b. 1952.
Text and music ©1984, 1985. Published by OCP Publications.

Wade in the Water

*OSTINATO REFRAIN: 1st time: Cantor/All repeat; thereafter: All
Freely (♩ = ca. 104)

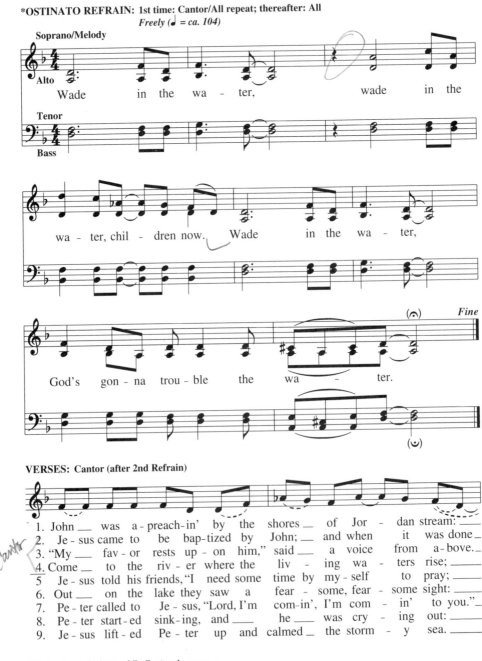

VERSES: Cantor (after 2nd Refrain)

1. John ___ was a-preach-in' by the shores ___ of Jor - dan stream: ___
2. Je-sus came to be bap-tized by John; ___ and when it was done ___
3. "My ___ fav-or rests up-on him," said ___ a voice from a-bove. ___
4. Come ___ to the riv-er where the liv - ing wa - ters rise; ___
5. Je-sus told his friends, "I need some time by my-self to pray; ___
6. Out ___ on the lake they saw a fear - some, fear - some sight: ___
7. Pe-ter called to Je-sus, "Lord, I'm com-in', I'm com - in' to you." ___
8. Pe-ter start-ed sink-ing, and ___ he ___ was cry - ing out: ___
9. Je-sus lift-ed Pe-ter up and calmed ___ the storm - y sea. ___

*Choir repeats Ostinato while Cantor sings verses.

Text: Refrain, Traditional; verses, M.D. Ridge ©1993, M.D. Ridge. Published by OCP Publications.
Music: Spiritual; choral arr. by M.D. Ridge ©1993, M.D. Ridge. Published by OCP Publications.

1. "Re - pent ____ of your sins and let the
2. a voice ____ from the heav-ens said: __
3. The crowd ____ saw the Spir - it in the
4. if you want to fol - low Je - sus, you must
5. take the boat a - cross the lake and
6. Je - sus walk-ing on the wa - ter
7. He walked on the wa - ter while the
8. "Save ___ me, Lord!"__ and Je - sus
9. Walk ___ on the wa - ter and let

1. wa - ter wash you clean."____
2. "This __ is my be - lov-ed Son."
3. form of a snow - white dove. ____
4. come __ and be bap - tized. ____
5. find ___ a place to stay." ____
6. on ___ that wind - y night. ____
7. storm - y night winds blew. ____
8. heard __ him, heard him shout. ____
9. Je - sus set you free. ____

D.C.

O

Wake from Your Sleep

VERSES: *Light and merrily (♩ = 144)*

1. Wake from your sleep, a Sav - ior is born.
2. Come from your fields as shep - herds of old.
3. Stay with us now, O Lord of the earth.
4. Now shall the earth take joy in her tears.

1. God's ho - ly child gives light to this morn,
2. Wel - come this child whom proph - ets fore - told.
3. Make of our hearts a place for your birth.
4. Now shall our hearts be turned from their fears.

1. all our dark - ness to dis - pel.
2. God has made the earth his home.
3. Though our cares be great or small,
4. All the earth shall sing God's praise.

1. Praise to our God whose glo - ry we tell.
2. Praise to our God, the Sav - ior has come.
3. Je - sus the Lord, be born in us all.
4. Je - sus the Lord, be born on this day.

Text: Dan Schutte, b.1947.
Music: Dan Schutte.
Text and music ©1977, 1978, Daniel L. Schutte and New Dawn Music.

We Gather Together

1. We gath - er to - geth - er to ask the Lord's bless - ing; He
2. Be - side us to guide us, our God with us join - ing, Whose
3. We all do ex - tol you, our lead - er tri - um - phant, And

1. chas - tens and has - tens his will to make known; The
2. king - dom calls all to the love which en - dures. So
3. pray that you still our de - fend - er will be. Let

1. wick - ed op - press - ing now cease from dis - tress - ing: Sing
2. from the be - gin - ning the fight we were win - ning: You,
3. your con - gre - ga - tion es - cape trib - u - la - tion: Your

1. prais - es to his name; he for - gets not his own.
2. Lord, were at our side; all ____ glo - ry be yours!
3. name be ev - er praised! O ____ Lord, make us free!

Text: 12 11 12 11; *Wilt heden nu treden*; tr. by Theodore Baker, 1851–1934, alt.
Music: KREMSER; *Nederlandtsch Gedenckclanck*, 1626; choral arr. by Edward Kremser, 1838–1914.

We Are Many Parts

Text: Based on 1 Corinthians 12, 13; Marty Haugen, b. 1950.
Music: Marty Haugen.
Text and music ©1980, 1986, G.I.A. Publications, Inc.

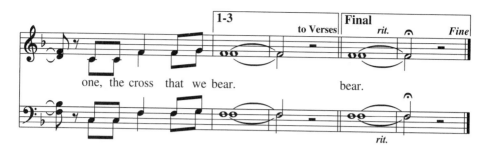

1-3 | to Verses | **Final** rit. Fine

one, the cross that we bear.   bear.

rit.

VERSES:

unison

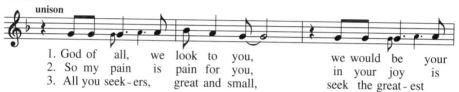

1. God of all, we look to you,   we would be your
2. So my pain is pain for you,   in your joy is
3. All you seek-ers, great and small,   seek the great-est

div.   D.C.

1. ser-vants true,   let us be your love to all the world.
2. my joy, too;   all is brought to-geth-er in the Lord.
3. gift of all;   if you love, then you will know the Lord.

We Are the Light of the World

VERSES:

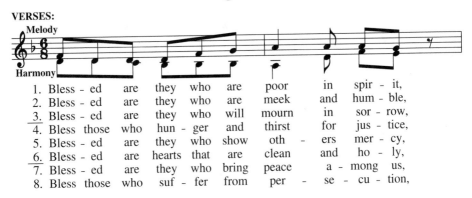

1. Bless - ed are they who are poor in spir - it,
2. Bless - ed are they who are meek and hum - ble,
3. Bless - ed are they who will mourn in sor - row,
4. Bless those who hun - ger and thirst for jus - tice,
5. Bless - ed are they who show oth - ers mer - cy,
6. Bless - ed are hearts that are clean and ho - ly,
7. Bless - ed are they who bring peace a - mong us,
8. Bless those who suf - fer from per - se - cu - tion,

1. Theirs is the king-dom of God.   Bless us, O Lord, make us
2. They will in - her - it the earth.   Bless us, O Lord, make us
3. They will be com - fort - ed.   Bless us, O Lord, when we
4. They will be sat - is - fied.   Bless us, O Lord, hear our
5. They will know mer - cy too.   Bless us, O Lord, hear our
6. They will be - hold ___ the Lord.   Bless us, O Lord, make us
7. They are the chil-dren of God.   Bless us, O Lord, may your
8. Theirs is the king-dom of God.   Bless us, O Lord, when they

1. poor in spir - it;
2. meek and hum - ble;
3. share their sor - row;
4. cry for jus - tice;   Bless us, O Lord, our God.
5. cry for mer - cy;
6. pure and ho - ly;
7. peace be with us;
8. per - se - cute us;

Text: Matthew 5; adapt. by Jean Anthony Greif, 1898–1981.
Music: Jean Anthony Greif; choral arr. by Randall DeBruyn, b. 1947.
Text and music ©1966, 1983, Vernacular Hymns Publishing Co.

REFRAIN:

Descant

Soprano

Alto — The light of the world, shine,

Soprano (Melody)

Alto — We are the light of the world, may our light shine be-fore

Tenor

Bass

shine be-fore all, see, see the good we do,

all, that they may see the good that we do, and give

1-7 *D.C.* **Final**

and give glo - ry to glo - ry to God. God.

1-7 *D.C.* **Final**

glo - ry to God. God.

glo - ry to God, to God. God.

We Believe

*Asterisk (*) over double bar line indicates that Cantor's pickup notes overlap with final measure of preceding Response.

Text: Bernadette Farrell, b. 1957.
Music: Bernadette Farrell.
Text and music ©1993, Bernadette Farrell. Published by OCP Publications.

VERSES 3-8:

3. We be-lieve in one Lord, Je-sus Christ:

Cantor:

4. who is flesh of our flesh, bone of our bone:

Cantor:

5. yet one be-ing with God, the liv-ing God.

Cantor:

6. We be-lieve in one Spir-it of our God:

Cantor:

7. Spir-it of the proph-ets, Spir-it of Je-sus:

Cantor:

8. Spir-it of us all, Spir-it of cre-a-tion.

(Hum)

We Walk by Faith

With quiet strength (♩ = 69-72)

1,5. We walk by faith, and not by sight: No
2. We may not touch his hands and side, Nor
3. Help then, O Lord, our un - be - lief, And
4. That when our life of faith is done In

Melody

Harmony

1,5. gra - cious words we hear Of him who spoke as
2. fol - low where he trod; Yet in his prom - ise
3. may our faith a - bound; To call on you when
4. realms of clear - er light We may be - hold you

1,5. none e'er spoke, But we be - lieve him near.
2. we re - joice And cry "My Lord and God!"
3. you are near, And seek where you are found:
4. as you are In full and end - less sight.

Text: CM; Based on John 20:24–29; Henry Alford, 1810–1871, alt.
Music: SHANTI; Marty Haugen, b. 1950 ©1984, G.I.A. Publications, Inc.

We Have Been Told

Text: David Haas, b. 1957.
Music: David Haas.
Text and music ©1983, G.I.A. Publications, Inc.

VERSES:

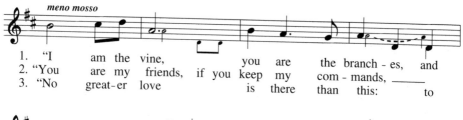

1. "I am the vine, you are the branch - es, and
2. "You are my friends, if you keep my com - mands, ____
3. "No great-er love is there than this: to

1. all ____ who live in me will bear great fruit."
2. no long - er slaves, I call you friends."
3. lay down one's life for ____ a friend."

We Praise You

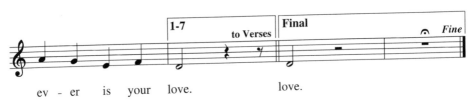

VERSES:

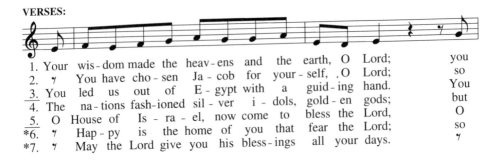

1. Your wis-dom made the heav-ens and the earth, O Lord; you
2. ⁊ You have cho-sen Ja-cob for your-self, O Lord; so
3. You led us out of E-gypt with a guid-ing hand. You
4. The na-tions fash-ioned sil-ver i-dols, gold-en gods; but
5. O House of Is-ra-el, now come to bless the Lord, O
*6. ⁊ Hap-py is the home of you that fear the Lord; so
*7. ⁊ May the Lord give you his bless-ings all your days. ⁊

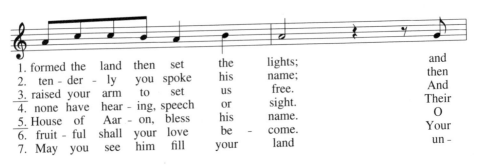

1. formed the land then set the lights; and
2. ten-der-ly you spoke his name; then
3. raised your arm to set us free. And
4. none have hear-ing, speech or sight. Their
5. House of Aar-on, bless his name. O
6. fruit-ful shall your love be-come. Your
7. May you see him fill your land un-

*Wedding verses

Text: Verses 1–5 based on Psalms 135, 136; verses 6–7 based on Psalm 128; Mike Balhoff, b. 1946.
Music: Darryl Ducote, b. 1945 and Gary Daigle, b. 1957.
Text and music ©1973, 1978, Damean Music.

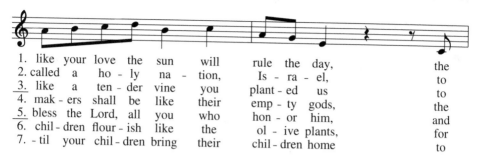

1. like your love the sun will   rule the day,   the
2. called a ho - ly na - tion,   Is - ra - el,   to
3. like a ten - der vine you   plant - ed us   to
4. mak - ers shall be like their   emp - ty gods,   the
5. bless the Lord, all you who   hon - or him,   and
6. chil - dren flour - ish like the   ol - ive plants,   for
7. - til your chil - dren bring their   chil - dren home   to

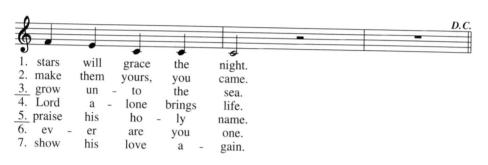

1. stars will grace the night.
2. make them yours, you came.
3. grow un - to the sea.
4. Lord a - lone brings life.
5. praise his ho - ly name.
6. ev - er are you one.
7. show his love a - gain.

We Remember

Text: Marty Haugen, b. 1950.
Music: Marty Haugen.
Text and music ©1980, G.I.A. Publications, Inc.

cel-e-brate,   we be-lieve.

VERSES:

Melody

Harmony

1. Here,   a   mil-lion wound-ed   souls   are   yearn-ing just to
2. Now   we   re-cre-ate your love,   we   bring the bread and
3. Christ,   the   Fa-ther's great "A - men" to   all the hopes and
4. See   the   face of Christ re - vealed in   ev - 'ry per - son

1. touch you and be   healed.   Gath - er all your
2. wine to share a   meal.   Sign of grace and
3. dreams of ev - 'ry heart,   Peace be - yond all
4. stand - ing by your side,   Gift to one an -

D.C.

1. peo - ple,   and   hold them to   your heart.
2. mer - cy,   the   pres - ence of   the   Lord.
3. tell - ing,   and   free - dom from all   fear.
4. oth - er,   and   tem - ples of your love.

We Shall Draw Water

REFRAIN: *Vigorous and bouncy (♩. = 60 minimum!)*

Descant

We shall draw wa - ter joy - ful - ly, sing - ing joy - ful - ly,

Melody

We shall draw wa - ter joy - ful - ly, sing - ing joy - ful - ly,

sing - ing joy - ful - ly; we shall draw wa - ter

sing - ing joy - ful - ly; we shall draw wa - ter

Fine

joy - ful - ly from the well - springs of sal - va - tion.

Fine

joy - ful - ly from the well - springs of sal - va - tion.

VERSE 1:

1. Tru - ly God is our sal - va - tion; we trust, we

1. shall not fear. For the Lord is our strength, the

D.C.

1. Lord is our song; he be - came our Sav - ior.

Text: Based on Isaiah 12:2–6; Paul Inwood, b. 1947.
Music: Paul Inwood.
Text and music ©1986, Paul Inwood. Published by OCP Publcations.

VERSE 2:

2. Give thanks, O give thanks to the Lord; give

2. praise to his ho - ly name! Make his might - y deeds known to

2. all of the na - tions; pro - claim his great - ness.

D.C.

VERSE 3:

3. Sing a psalm, sing a psalm to the Lord for he has done

3. glo - rious deeds. Make known his works to all of the earth;

3. peo - ple of Zi - on, sing for joy, for great in your midst,

D.C. al fine

3. great in your midst is the Ho - ly One of Is - rael.

We Three Kings of Orient Are

VERSES:

1. We three kings of O - ri - ent are, Bear - ing gifts we
2. Born a King on Beth - le - hem's plain, Gold I bring to
3. Frank - in - cense to of - fer have I: In - cense owns a
4. Myrrh is mine: its bit - ter per - fume Breathes a life of
5. Glo - rious now be - hold him a - rise, King and God and

1. tra - verse a - far, Field and foun - tain, Moor and moun - tain,
2. crown him a - gain, King for - ev - er, Ceas - ing nev - er
3. De - i - ty nigh; Prayer and prais - ing, Glad - ly rais - ing,
4. gath - er - ing gloom; Sor - rowing, sigh - ing, Bleed - ing, dy - ing,
5. Sac - ri - fice; Al - le - lu - ia, Al - le - lu - ia!

REFRAIN:

1. Fol - low - ing yon - der star.
2. O - ver us all to reign.
3. Wor - ship him, God on high.
4. Sealed in the stone-cold tomb.
5. Sounds thru' the earth and skies.

O star of won-der, star of

night, Star with roy - al beau - ty bright; West - ward

Text: 88 44 6 with refrain; Matthew 2:1–11; John H. Hopkins, Jr., 1820–1891.
Music: KINGS OF ORIENT; John H. Hopkins, Jr.

526

lead - ing, still pro - ceed - ing, Guide us to thy per - fect light!

We Will Rise Again

VERSES 1,2,4: (♩ = 100-104)

Descant

4. Fear not, I am with you; I

Melody

1. Like a shep-herd I will feed you; I will gath - er
2. I am strength to the wea - ry; to the weak I
4. Fear not, I am with you; I

4. am your God. I will strength-en you, and

1. you with care. I will lead you and
2. am new life. Though the young may grow
4. am your God. I will strength-en you, and

4. help you; up - hold you with my hand.

1. hold you close to my heart.
2. wea - ry, I will be their hope.
4. help you; up - hold you with my hand.

REFRAIN:

We will run for our

We will run and not grow wea - ry, for our

Text: Based on Isaiah 40, 41; David Haas, b. 1957.
Music: David Haas.
Text and music ©1985, David Haas. Published by OCP Publications.

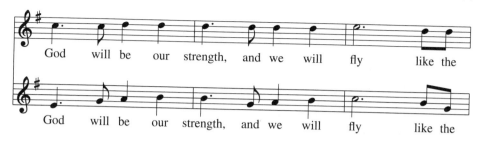

God will be our strength, and we will fly like the

God will be our strength, and we will fly like the

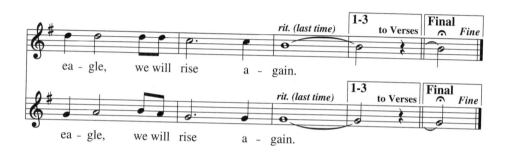

rit. (last time) **1-3** to Verses | **Final** ⌢ *Fine*

ea - gle, we will rise a - gain.

rit. (last time) **1-3** to Verses | **Final** ⌢ *Fine*

ea - gle, we will rise a - gain.

VERSE 3:

3. Lift up your eyes, and see who made the stars. I

D.S. al fine

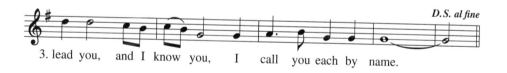

3. lead you, and I know you, I call you each by name.

Were You There

1. Were you there when they cru - ci - fied my Lord? Were you
2. Were you there when they nailed him to the tree? Were you
3. Were you there when they laid him in the tomb? Were you

1. there when they cru - ci - fied my Lord? Oh!
2. there when they nailed him to the tree? Oh!
3. there when they laid him in the tomb? Oh!

1.
2.
3.
Some-times it caus-es me to trem-ble, trem-ble,
Some-times it caus-es me to trem-ble, trem-ble,
Some-times it caus-es me to trem-ble, trem-ble,

1. trem-ble. Were you there when they cru - ci-fied my Lord?
2. trem-ble. Were you there when they nailed him to the tree?
3. trem-ble. Were you there when they laid him in the tomb?

Text: 10 10 14 10; Spiritual.
Music: WERE YOU THERE; Spiritual.

What Child Is This

VERSES:

1. What child is this, who, laid to rest, On Ma-ry's lap is sleep-ing?
2. Why lies he in such mean es-tate Where ox and ass are feed-ing?
3. So bring him in-cense, gold, and myrrh, Come peas-ant, King, to own him;

1. Whom an-gels greet with an-thems sweet, While shep-herds watch are keep-ing?
2. Good Chris-tian, fear, for sin-ners here The si-lent Word is plead-ing.
3. The King of kings sal-va-tion brings, Let lov-ing hearts en-throne him.

REFRAIN:

This, this is Christ the King, Whom shep-herds guard and an-gels sing;

Haste, haste to bring him laud, The babe, the son of Ma-ry.

Text: 87 87 with refrain; William C. Dix, 1837–1898.
Music: GREENSLEEVES; English melody, 16th cent.

531

What Is This Place

1. What is this place, where we are meet-ing? On-ly a house, the
2. Words from a - far, stars that are fall - ing. Sparks that are sown in
3. And we ac - cept bread at this ta - ble, Bro - ken and shared, a

1. earth its floor. Walls and a roof, shel - ter-ing peo - ple, Win-dows for
2. us like seed: Names for our God, dreams, signs and won-ders Sent from the
3. liv - ing sign. Here in this world, dy - ing and liv-ing, We are each

1. light, an o - pen door. Yet it be-comes a bod - y that lives When
2. past are all we need. We in this place re - mem-ber and speak A -
3. oth-er's bread and wine. This is the place where we can re - ceive What

1. we are gath-ered here, And know our God is near.
2. gain what we have heard: God's free re - deem-ing word.
3. we need to in - crease: Our jus - tice and God's peace.

Text: 98 98 9 66; Huub Oosterhuis, b. 1933; tr by David Smith, b. 1933.
Music: KOMT NU MET ZANG; Trad. Dutch Hymn, 1626; choral arr. by Bernard Huijbers, b. 1922.
Text and music ©1967, Gooi en Sticht, bv., Baarn, The Netherlands. Exclusive agent for English-language countries: OCP Publications.

What Star Is This

1. What star is this, with beams so bright, More love - ly
2. 'Tis now ful - filled what God de - creed, "From Ja - cob
3. O Je - sus, while the star of grace Im - pels us
4. To God, the Fa - ther, heav'n - ly Light, To Christ, re -

1. than the noon - day light? 'Tis sent to an - nounce a
2. shall a star pro - ceed"; And lo! the __ east - ern
3. on to seek thy face, Let not our __ sloth - ful
4. vealed in earth - ly night, To God the __ Ho - ly

1. new - born king, Glad tid - ings of our God to bring.
2. sag - es stand To read in heav'n the Lord's com - mand.
3. hearts re - fuse The guid - ance of thy light to use.
4. Spir - it raise An end - less song of thank - ful praise!

Text: LM; *Quem stella sole pulchrior;* Charles Coffin, 1676–1749; tr. by John Chandler, 1806–1876, alt.
Music: PUER NOBIS; adapt. by Michael Praetorius, 1571–1621; choral arr. by George Woodward, 1843–1934.

What Wondrous Love Is This

1. What won-drous love is this, O my soul, O my soul? What won-drous love is this, O my soul? What this That caused the Lord of Bliss To bear the dread-ful curse for my soul, for my soul, To bear the dread-ful curse for my soul?

2. To God and to the Lamb, I will sing, I will sing, To God and to the Lamb, I will sing. What won-drous love is Lamb Who is the great I AM, While mil-lions join the theme, I will sing, I will sing, While mil-lions join the theme I will sing.

3. And when from death I'm free, I'll sing on, I'll sing on, And when from death I'm free, I'll sing on. To God and to the And when from death I'm free I'll sing and joy-ful be, And through e-ter-ni-ty I'll sing on, I'll sing on, And through e-ter-ni-ty, I'll sing on.

Text: 12 9 12 12 9; Anon; first appeared in *A General Selection of the Newest and Most Admired Hymns and Spiritual Songs...*, 1811.
Music: WONDROUS LOVE; William Walker's *Southern Harmony*, 1840; choral arr. by Randall DeBruyn, b. 1947 ©1990, OCP Publications.

Whatsoever You Do

REFRAIN:

What-so - ev - er you do to the least of my peo - ple, that you do un - to me.

VERSES:

Fine

1. When I was hun - gry, you gave me to
2. When I was home-less, you o - pened your
3. When I was wea - ry, you helped me find
4. When in a pris - on, you came to my
5. When I was laughed at, you stood by my

1. eat; When I was thirst - y, you gave me to drink.
2. door; When I was na - ked, you gave me your coat.
3. rest; When I was anx - ious, you calmed all my fears.
4. cell; When on a sick - bed, you cared for my needs.
5. side; When I was hap - py, you shared in my joy.

D.C.

1-5. Now en - ter in - to the home of my Fa - ther.

Text: Willard F. Jabusch, b. 1930.
Music: Willard F. Jabusch; choral arr. by Owen Alstott, b. 1947.
Text and music ©1967, 1977, Willard F. Jabusch. Administered by OCP Publications.

When I Survey the Wondrous Cross

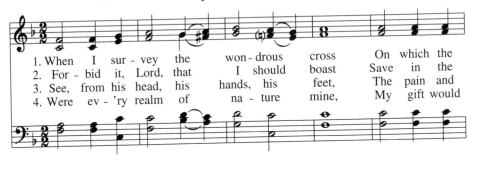

1. When I sur-vey the won-drous cross On which the
2. For-bid it, Lord, that I should boast Save in the
3. See, from his head, his hands, his feet, The pain and
4. Were ev-'ry realm of na-ture mine, My gift would

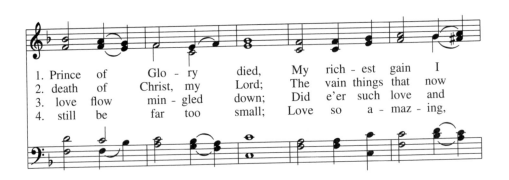

1. Prince of Glo-ry died, My rich-est gain I
2. death of Christ, my Lord; The vain things that now
3. love flow min-gled down; Did e'er such love and
4. still be far too small; Love so a-maz-ing,

1. count but loss, And pour con-tempt on all my pride.
2. tempt me most, I sac-ri-fice them to his blood.
3. sor-row meet, Or thorns com-pose so rich a crown?
4. so di-vine, De-mands my soul, my life, my all.

Text: LM; Isaac Watts, 1674–1748, alt.
Music: HAMBURG; Lowell Mason, 1792–1872.

While Shepherds Watched Their Flocks

1. While shep-herds watched their flocks by night, All seat-ed
2. "Fear not," said he, for might-y dread Had seized their
3. "To you, in Da-vid's town this day, Is born of
4. "The heav'n-ly Babe you there shall find To hu-man
5. Thus spoke the ser-aph, and forth-with Ap-peared a
6. "All glo-ry be to God on high, And on the

1. on the ground, The an-gel of the Lord came down, And
2. trou-bled mind. "Glad tid-ings of great joy I bring To
3. Da-vid's line The Sav-ior, who is Christ, the Lord, And
4. view dis-played, All mean-ly wrapped in swath-ing bands, And
5. shin-ing throng Of an-gels prais-ing God, who thus Ad-
6. earth be peace: Good will hence-forth, from heav'n to all, Be-

1. glo-ry shone a-round, And glo-ry shone a-round.
2. you and hu-man-kind, To you and hu-man-kind.
3. this shall be the sign, And this shall be the sign:
4. in a man-ger laid, And in a man-ger laid."
5. dressed their joy-ful song, Ad-dressed their joy-ful song:
6. gin and nev-er cease! Be-gin and nev-er cease!"

Text: CM, with repeat; Luke 2:8–14; Nahum Tate, 1652–1715.
Music: CHRISTMAS; George F. Handel, 1685–1759; adapt. in *The Psalms of David for the use of Parish Churches*, London, 1791.

When We Eat This Bread

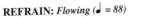

REFRAIN: *Flowing (♩ = 88)*

Cantor/All (melody):

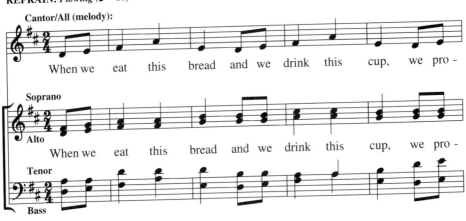

When we eat this bread and we drink this cup, we pro-

Soprano

Alto

When we eat this bread and we drink this cup, we pro-

Tenor

Bass

Fine

claim your death un - til you come.

Fine

claim your death un - til you come.

VERSES:

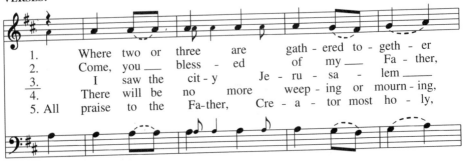

1. Where two or three are gath - ered to - geth - er
2. Come, you __ bless - ed of my __ Fa - ther,
3. I saw the cit - y Je - ru - sa - lem __
4. There will be no more weep - ing or mourn - ing,
5. All praise to the Fa - ther, Cre - a - tor most ho - ly,

Text: Refrain based on 1 Corinthians 11:26 ©1973, I.C.E.L., Inc. Verses based on Matthew 18, Revelation 21 ©1981, 1982, Michael Joncas, b. 1951. Published by Cooperative Ministries, Inc. Exclusive agent: OCP Publications.
Music: Michael Joncas ©1981, 1982, Michael Joncas. Published by Cooperative Ministries, Inc. Exclusive agent: OCP Publications.

div.

1. in my name, _____ where two or
2. come to me. _____ En - ter _____
3. come from God, _____ all clothed and a -
4. nev - er - more: _____ and God will _____
5. praise to him. _____ All praise to the

div.

1. three _____ are _____ gath - ered to - geth - er, there am
2. in - to _____ God's ho - ly _____ king - dom, full of
3. dorned _____ as a bride for her hus - band, filled with
4. dwell _____ with his ho - ly _____ peo - ple ev - er -
5. Son, _____ our _____ Sav - ior and broth - er, praise to

1. I. How bless - ed are they who are
2. joy. How bless - ed are they who are
3. love. How bless - ed are they who are
4. more. How bless - ed are they who are
5. him; All glo - ry and praise to the

D.C.

1-4. called to the ban - quet of the Lord.
5. Spir - it of God who makes us one.

Where There Is Love

Descant (final Refrain only)

Where there is love, there is God. The

Melody *(a tempo)*

Where there is love, there is God.

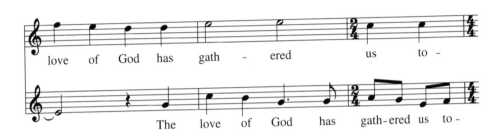

love of God has gath - ered us to -

The love of God has gath-ered us to -

1-3 to Verses

geth - er; Al - le - lu - ia.

1-3 to Verses

geth - er; Al - le - lu - ia.

Final
rit. Fine

VERSE 1:

1. Love is pa-tient, love is kind,

1. nev - er jeal - ous, nev - er proud, nev - er seek-ing for one's

Text: Based on 1 John 4, 1 Corinthians 13; David Haas, b. 1957.
Music: David Haas.
Text and music ©1985, David Haas. Published by OCP Publications.

1. self.　　Love nev-er leads　to　　an - ger.

VERSE 2:

2. Love is gra-cious and for - giv - ing,　　tak-ing no de-light in wrong;

2. Love re-joic - es　　in the truth;　Love will en - dure.

VERSE 3:

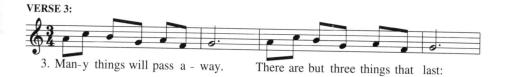

3. Man-y things will pass a - way.　There are but three things that last:

3. Faith, Hope, and Love;　the great-est of these is　　Love.

Without You

Text: Based on a Prayer of St. Francis, 1182–1226; Tom Kendzia.
Music: Tom Kendzia.
Text and music ©1991, Tom Kendzia and North American Liturgy Resources (N.A.L.R.).

1. love and your care, in the face of de-spair, be your
2. dark-ness of night, you a-lone are our light. You a-

rall.   *a tempo*   **D.C.**

1. peace a - live in the world.
2. lone, O God, are peace.

VERSE 3: *animato*

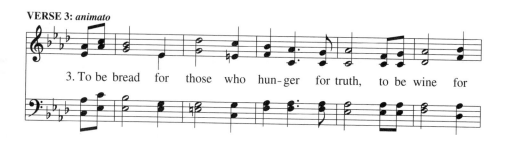

3. To be bread for those who hun-ger for truth, to be wine for

3. all thirst-ing for you. In your Spir-it a - live, we are

rit.   *gently, ad lib.*   **D.C. al fine**

3. sight to the blind. We are love when love can't be found.

rit.   *gently, ad lib.*

Wood of the Cross

Text: Based on Good Friday Liturgy, Psalm 22; Owen Alstott, b. 1947.
Music: Owen Alstott; choral arr. by Randall DeBruyn, b. 1947.
Text and music ©1982, 1987, OCP Publications.

Yahweh

REFRAIN: *Gently*

Yah-weh is the God of my sal - va - tion: I trust in him and have no fear. I sing of the joy which his love gives to me, and I draw deep-ly from the gives me, springs of his great kind - ness.

1-4 *to Verses* | Final | *Fine*

Text: Isaiah 12:2–3; Weston Priory, Gregory Norbet, OSB, b. 1940.
Music: Weston Priory, Gregory Norbet, OSB.
Text and music ©1972, 1980, from the recording *Wherever You Go*, The Benedictine Foundation of the State of Vermont, Inc., Weston, VT.

VERSES:

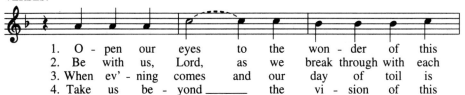

1. O - pen our eyes to the won - der of this
2. Be with us, Lord, as we break through with each
3. When ev' - ning comes and our day of toil is
4. Take us be - yond _____ the vi - sion of this

1. mo - ment, the be - gin - ning of _____ an -
2. oth - er, to find ____ the truth _____ and
3. o - ver, give us rest, ____ O Lord, in the
4. day to the deep and wide ways of your

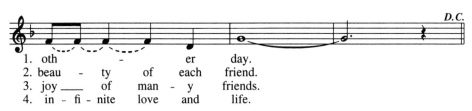

1. oth - er day.
2. beau - ty of each friend.
3. joy ____ of man - y friends.
4. in - fi - nite love and life.

Ye Sons and Daughters

ANTIPHON:

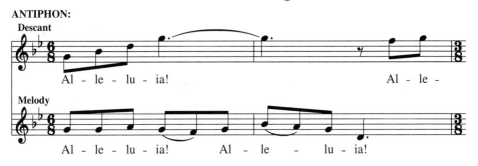

Descant: Al - le - lu - ia!   Al - le -

Melody: Al - le - lu - ia!   Al - le - lu - ia!

VERSES:

lu - ia! Al - le - lu - ia!   Al - le -

Al - le - lu - ia!

Do All verses

1. Ye sons and daugh - ters
2. That Eas - ter morn, at
3. An an - gel clad in
4. That night the a - pos - tles
5. When Thom - as first the
6. "My pier - céd side, O
7. No long - er Thom - as
8. How blest are they who
9. On this most ho - ly

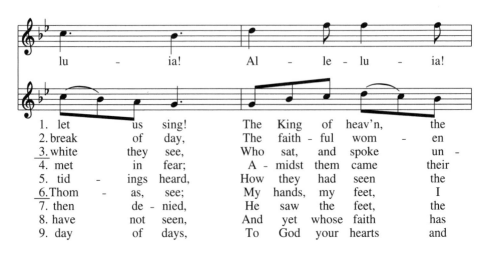

lu - ia!   Al - le - lu - ia!

1. let us sing! The King of heav'n, the
2. break of day, The faith - ful wom - en
3. white they see, Who sat, and spoke un -
4. met in fear; A - midst them came their
5. tid - ings heard, How they had seen the
6. Thom - as, see; My hands, my feet, I
7. then de - nied, He saw the feet, the
8. have not seen, And yet whose faith has
9. day of days, To God your hearts and

Text: 888 with alleluias; attr. to Jean Tisserand, d. 1494; tr. by John M. Neale, 1818–1866.
Music: O FILII ET FILIAE; melody fr. *Airs sur les hymnes sacrez, odes et noëls*, 1623; Mode II; descant by Randall DeBruyn, b. 1947
©1990, OCP Publications.

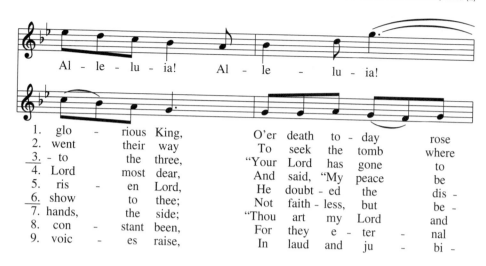

Al - le - lu - ia!   Al - le - lu - ia!

1. glo - rious King,   O'er death to - day   rose
2. went their way   To seek the tomb   where
3. - to the three,   "Your Lord has gone   to
4. Lord most dear,   And said, "My peace   be
5. ris - en Lord,   He doubt - ed the   dis -
6. show to thee;   Not faith - less, but   be -
7. hands, the side;   "Thou art my Lord   and
8. con - stant been,   For they e - ter - nal
9. voic - es raise,   In laud and ju - bi -

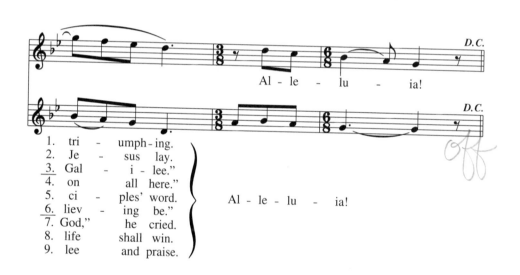

Al - le - lu - ia!

1. tri - umph - ing.
2. Je - sus lay.
3. Gal - i - lee."
4. on all here."
5. ci - ples' word.   Al - le - lu - ia!
6. liev - ing be."
7. God," he cried.
8. life shall win.
9. lee and praise.

549

Ye Watchers and Ye Holy Ones

1. Ye watch-ers and ye ho-ly ones,
2. Re-spond, ye souls in end-less rest,
3. O friends, in glad-ness let us sing,

Bright
Ye
Tri-

1. ser-aphs, cher-u-bim, and thrones,
2. pa-tri-archs and proph-ets blest,
3. um-phant an-thems e-cho-ing,

Raise the glad-strain,
Al-le-lu-ia!
Al-le-lu-ia!

1. al-le-lu-ia! Cry out, do-min-ions, prince-doms,
2. Al-le-lu-ia! Ye ho-ly twelve and mar-tyrs
3. Al-le-lu-ia! To God the Fa-ther, God the

1. powers, Vir-tues, arch-an-gels, an-gels' choirs, } (Melody)
2. strong, All saints tri-um-phant, raise the song, } 1-3. Al-le-
3. Son, And God the Spir-it, Three in One, } 1-3. Al-

Text: LM with additions; J. Athelstan Riley, 1858–1945, alt. © Oxford University Press, London.
Music: LASST UNS ERFREUEN; melody fr. *Auserlesene, Catholische, Geistliche Kirchengesäng*, Cologne, 1623; choral arr. by Randall DeBruyn, b.1947 ©1994, OCP Publications.

You Are Mine

VERSES 1-3: *Tenderly, legato (♩ = ca. 72-80)*

1. I will come to you in the si - lence, I will lift you
2. I am hope for all who are hope-less, I am eyes for
3. I am strength for all the de - spair-ing, heal-ing for the

1. from ___ all your fear.
2. all who long to see. In the shad-ows of the night, ___
3. ones who dwell in shame. All the blind will see, the

You will hear my voice, I

1. claim you as my choice, be still and know I am here. **(to Vs 2)**
2. I will be your light, ___ come and rest in me. **(to Refrain)**
3. lame will all run free, and all will know my name. **(to Refrain)**

℗ REFRAIN:

Melody

Harmony

Do not be a-fraid, I am with you. I have called you each by

name. Come and fol-low me, I will bring you home; I

Final *Fine*
(to Verses)

love you and you are mine.

(4. I)

Text: David Haas, b. 1957.
Music: David Haas; choral arr. by David Haas and Kate Cuddy.
Text and music ©1991, G.I.A. Publications, Inc.

552

VERSE 4:

4. am the Word that leads all to free-dom,   I   am the peace the

4. world can-not give.   I will call your name, em - brac-ing all your

(Melody)

D.S. al fine

Harmony

4. pain,   stand up,   now   walk,   and   live!

You Are Near

ANTIPHON: *Peacefully (♩ = 80)*

2ND Descant

Yah-weh, I know you are near, stand-ing

1ST Melody

Yah-weh, I know you are near, stand-ing

al - ways at my side. You guard me from the

al - ways at my side. You guard me from the

Fine

foe, and you lead me in ways ev - er - last-ing.

Fine

foe, and you lead me in ways ev - er - last-ing.

VERSES:

1. Lord, — you have searched my heart, and you know when I
2. Where — can I run from your love? If I climb to the
3. You — know my heart and its ways, you who formed me be -
4. Mar-vel-ous to me are your works; how pro - found are your

Text: Based on Psalm 139; Dan Schutte, b. 1947.
Music: Dan Schutte.
Text and music ©1971, 1979, Daniel L. Schutte. Administered by New Dawn Music.

1. sit and when I stand.
2. heav-ens you are there;
3. -fore I was born,
4. thoughts, my _ Lord.

Your _ hand is up - on me pro -
if I fly to the sun - rise or
in the se - cret of dark - ness be -
E - ven if I could count them, they

rit. **D.C.**

1. tect-ing me from death,
2. sail be - yond the sea,
3. fore I saw the sun,
4. num-ber as the stars,

keep - ing me from harm.
still I'd find you there.
in my moth-er's womb.
you would still be there.

You Are Our Living Bread

REFRAIN: *Flowing; in deep faith* (♩ = ca. 100) **1st time: Cantor; thereafer: All**

You are our liv-ing bread; you are our

Fine

ho - ly wine, Lord Je - sus Christ!

VERSES: Cantor

1. I feed my peo-ple on the fin - est ___ of bread, on my
2. I feed my peo-ple on the fin - est ___ of wine, on my
3. Where two or three ___ have ___ gath-ered in my name, there am

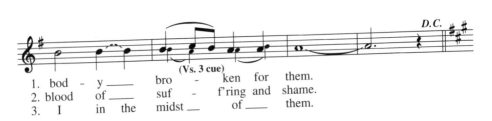

D.C.

(Vs. 3 cue)

1. bod - y ___ bro - ken for them.
2. blood of ___ suf - f'ring and shame.
3. I in the midst ___ of ___ them.

Text: Michael Joncas, b. 1951.
Music: Michael Joncas.
Text and music ©1979, New Dawn Music.

MORNING PRAYER
EVENING PRAYER
CHRISTIAN INITIATION OF ADULTS
CHRISTIAN FUNERALS

Opening Dialogue

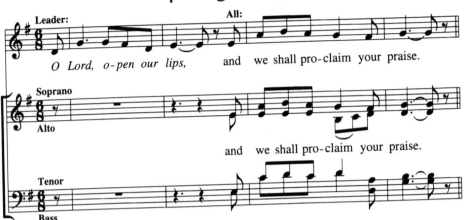

O Lord, o-pen our lips, and we shall pro-claim your praise.

and we shall pro-claim your praise.

Text: Based on Psalm 51:15; Michael Joncas, b. 1951.
Music: Michael Joncas.
Text and music ©1985, New Dawn Music.

Morning Hymn: Psalm 95

1. O come and sing to God, the Lord, To him our voic - es raise; Let us in our most joy - ful songs, The Lord, our Sav - ior, praise.
2. Be - fore his pres - ence let us come With praise and thank - ful voice; Let us sing psalms to him with joy, With grate - ful hearts re - joice.
3. He is a great and might - y king, A - bove all gods his throne; The depths of earth are in his hand, The moun - tains are his own.
4. To him the spa - cious sea be - longs, He made its waves and tides; And by his hand the ris - ing land Was formed and still a - bides.
5. O come, and bow - ing down to him Our wor - ship let us bring; Yes, let us kneel be - fore the Lord, Our Mak - er and our king.

(⌒) Last time

Text: Psalm 95:1–6; *The Psalter,* 1912, alt. by Michael Joncas, b. 1951.
Music: Michael Joncas.
Text and music ©1985, New Dawn Music.

Canticle of Zachary

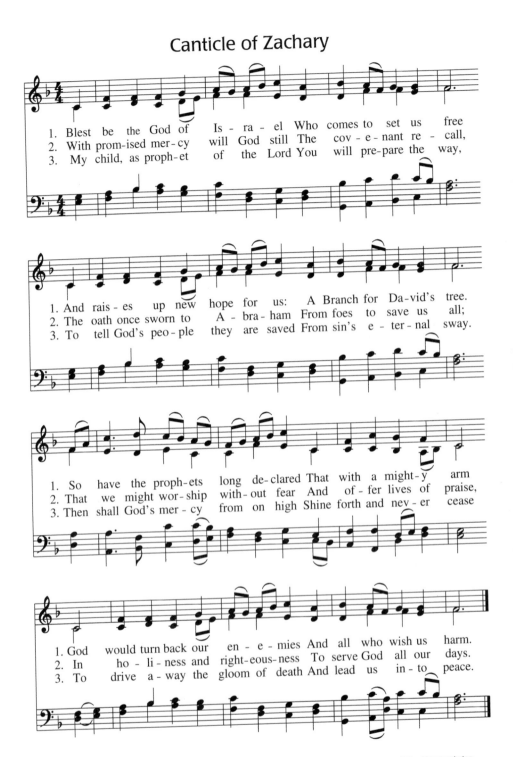

1. Blest be the God of Is - ra - el Who comes to set us free
2. With prom-ised mer-cy will God still The cov - e - nant re - call,
3. My child, as proph-et of the Lord You will pre-pare the way,

1. And rais - es up new hope for us: A Branch for Da-vid's tree.
2. The oath once sworn to A - bra - ham From foes to save us all;
3. To tell God's peo - ple they are saved From sin's e - ter - nal sway.

1. So have the proph-ets long de-clared That with a might-y arm
2. That we might wor-ship with-out fear And of - fer lives of praise,
3. Then shall God's mer - cy from on high Shine forth and nev - er cease

1. God would turn back our en - e - mies And all who wish us harm.
2. In ho - li - ness and right-eous-ness To serve God all our days.
3. To drive a - way the gloom of death And lead us in - to peace.

Text: CMD; Luke 1:68–79; adapt. by Carl P. Daw Jr., b. 1944 ©1989, Hope Publishing Co. All rights reserved. Used by permission.
Music: FOREST GREEN; Trad. English Melody; *The English Hymnal*; collected and arr. by Ralph Vaughan Williams, 1872–1958. Used with permission of Oxford University Press.

Proclamation of Light

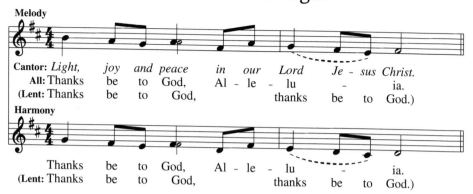

Melody

Cantor: *Light, joy and peace in our Lord Je - sus Christ.*
All: Thanks be to God, Al - le - lu - ia.
(Lent: Thanks be to God, thanks be to God.)

Harmony

Thanks be to God, Al - le - lu - ia.
(Lent: Thanks be to God, thanks be to God.)

Music: Paul Inwood, b. 1947 ©1984, 1985, Paul Inwood. Published by OCP Publications.

Evening Hymn: Phos Hilaron/O Radiant Light

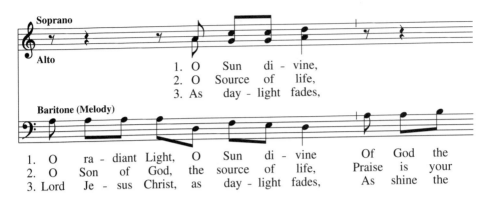

Soprano

Alto

1. O Sun di - vine,
2. O Source of life,
3. As day - light fades,

Baritone (Melody)

1. O ra - diant Light, O Sun di - vine Of God the
2. O Son of God, the source of life, Praise is your
3. Lord Je - sus Christ, as day - light fades, As shine the

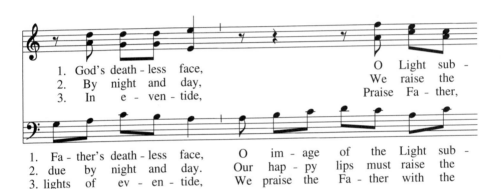

1. God's death - less face, O Light sub -
2. By night and day, We raise the
3. In e - ven - tide, Praise Fa - ther,

1. Fa - ther's death - less face, O im - age of the Light sub -
2. due by night and day. Our hap - py lips must raise the
3. lights of ev - en - tide, We praise the Fa - ther with the

1. lime, The dwell - ing place.
2. strain: Your splen - did name.
3. Son, And Spir - it, one.

1. lime That fills the heav'n - ly dwell - ing place.
2. strain Of your es - teemed and splen - did name.
3. Son, The Spir - it blest, and with them one.

Text: LM; *Phos Hilaron*, Greek, ca. 200; tr. by William G. Storey, b. 1923 © William G. Storey.
Music: JESU DULCIS MEMORIA; Mode I; choral arr. by Randall DeBruyn, b. 1947 ©1991, OCP Publications.

Gospel Canticle: Magnificat
(Great is the Lord)

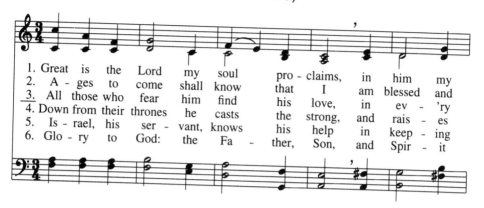

1. Great is the Lord my soul pro - claims, in him my
2. A - ges to come shall know that I am blessed and
3. All those who fear him find his love, in ev - 'ry
4. Down from their thrones he casts the strong, and rais - es
5. Is - rael, his ser - vant, knows his help in keep - ing
6. Glo - ry to God: the Fa - ther, Son, and Spir - it

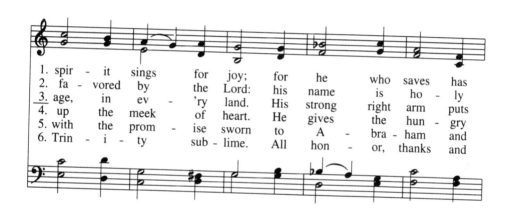

1. spir - it sings for joy; for he who saves has
2. fa - vored by the Lord: his name is ho - ly
3. age, in ev - 'ry land. His strong right arm puts
4. up the meek of heart. He gives the hun - gry
5. with the prom - ise sworn to A - bra - ham and
6. Trin - i - ty sub - lime. All hon - or, thanks and

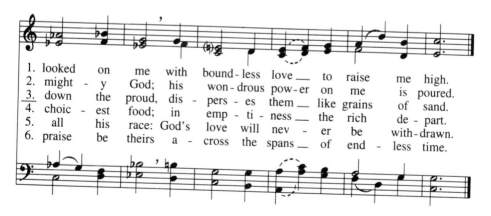

1. looked on me with bound - less love __ to raise me high.
2. might - y God; his won - drous pow - er on me is poured.
3. down the proud, dis - pers - es them __ like grains of sand.
4. choic - est food; in emp - ti - ness __ the rich de - part.
5. all his race: God's love will nev - er be with - drawn.
6. praise be theirs a - cross the spans __ of end - less time.

Text: Based on Luke 1:46-55; Paul Inwood, b. 1947.
Music: Paul Inwood.
Text and music ©1984, Paul Inwood. Published by OCP Publications.

Signing of the Senses

VERSE 1: Presider/Cantor

1. Receive the cross on your fore-head. It is Christ himself who
1. now strengthens you with this sign of his love. Learn to know and fol-low him.

RESPONSE: First time only: Cantor/All repeat; Other times: All

Soprano/Melody

Alto

By this sign may you re - ceive Christ's love and

Tenor

Bass

al - ways fol - low him.

VERSES 2-6: Presider/Cantor

S

2. Receive the sign of the cross on your ears,
3. Receive the sign of the cross on your eyes,
4. Receive the sign of the cross on your lips,
5. Receive the sign of the cross o - ver your heart,
6. Receive the sign of the cross on your should - ers,

A

2. (H)mm

T

B

Text: ©1985, I.C.E.L., Inc.
Music: Randall DeBruyn, b. 1947 ©1987, OCP Publications.

All repeat Response

2. that you may hear the voice of the Lord.
3. that you may see the glo - ry of God.
4. that you may respond to the word of God.
5. that Christ may dwell there by faith.
6. that you may bear the gentle yoke of Christ.

All repeat Response

(Hmm)

BLESSING: Presider

7. I sign you with the sign of eternal life in the name of the

rit. - - - - - - - - - - - - - - - - - - - (to Amen)

7. Fa - ther, and of the Son, and of the Ho - ly Spir - it.

AMEN: All

A - men. A -

men. A - men.

Those Who Seek Your Face

REFRAIN: (♩ = ca. 56)

Descant

Those who seek your face, Lord, with a pure heart shall

Soprano

Alto

Those who seek your face, Lord, with a pure heart shall

Tenor

Bass

stand in your ho - ly place. place.

1-6 to Verses | Final Fine

stand in your ho - ly place. place.

*VERSES: (♩ = o)

1. Lord, you are my light and my help.
2. My God, there is one thing I ask:
3. O Lord, hear my voice when I call.
4. O Lord, do not turn me a - way,
5. I know in this life I will see
6. To you our Cre - a-tor we pray;

*Verses for R.C.I.A. Rite of Acceptance (Ps 27).

Text: Psalms 27, 26, 32; Christopher Walker, b. 1947.
Music: Christopher Walker.
Text and music ©1987, Christopher Walker. Published by OCP Publications.

1. With you there is no one I fear,
2. to live in your house all my life;
3. O Lord, in your mer - cy give answer.
4. O Lord, do not leave me a - lone!
5. the goodness of God all a - round me.
6. to you, God the Son, we give glory.

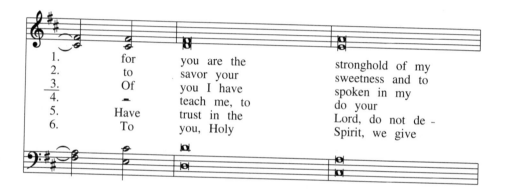

1. for you are the stronghold of my
2. to savor your sweetness and to
3. Of you I have spoken in my
4. — teach me, to do your
5. Have trust in the Lord, do not de -
6. To you, Holy Spirit, we give

D.C.

1. life; I will not be a - fraid.
2. ask you to guide my ways.
3. heart; I seek your face.
4. will and lead me in your paths.
5. spair but have faith in your God.
6. praise both now and ever - more!

ALTERNATE VERSES:

*1. Ex - amine me, God, test my motives. My
2. My hands I have washed in my innocence. I
3. O God how I love where you live, the
4. I walk on the path of per - fection. Re -

**1. O happy are those you for - give, the
2. O God when I grieved at my guilt my
3. But then I con - fessed all my sins, I
4. God, you are the place where I hide. When

1. thoughts and de - sires you can see. Your love, ever
2. worship your name at your altar. A hymn of thanks-
3. place where you dwell in your glory. O spare me from
4. deem me and show me your mercy. O God, from all

1. people whose sin you have pardoned; O happy the
2. days were ex - haust - ed with crying; your hand was up -
3. did not con - ceal my wrong - doings. To you I con -
4. I am in trou - ble you save me. A - loud I will

1. constant, is my guide; O lead me in your truth.
2. giving I will sing to tell your wondrous deeds.
3. evil and the fate of those who sin a - gainst you.
4. danger keep me safe, I bless you with your people.

1. guiltless for their hearts are free from all de - ceit.
2. on me night and day, my strength drained a - way.
3. fessed them and in love you have for - given me.
4. sing of your sal - vation. God, pro - tect my soul.

*Alternate Verses for Scrutinies (Ps 26).
**Alternate Verses for Scrutinies (Ps 32).

568

Grant Them Eternal Rest

REFRAIN:

Descant: Grant them e-ter-nal

Harmony: Grant them e-ter-nal rest, O Lord.

Melody: Grant them e-ter-nal rest, O Lord, and let per-rest. Let light shine up-on them.

Let light shine up-on them.

pet-u-al light shine up-on them.

Fine | 2

VERSES: (Interlude)

Soprano / Alto

1. Out of the depths I cry to you, O Lord. I
2. One thing I ask, just one thing do I seek: to
3. Hear me, O God. Hide not your face from me. Re-

Tenor / Bass

1. know you are my on-ly hope. Save me, O God!
2. dwell for-ev-er in your house, Lord, God of Hosts!
3. mem-ber that your mer-cies, Lord, are from of old.

D.C.

Text: Owen Alstott, b. 1947.
Music: Owen Alstott.
Text and music ©1983, OCP Publications.

Song of Farewell

REFRAIN: (♩ = 72) **1st time: Cantor / All repeat**

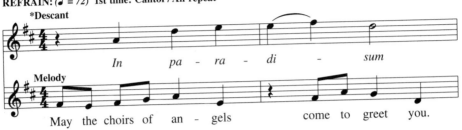

Descant
In pa - ra - di - sum

Melody
May the choirs of an - gels come to greet you.

de - du - cant an - ge - li; in pa - ra -

May they speed you to par - a - dise. May the Lord en - fold you

di - sum de - du - cant te. *Fine*

in his mer - cy. May you find e - ter - nal life. *Fine*

VERSES: *Moving on* (♩ = ca. 92) **Choir**

Soprano

Alto
1. The ___ Lord is my light and my help; ___ it is
2. There is one thing I ask of the Lord; ___ that he
3. O ___ Lord, hear my voice when I cry; ___ have ___
4. I am sure I shall see the Lord's good-ness; ___ I shall

Tenor

Bass

*Descant after Verses 3 and 4.

Text: Refrain, *In Paradisum*; based on Psalm 27; verses, Ernest Sands, b. 1949 ©1990, Ernest Sands. Published by OCP Publications.
Music: Ernest Sands ©1990, Ernest Sands. Published by OCP Publications.

1. he who pro - tects me from harm. _____ The _____
2. grant me my heart - felt de - sire. _____ To _____
3. mer - cy on me and give an - swer. _____ Do not
4. dwell in the land of the liv - ing. _____ Hope in

1. Lord is the strength of my days; _____ be - fore
2. dwell in the courts of our God _____ ev - 'ry
3. cast me a - way in your an - ger, _____ for _____
4. God, _____ stand firm and take heart, _____

1. whom should I trem - ble with fear? _____
2. day of my life in his pres - ence. _____
3. you are the God of my help. _____
4. place all your trust in the Lord. _____

rall.

D.C.

Song of Farewell

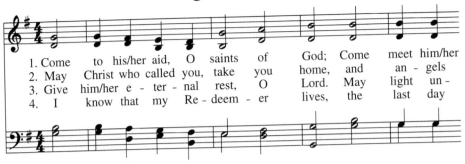

1. Come to his/her aid, O saints of God; Come meet him/her
2. May Christ who called you, take you home, and an - gels
3. Give him/her e - ter - nal rest, O Lord. May light un -
4. I know that my Re - deem - er lives, the last day

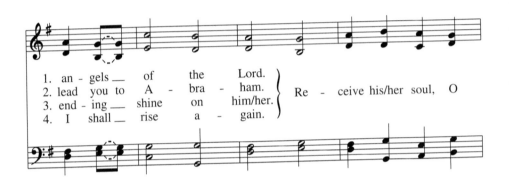

1. an - gels __ of the Lord.
2. lead you to A - bra - ham. } Re - ceive his/her soul, O
3. end - ing __ shine on him/her.
4. I shall __ rise a - gain.

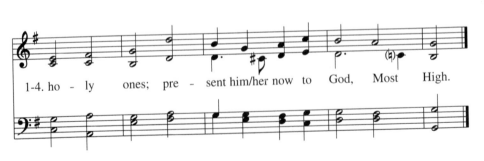

1-4. ho - ly ones; pre - sent him/her now to God, Most High.

Text: LM; *Subvenite;* Job 19:25–27; tr. by Dennis C. Smolarski, SJ, b. 1947 ©1981, Dennis C. Smolarski, SJ.
Music: OLD HUNDREDTH; melody fr. *Pseaumes octante trois de David,* 1551; harm. attr. to Louis Bourgeois, ca. 1510–1561.

MASS SETTINGS

Sprinkling Rite

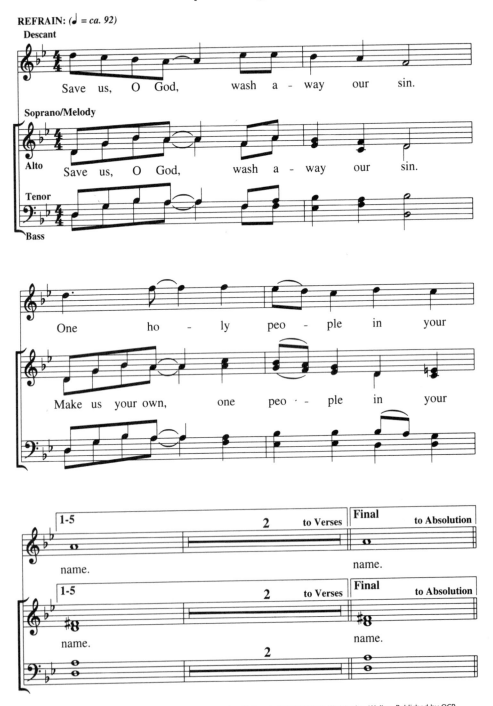

Text: Absolution ©1973, I.C.E.L., Inc. Sprinkling Rite, Christopher Walker, b. 1947 ©1996, Christopher Walker. Published by OCP Publications.
Music: *Celtic Mass*; Christopher Walker ©1996, Christopher Walker. Published by OCP Publications.

VERSES: Choir or All

1. With wa - ter of life, re - fresh us.
2. Re - new us in soul and bod - y.
3. Your Spir - it re - news cre - a - tion.
4. By dy - ing to sin with Je - sus:
5. By ris - ing with Christ in glo - ry:

Give us new

All: (div.) *D. C.*

1-5. life. Give us new life.

ABSOLUTION:

Priest:

May almighty God have mercy on us, for - give us our sins,

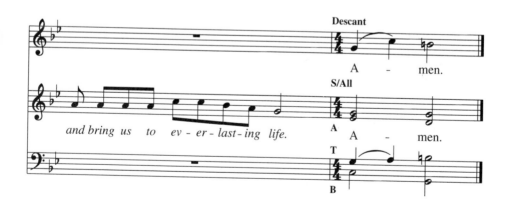

Descant

A - men.

S/All

and bring us to ev - er - last - ing life.

A - men.

T

B

Penitential Rite B

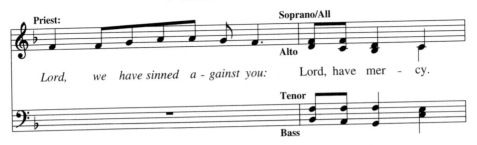

Priest: Lord, we have sinned a-gainst you:

Soprano/All / Alto / Tenor / Bass: Lord, have mer - cy.

Priest: Lord, show us your mer-cy and love.

S/All / A / T / B: And grant us your sal - va - tion.

ABSOLUTION:

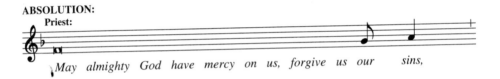

Priest: May almighty God have mercy on us, forgive us our sins,

and bring us to ev - er - last-ing life.

S/All / A / T / B: A - men.

Text: ©1973, I.C.E.L., Inc.
Music: *Celtic Mass*; Christopher Walker, b. 1947 ©1996, Christopher Walker. Published by OCP Publications.

Litany of Praise

Priest:

*Lord Je - sus, you came to heal the con-trite: *Lord, have mer - cy.*

Soprano/All
Alto
Lord, have mer - cy. Lord, have mer - cy. Lord, have mer - cy.

Tenor
Bass

Priest:

You came to call sin - ners: *Christ, have mer - cy.*

S/All
A
Christ, have mer - cy. Christ, have mer - cy. Christ, have mer - cy.

T
B

Priest:

You plead for us at the right hand of the Fa-ther: *Lord, have mer - cy.*

*Other invocations may be used.

Text: ©1973, I.C.E.L., Inc.
Music: *Celtic Mass*; Christopher Walker, b. 1947 ©1996, Christopher Walker. Published by OCP Publications.

577

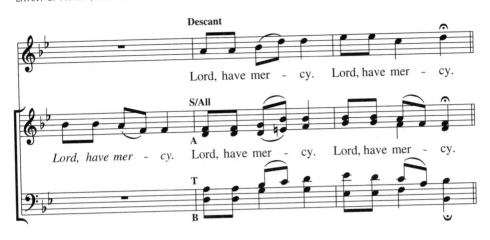

Descant

Lord, have mer - cy. Lord, have mer - cy.

S/All

A

Lord, have mer - cy. Lord, have mer - cy. Lord, have mer - cy.

T

B

ABSOLUTION:

Priest:

May almighty God have mercy on us, for - give us our sins,

S/All

A

and bring us to ev - er - last - ing life. A - men.

T

B

Kyrie

Music: *Celtic Mass*; Christopher Walker, b. 1947 ©1996, Christopher Walker. Published by OCP Publications.

Lord, Have Mercy

Music: *Celtic Mass*; Christopher Walker, b. 1947 ©1996, Christopher Walker. Published by OCP Publications.

Glory to God (with Optional Refrain)

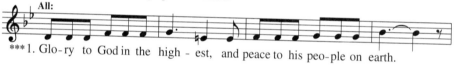

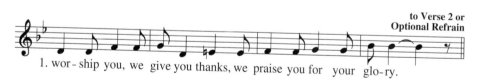

*Begin piece at Verse 1 if not using Optional Refrain.
**When used with full brass, ♩. = ca. 66.
***Alternate text offered in original songbook.

Music: *Celtic Mass*; Christopher Walker, b. 1947 ©1996, Christopher Walker. Published by OCP Publications.

VERSE 3: All

3. For you a-lone are the Ho-ly One, you a-lone are the

3. Lord, you a-lone are the Most High,

3. Je - sus Christ, with the Ho - ly Spir-it, in the

to Coda ⊕ or
Optional Refrain & Coda ⊕

3. glo-ry of God, the glo-ry of God the Fa-ther.

⊕ CODA

Melody — rall.

A - men, a - men, a - men.

S — rall. — div.

A - men, a - men, a - men, a - men.

T

B — rall.

Celtic Alleluia

REFRAIN: (♩. = *ca. 66*)

Descant

Al - le - lu - ia, al - le - lu - ia. Al -

Soprano/Melody

Alto

Al - le - lu - ia, al - le - lu - ia. Al -

Tenor

Bass

le - lu - ia, al - le - lu - ia.

1, Final *D.C. Fine* div.

2 to Verse(s) div.

ia.

le - lu - ia, al - le - lu - ia.

1, Final *D.C. Fine*

2 to Verse(s)

ia.

VERSES:

1. Speak, Lord, your ser - vant is lis - t'ning. _____
2. The Word of the Lord lasts for ev - er. _____
3. "Fa - ther, of all you are blessed, _____ cre -
4. "I call you friends," says the Lord, _____
5. "The sheep of my flock," says the Lord, _____
6. The Word of the Lord is a - live. _____ The
7. "E - ven if you have to die, _____

Text: *Celtic Mass*; Christopher Walker, b. 1947.
Music: *Celtic Mass*; Fintan O'Carroll, d. 1977 and Christopher Walker.
Text and music ©1985, 1996, Fintan O'Carroll and Christopher Walker. Published by OCP Publications.

Melody

Harmony

1. Speak ____ your words ____ of wis - dom, for the
2. What is the word that is liv - ing? It is
3. - a - tor of earth ____ and heav - en, for the
4. "you who are my ____ dis - ci - ples. I make
5. "hear - ing my voice, ____ will lis - ten. They will
6. Word of the Lord ____ is ac - tive. It can
7. close to my Word ____ keep faith - ful: for your

D.C.

1. words you speak ____ are ev - er - last - ing life. ____
2. brought to us ____ through God's son: ____ Je - sus Christ. ____
3. mys - ter - ies ____ of the King-dom __ shown to chil-dren." __
4. known to you ____ all I've learned ____ from my Fa - ther." __
5. fol - low me, ____ for I know them; __ they are mine." ____
6. judge our thoughts, __ bring us clos - er ____ to the Fa - ther. ____
7. faith - ful - ness ____ I will give you the crown of life." ____

Advent
Stay awake, pray at all times,
praying that you may be strengthened,
that with confidence
you can meet the Son of Man.

Christmas
"I bring you news of great joy,
joy for all nations,
for today is born
our savior, Christ the Lord."

Epiphany
A holy day has dawned.
Adore the Lord, you nations,
for today a light
has come on the earth.

Easter
1. Give thanks to the Lord, who is good.
The love of the Lord knows no ending.
All in Israel say,
"God's love has no end."

2. The Right Hand of God raised me up.
The hand of the Lord has triumphed.
I shall never die,
I shall live, telling God's deeds.

Easter (continued)
3. The stone which the builders rejected,
becomes the cornerstone chosen.
Praise the work of God
for this marvel in our eyes.

Pentecost
Come, Holy Spirit.
Fill the hearts of your faithful
and enlighten them
with the fire of your love.

Wedding
All those who live in love
with God are united,
for they live with God
and God lives in them.

Feasts of Mary
Hail: full of grace,
Mary, most blessed among women;
who believed that it
would be as God promised.

585

Lenten Gospel Acclamations
(including Scrutinies for Sundays 3, 4, 5)

*after 1st time

Text: ©1969, 1981, I.C.E.L., Inc.
Music: *Celtic Mass*; Christopher Walker, b. 1947 ©1996, Christopher Walker. Published by OCP Publications.

VERSES: Sundays 1, 2

1st Sunday: We____ do not live on bread a - lone, but on
2nd Sunday: From the bright____ cloud a voice was heard: "This is

1st Sunday: We____ do not live on bread a - lone, but on
2nd Sunday: From the bright____ cloud a voice was heard: "This is

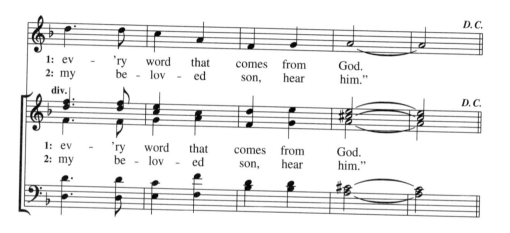

1: ev - 'ry word that comes from God.
2: my be - lov - ed son, hear him."

1: ev - 'ry word that comes from God.
2: my be - lov - ed son, hear him."

AFTER THE GOSPEL READING:

The Gos - pel of the Lord.

587

VERSES: Sundays 3–5

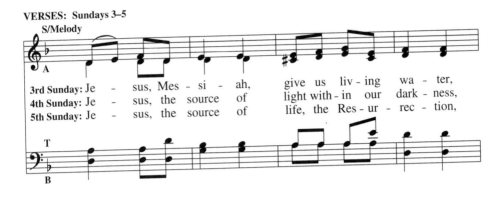

3rd Sunday: Je - sus, Mes - si - ah, give us liv - ing wa - ter,
4th Sunday: Je - sus, the source of light with - in our dark - ness,
5th Sunday: Je - sus, the source of life, the Res - ur - rec - tion,

3: wa - ter that brings e - ter - nal life.
4: come, _____ Lord Je - sus, help us see.
5: come, _____ Lord Je - sus, set us free.

AFTER THE GOSPEL READING:

The Gos - pel of the Lord.

Dismissal of the Catechumens

Text: *Celtic Mass*, Christopher Walker, b. 1947.
Music: *Celtic Mass*; Christopher Walker.
Text and music ©1996, Christopher Walker. Published by OCP Publications.

We Believe
(Renewal of Baptismal Promises)

(Before song begins)

Priest: Do you reject sin,
so as to live in the freedom of God's children?

All: I do.

Priest: Do you reject the glamor of evil,
and refuse to be mastered by sin?

All: I do.

Priest: Do you reject Satan, father of sin and prince of darkness?

All: I do.

Do you believe in God, the Father almighty, creator of heaven and earth?

we be-lieve. Lord, help our un - be-lief!

we be-lieve. Lord, help our un - be-lief!

Choir continues while Priest continues proclaiming the Renewal Of Baptismal Promises.

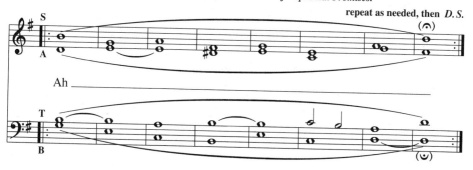

Ah _____

Priest: Do you believe in Jesus Christ, his only Son, our Lord,
who was born of the Virgin Mary,
was crucified, died, and was buried,
rose from the dead,
and is now seated at the right hand of the Father? **(to Refrain)**

Do you believe in the Holy Spirit,
the holy Catholic Church, the communion of saints,
the forgiveness of sins, the resurrection of the body,
and life everlasting? **(to Refrain)**

We Believe
(Apostles' and Nicene Creeds)

Choir continues while Priest proclaims the Creed.

repeat as needed, then *D. C.*

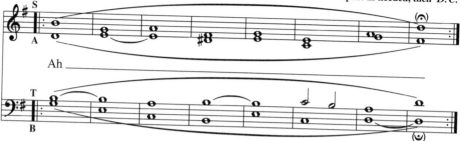

Ah

NICENE CREED

Priest:

We believe in one God,
  the Father, the Almighty,
  maker of heaven and earth,
  of all that is seen and unseen.

We believe in one Lord, Jesus Christ,
  the only Son of God,
  eternally begotten of the Father, **(to Refrain)**

God from God, Light from Light,
  true God from true God,
begotten, not made, one in Being with the Father.
Through him all things were made.
For us men and for our salvation
  he came down from heaven:
by the power of the Holy Spirit
he was born of the Virgin Mary,
  and became man. **(to Refrain)**

For our sake he was crucified under Pontius Pilate;
he suffered, died, and was buried.
On the third day he rose again
  in fulfillment of the Scriptures;
he ascended into heaven
  and is seated at the right hand of the Father.
He will come again in glory to judge the living and the dead,
  and his kingdom will have no end. **(to Refrain)**

We believe in the Holy Spirit, the Lord, the giver of life,
  who proceeds from the Father and the Son.
With the Father and the Son he is worshiped and
  glorified.
He has spoken through the Prophets. **(to Refrain)**

We believe in one holy catholic and apostolic Church.
We acknowledge one baptism for the forgiveness
  of sins.
We look for the resurrection of the dead,
  and the life of the world to come. **(to Refrain)**

APOSTLES' CREED

Priest:

We believe in God, the Father almighty,
  creator of heaven and earth.

We believe in Jesus Christ, his only Son, our Lord.
  He was conceived by the power of the Holy Spirit
  and born of the Virgin Mary. **(to Refrain)**

He suffered under Pontius Pilate,
  was crucified, died, and was buried.
He descended to the dead.
On the third day he rose again.
He ascended into heaven,
  and is seated at the right hand of the Father.
He will come again to judge the living
  and the dead. **(to Refrain)**

We believe in the Holy Spirit,
  the holy catholic Church,
  the communion of saints,
  the forgiveness of sins,
  the resurrection of the body,
  and the life everlasting. **(to Refrain)**

General Intercessions

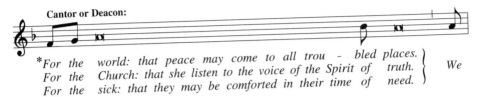

Cantor or Deacon:

For the world: that peace may come to all trou - bled places.
For the Church: that she listen to the voice of the Spirit of truth.
For the sick: that they may be comforted in their time of need. We

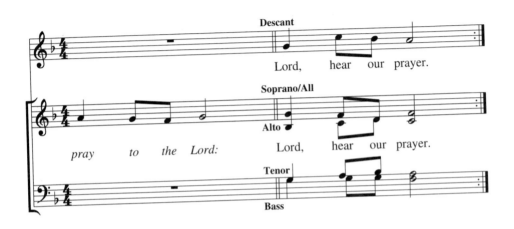

Descant

Lord, hear our prayer.

Soprano/All

Alto

pray to the Lord: Lord, hear our prayer.

Tenor

Bass

CONCLUDING PRAYER:

Priest:

Loving God, we ask these prayers through Jesus Christ, your Son,

who lives and reigns with you in the unity of the Holy Spirit, one God for

S/All

A

ev - er and ev - er. A - men.

T

B

Additional or alternative prayers may be used.

Music: *Celtic Mass*; Christopher Walker, b. 1947 ©1996, Christopher Walker. Published by OCP Publications.

Advent Intercessions

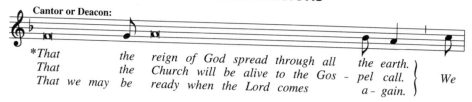

Cantor or Deacon:

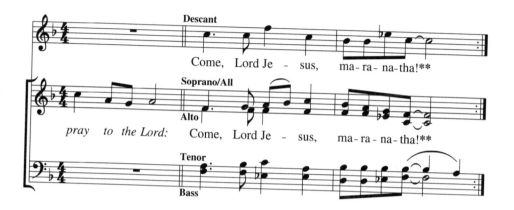

*That the reign of God spread through all the earth.
That the Church will be alive to the Gos - pel call.
That we may be ready when the Lord comes a - gain.

We pray to the Lord:

Descant

Come, Lord Je - sus, ma - ra - na - tha!**

Soprano/All

Alto

Come, Lord Je - sus, ma - ra - na - tha!**

Tenor

Bass

CONCLUDING PRAYER:

Priest:

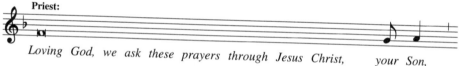

Loving God, we ask these prayers through Jesus Christ, your Son,

who lives and reigns with you in the unity of the Holy Spirit, one God for

S/All

ev - er and ev - er.

A

A - men.

T

B

*Additional or alternative prayers may be used.
**Maranatha is Aramaic for "Come, Lord."

Text: *Celtic Mass*; Christopher Walker, b. 1947.
Music: *Celtic Mass*; Christopher Walker.
Text and music ©1996, Christopher Walker. Published by OCP Publications.

Preface Dialogue

Music: *Celtic Mass*; Christopher Walker, b. 1947 ©1996, Christopher Walker. Published by OCP Publications.

Preface

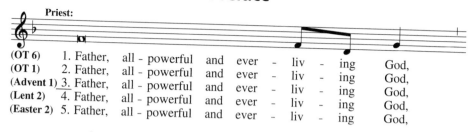

Priest:

(OT 6)   1. Father, all - powerful and ever - liv - ing God,
(OT 1)   2. Father, all - powerful and ever - liv - ing God,
(Advent 1) 3. Father, all - powerful and ever - liv - ing God,
(Lent 2) 4. Father, all - powerful and ever - liv - ing God,
(Easter 2) 5. Father, all - powerful and ever - liv - ing God,

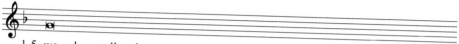

1-5. we do well always and everywhere to...

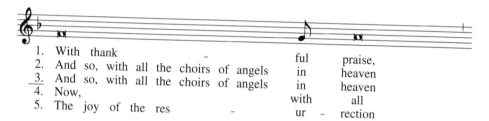

1. With thank — ful praise,
2. And so, with all the choirs of angels in heaven
3. And so, with all the choirs of angels in heaven
4. Now, with all
5. The joy of the res — ur - rection

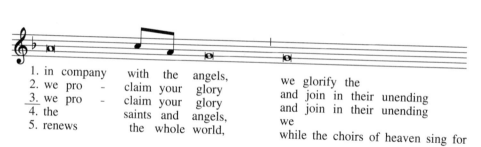

1. in company with the angels, we glorify the
2. we pro - claim your glory and join in their unending
3. we pro - claim your glory and join in their unending
4. the saints and angels, we
5. renews the whole world, while the choirs of heaven sing for

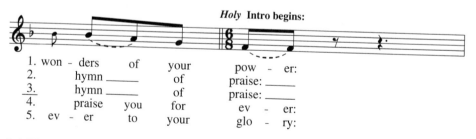

***Holy* Intro begins:**

1. won - ders of your pow - er:
2. hymn _____ of praise: _____
3. hymn _____ of praise: _____
4. praise you for ev - er:
5. ev - er to your glo - ry:

Text: ©1973, I.C.E.L., Inc.
Music: *Celtic Mass*; Christopher Walker, b. 1947 ©1996, Christopher Walker. Published by OCP Publications.

Holy

*(♩. = ca. 63)**

Soprano/Melody

Alto

Ho-ly, ho-ly, ho-ly Lord, God of pow-er, God of might.

Tenor

Bass

Descant

Heav-en and earth are full of your glo - ry. Ho - san - na

Heav-en and earth are full of your glo - ry. Ho - san - na

in the high - est, ho - san - na, ho - san - na, ho -

in the high - est, ho - san-na in the high - est, ho -

*When using full brass, ♩. = ca. 52.

Music: *Celtic Mass*; Christopher Walker, b. 1947 ©1996, Christopher Walker. Published by OCP Publications.

- san - na, ho - san - na.

- san-na in the high - est. Bless-ed is he who comes in the

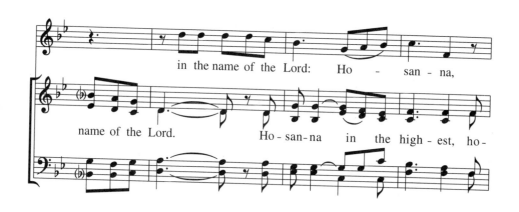

in the name of the Lord: Ho - san - na,

name of the Lord. Ho - san-na in the high - est, ho -

ho - san - na, ho - san - na, ho-san - na!

san - na in the high-est, ho - san-na in the high - est!

Memorial Acclamation A

Memorial Acclamation B

Priest:

Let us proclaim the mys - ter - y of faith:

(♩ = ca. 108)

Soprano/All

Alto

Tenor

Bass

Dy - ing you de - stroyed our death,

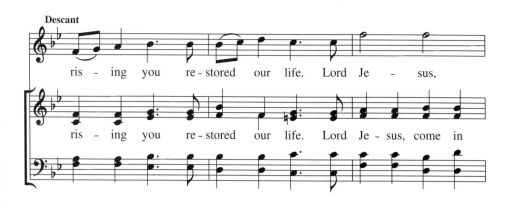

Descant

ris - ing you re - stored our life. Lord Je - sus,

ris - ing you re - stored our life. Lord Je - sus, come in

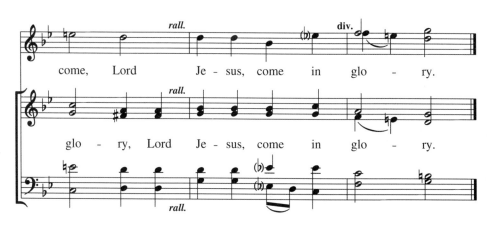

rall.   div.

come, Lord Je - sus, come in glo - ry.

rall.

glo - ry, Lord Je - sus, come in glo - ry.

rall.

Memorial Acclamation C

Priest:

Let us proclaim the mys - ter - y of faith:

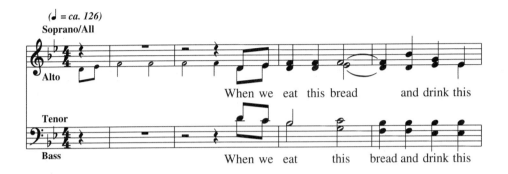

(♩ = ca. 126)

Soprano/All

Alto

When we eat this bread and drink this

Tenor

Bass

When we eat this bread and drink this

Descant

un -

cup, we pro-claim your death, Lord Je - sus Christ, un -

cup, we pro-claim your death, Lord Je - sus Christ,

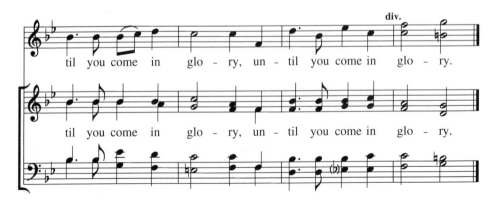

div.

til you come in glo - ry, un - til you come in glo - ry.

til you come in glo - ry, un - til you come in glo - ry.

Text: ©1973, I.C.E.L., Inc.
Music: *Celtic Mass*; Christopher Walker, b. 1947 ©1996, Christopher Walker. Published by OCP Publications.

Memorial Acclamation D

Priest: (♩ = ca. 108)

Let us proclaim the mys-ter-y of faith:

Descant

Lord, by your cross and res-ur-rec-tion you have

Soprano/All

Lord, by your cross and res-ur-rec-tion you have

Alto

Tenor

Bass

set us free. You are the Sav-ior of the

set us free. You are the Sav-ior of the

div.

world, the Sav-ior of the world.

world, the Sav-ior of the world.

Doxology/Amen

Through him, with him, in him, in the u-ni-ty of the Ho-ly Spir-it, all glo-ry and hon-or is yours, al-might-y Fa-ther, for ev-er and ev-er.

OPTIONAL INTRO:
2

Descant
A - men, a - men, a - men,

Soprano/All

Alto
A - men, a - men, a - men,

Tenor

Bass
a - men, a - men, a - men.

a - men, a - men, a - men.

The Lord's Prayer

Our Fa-ther, who art in heav-en, hal-lowed be thy name; thy king-dom come; thy will be done on earth as it is in heav-en. Give us this day our dai-ly bread; and for-give us our tres-pas-ses as we for-give those who tres-pass a-gainst us; and lead us not in-to temp-ta-tion, but de-li-ver us from e-vil.

Priest: Deliver us, Lord, from ev-ery e-vil, and grant us peace in our day.

*The Lord's Prayer can end here when used during Liturgy of the Hours or in other situations outside of the eucharistic liturgy. Two other options are:
1) Proceed to "For the Kingdom . . ."
2) Proceed to "Amen" in the Peace Prayer.

Music: *Celtic Mass*; Christopher Walker, b. 1947 ©1996, Christopher Walker. Published by OCP Publications.

In your mercy keep us free from sin and protect us from all anx - i - e - ty

as we wait in joy - ful hope for the coming of our Savior, Je - sus

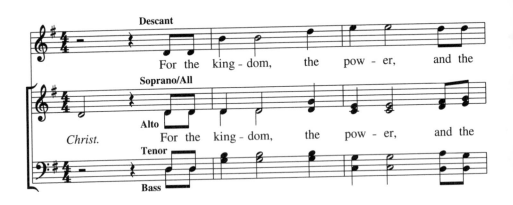

Descant

For the king - dom, the pow - er, and the

Soprano/All

Alto

Christ. For the king - dom, the pow - er, and the

Tenor

Bass

*attacca Peace Prayer

glo - ry are yours, now and for ev - er.

*attacca Peace Prayer

glo - ry are yours, now and for ev - er.

*or attaca "Amen" in the *Peace Prayer*.

Peace Prayer

Lord Jesus Christ, you said to your a-pos-tles: Peace I leave with you, my peace I give you. Look not on our sins, but on the faith of your Church, and grant us the peace and unity of your king-dom where you live for ev-er and ev-er.

(♩ = ca. 108)

Descant
A - men, a - men.

Soprano/All
Alto
A - men, a - men.

Tenor
Bass

Priest: The peace of the Lord be with you al-ways. All: And al-so

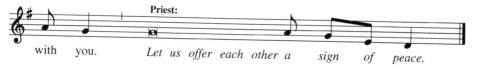

with you. Priest: Let us offer each other a sign of peace.

Text: ©1973, I.C.E.L., Inc.
Music: *Celtic Mass*; Christopher Walker, b. 1947 ©1996, Christopher Walker. Published by OCP Publications.

Jesus, Lamb of God Litany

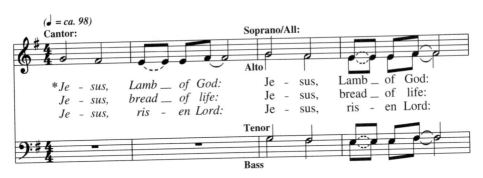

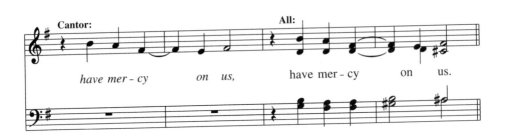

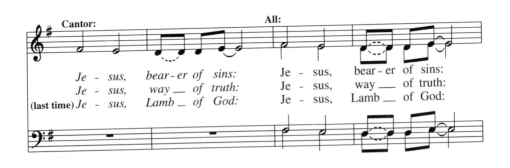

*Other invocations may be used.

Music: *Celtic Mass*; Christopher Walker, b. 1947 ©1996, Christopher Walker. Published by OCP Publications.

Final

Cantor: *rall.* All:

grant us peace, grant us peace.

rall.

ADDITIONAL VERSES

General
Jesus, Son of God...
Jesus, Light from Light...
Jesus, begotten, not made...
Jesus, Word of God...
Jesus, way of truth...
Jesus, bread from heaven...
Jesus, Savior of all...
Jesus, way to the Father...
(other invocations may be used)

Advent
(First Sunday)
Jesus, who is to come...
Jesus, Son of Man...
Jesus, promise of God...

(Second and Third Sundays)
Jesus, hope of all...
Jesus, wisdom of God...
Jesus, Morning Star...

(Fourth Sunday)
Jesus, promise of God...
Jesus, David's key...
Jesus, Emmanuel...

Christmas
Jesus, Word made flesh...
Jesus, one like us...
Jesus, Emmanuel...

Lent/Holy Week
Jesus, crucified...
Jesus, Savior of all...
Jesus, hope of sinners...

Easter
Jesus, risen Lord...
Jesus, splendor of God...
Jesus, reigning on high...

Lamb of God

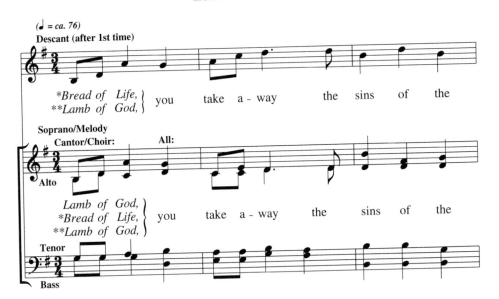

*Other invocations may be used.
**Last time.

Text: *Celtic Mass*; Christopher Walker, b. 1947.
Music: *Celtic Mass*; Christopher Walker.
Text and music ©1996, Christopher Walker. Published by OCP Publications.

ADDITIONAL VERSES

Word made flesh, you take away…
Saving help, you take away…
Wine poured out, you take away…
God from God, you take away…
Mary's Son, you take away…
Broken Lord, you take away…
Lasting joy, you take away…
Lord of all, you take away…

(other invocations may be used)

Blessing and Dismissal

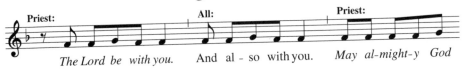

Priest: The Lord be with you. All: And al-so with you. Priest: May al-might-y God

bless you, the Fa-ther, and the Son, and the Ho - ly Spir-it.

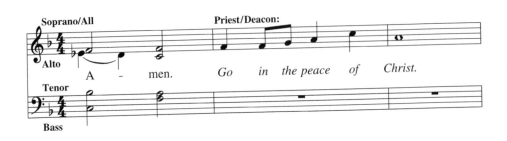

Soprano/All / Alto: A - men. Priest/Deacon: Go in the peace of Christ.

Tenor / Bass

Descant: Thanks be to God.

S/All / A: Thanks be to God.

T / B

Text: ©1973, I.C.E.L., Inc.
Music: *Celtic Mass*; Christopher Walker, b. 1947 ©1996, Christopher Walker. Published by OCP Publications.

Easter Blessing and Dismissal

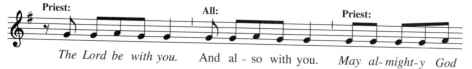

Priest: The Lord be with you. **All:** And al-so with you. **Priest:** May al-might-y God

bless you, the Fa-ther, and the Son, and the Ho - ly Spir-it. A - men.

Soprano/All

Alto

Tenor

Bass

Priest/Deacon: Go in peace to serve the Lord, Al - le - lu - ia.

Descant

Thanks be to God, Al - le - lu - ia.

S/All

A

Thanks be to God, Al - le - lu - ia.

T

B

Text: ©1973, I.C.E.L., Inc.
Music: *Celtic Mass*; Christopher Walker, b. 1947 and Fintan O'Carroll, d. 1977 ©1985, 1996, Fintan O'Carroll and Christopher Walker.
Published by OCP Publications.

Eucharistic Prayer II: Preface Dialogue

Presider: *The Lord be with you.*

All: *And al - so with you.*

Lift up your hearts.

We lift them up to the

Let us give thanks to the Lord our God.

Lord.

(Assembly:) It is right to

(All:) *give him thanks and praise.*

Choir:
Soprano

Alto

It is right to give him thanks and

Tenor

Bass

*A portion of the choir (perhaps the soprano section) should be designated to reinforce the assembly's part here.

Text: ©1973, I.C.E.L., Inc.
Music: *Mass of Glory*; Ken Canedo and Bob Hurd, b. 1950; choral arr. by Craig S. Kingsbury, b. 1952 ©1991, 1993, Ken Canedo and Bob Hurd. Published by OCP Publications.

It is right to give him thanks and praise.

praise,   thanks and praise.

Holy

Ho - ly, ho - ly, ho - ly Lord, God of pow - er and might. Heav - en and earth are full of your glo - ry. Ho - san - na, ho - san - na, ho - san - na in the high-est.

Text: ©1973, I.C.E.L., Inc.
Music: *Mass of Glory*; Ken Canedo and Bob Hurd, b. 1950; choral arr. by Craig S. Kingsbury, b. 1952 ©1991, 1993, Ken Canedo and Bob Hurd. Published by OCP Publications.

Bless - ed is he who comes in the name of the Lord. Ho-san - na, ho - san - na, ho - san - na in the high - est.

Memorial Acclamation A

Christ has died. Christ is ris-en,

Christ will come, will come a-gain.

Text: ©1973, I.C.E.L., Inc.
Music: *Mass of Glory*; Ken Canedo and Bob Hurd, b. 1950; choral arr. by Craig S. Kingsbury, b. 1952 ©1991, 1993, Ken Canedo and Bob Hurd. Published by OCP Publications.

Eucharistic Prayer II: Post-Narrative 2

After the first three measures, the Priest begins the prayer, which is spoken rather than sung. The refrain is sung in response to each section of the prayer as indicated below. Since the various sections of the prayer are of different lengths, use the following rule for pacing: play the instrumental ostinato twice through to accompany sections one and four ("In memory…" and "Have mercy…"); play the instrumental ostinato only once through for sections two and three ("Lord, remember…" and "Remember our brothers and sisters…").

INSTRUMENTAL OSTINATO: (♩ = 88-93) *with a gospel swing*

16

(repeat as needed under Priest's prayer)

Priest: In memory of his death and resurrection,
we offer you, Father, this life-giving bread,
this saving cup.
We thank you for counting us worthy
to stand in your presence and serve you.
May all of us who share in the body
and blood of Christ
be brought together in unity by the
Holy Spirit.
(Refrain)

Music: *Mass of Glory*; Ken Canedo and Bob Hurd, b. 1950; choral arr. by Craig S. Kingsbury, b. 1952 ©1991, 1993, Ken Canedo and Bob Hurd. Published by OCP Publications.

REFRAIN: Choir/All

Hear our prayer. Hear our prayer.

God of mer-cy, hear our prayer.

Priest: Lord, remember your Church
throughout the world;
make us grow in love,
together with John Paul our Pope,
N. our bishop, and all the clergy. **(Refrain)**

Priest: Remember our brothers and sisters
who have gone to their rest
in the hope of rising again;
bring them and all the departed
into the light of your presence. **(Refrain)**

Priest: Have mercy on us all;
make us worthy to share eternal life
with Mary, the virgin Mother of God,
with the apostles, and with all the saints
who have done your will throughout
the ages.
May we praise you in union with them,
and give you glory
through your Son, Jesus Christ. **(Final Refrain)**

Eucharistic Prayer II: Amen 2

*Alternate words for use during Lent.

Music: *Mass of Glory*; Ken Canedo and Bob Hurd, b. 1950; choral arr. by Craig S. Kingsbury, b. 1952 ©1991, 1993, Ken Canedo and Bob Hurd. Published by OCP Publications.

Lamb of God

Cantor or Choir:

Soprano (Melody) All:

Alto

*Lamb   of   God,
 Prince   of   Peace,
**Word   made flesh,   you take a-way the   sins of the

Tenor

Bass

world: (of   the   world:)   have mer - cy   on us;   have

mer - cy   on   us.   (Repeat as needed) | Final
                              world:)   grant   us

peace;   grant   us   peace.

*"Lamb of God," final time.
**Additional invocations may be added as needed: Son of God, Promise of Life, etc.
  Complete score with modulation is available from the publisher.

Music: *Mass of Glory*; Bob Hurd, b. 1950; choral arr. by Craig S. Kingsbury, b. 1952 ©1991, 1993, Bob Hurd. Published by OCP
Publications.

Holy

Ho - ly, ho - ly, ho - ly, Lord God of pow'r, ___
Bless - ed, bless - ed, bless - ed, bless - ed is he who

Lord God of might, ___ Lord God of pow'r and might.
comes in the name, who comes in the Lord's own name.

1

Heav'n and earth are full of your glo - ry. Ho - san - na

in the high - est. Ho - san - na, ho - san -

na, ho - san - na in the high - est.

2 D.C.

2
Soprano I

Ho - san - na, ho - san - na, ho - san -

2
Soprano II/Melody

Alto

Ho - san - na, ho - san - na, ho - san - na

Tenor

Bass

Music: *Mass of Hope*; Bernadette Farrell, b. 1957 ©1985, Bernadette Farrell. Published by OCP Publications.

Memorial Acclamation A

Text: ©1973, I.C.E.L., Inc.
Music: *Mass of Hope*; Bernadette Farrell, b. 1957; choral arr. by Paul Inwood, b. 1947 ©1985, 1989, Bernadette Farrell. Published by
OCP Publications.

Amen

(for use with Memorial Acclamation A)

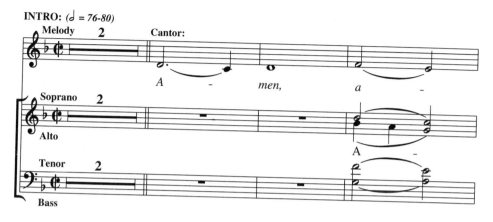

Music: *Mass of Hope*; Bernadette Farrell, b. 1957; choral arr. by Paul Inwood, b. 1947 ©1986, 1989, Bernadette Farrell. Published by OCP Publications. All rights reserved.

Memorial Acclamation B

Dy - ing you de - stroyed our death, ris - ing

you re - stored our life. Lord Je - sus,

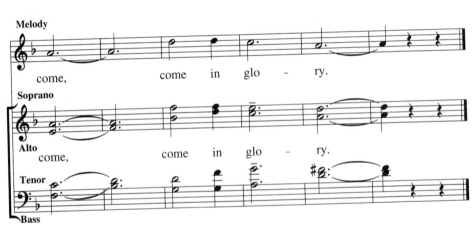

come, come in glo - ry.

come, come in glo - ry.

Text: ©1973, I.C.E.L., Inc.
Music: *Mass of Hope*; Bernadette Farrell, b. 1957; choral arr. by Paul Inwood, b. 1947 ©1985, 1989, Bernadette Farrell. Published by OCP Publications.

Memorial Acclamation C

(♩. = ca. 56)

unison

When we eat this bread and drink this cup,

we pro - claim your death, Lord Je - sus Christ,

un - til you come in glo - ry, un -

Melody

til you come in glo - ry, un - til you come in

Soprano

til you come in glo - ry, un - til you come in

Alto

Tenor

Bass

glo - ry, Je - sus Christ.

glo - ry, Je - sus Christ.

Text: ©1973, I.C.E.L., Inc.
Music: *Mass of Hope*; Bernadette Farrell, b. 1957; choral arr. by Paul Inwood, b. 1947 ©1985, 1989, Bernadette Farrell. Published by OCP Publications.

Amen
(when Doxology is spoken)

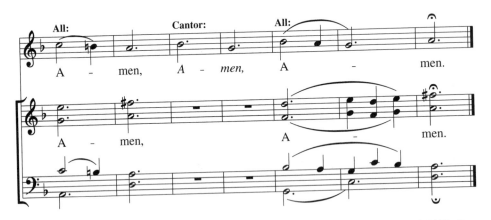

Music: *Mass of Hope*; Bernadette Farrell, b. 1957; choral arr. by Paul Inwood, b. 1947 ©1985, 1989, Bernadette Farrell. Published by OCP Publications.

Jesus, Lamb of God

VERSES: (♩ = ca. 78)

Cantor/Choir:

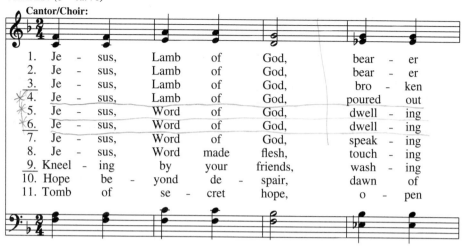

1. Je - sus, Lamb of God, bear - er
2. Je - sus, Lamb of God, bear - er
3. Je - sus, Lamb of God, bro - ken
4. Je - sus, Lamb of God, poured out
5. Je - sus, Word of God, dwell - ing
6. Je - sus, Word of God, dwell - ing
7. Je - sus, Word of God, speak - ing
8. Je - sus, Word made flesh, touch - ing
9. Kneel - ing by your friends, wash - ing
10. Hope be - yond de - spair, dawn of
11. Tomb of se - cret hope, o - pen

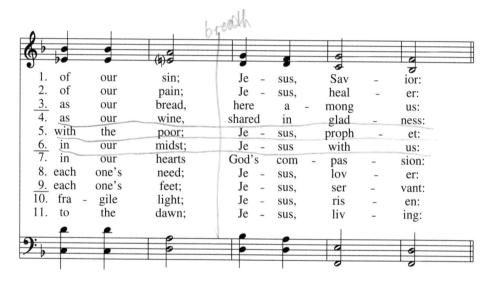

1. of our sin; Je - sus, Sav - ior:
2. of our pain; Je - sus, heal - er:
3. as our bread, here a - mong us:
4. as our wine, shared in glad - ness:
5. with the poor; Je - sus, proph - et:
6. in our midst; Je - sus with us:
7. in our hearts God's com - pas - sion:
8. each one's need; Je - sus, lov - er:
9. each one's feet; Je - sus, ser - vant:
10. fra - gile light; Je - sus, ris - en:
11. to the dawn; Je - sus, liv - ing:

Text: *Mass of Hope*; Bernadette Farrell, b. 1957.
Music: *Mass of Hope*; Bernadette Farrell.
Text and music ©1991, Bernadette Farrell. Published by OCP Publications.

REFRAIN: All

Ah _____ Ah _____

Hear our prayer, hear our prayer; through this bread and

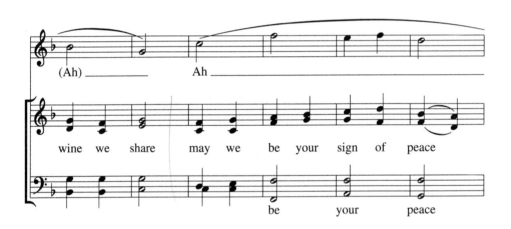

(Ah) _____ Ah _____

wine we share may we be your sign of peace

be your peace

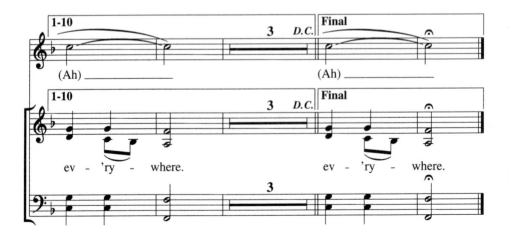

(Ah) _____ (Ah) _____

ev - 'ry - where. ev - 'ry - where.

Lord, Have Mercy

Music: *Heritage Mass;* Owen Alstott, b. 1947 ©1978, OCP Publications.

Glory to God

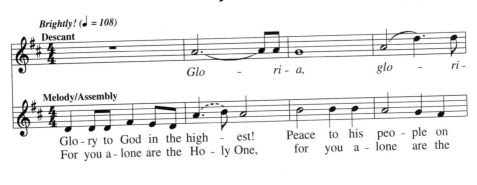

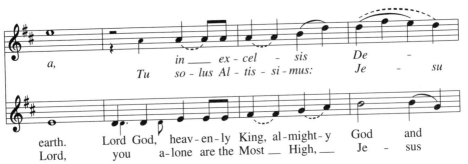

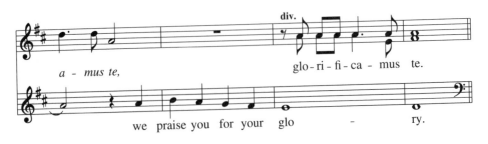

Music: *Heritage Mass;* Owen Alstott, b. 1947 ©1978, 1987, OCP Publications.

Holy

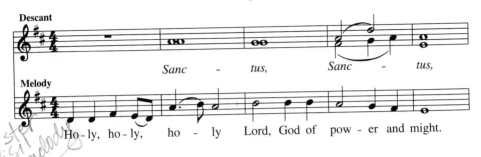

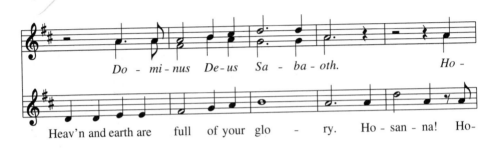

Music: *Heritage Mass*; Owen Alstott, b. 1947 ©1978, OCP Publications.

Memorial Acclamation A

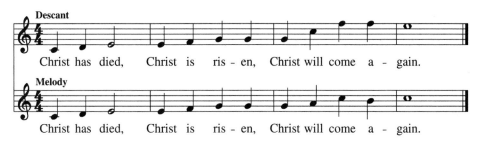

Descant

Christ has died, Christ is ris-en, Christ will come a-gain.

Melody

Christ has died, Christ is ris-en, Christ will come a-gain.

Text: ©1973, I.C.E.L., Inc.
Music: *Heritage Mass;* Owen Alstott, b. 1947 ©1988, OCP Publication.

Memorial Acclamation B

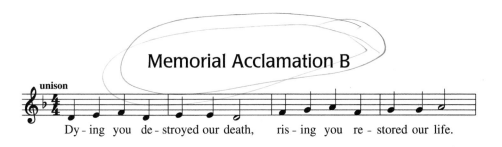

unison

Dy-ing you de-stroyed our death, ris-ing you re-stored our life.

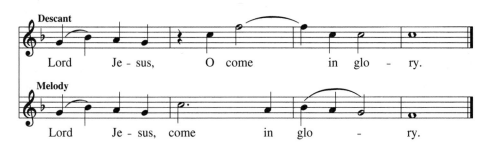

Descant

Lord Je-sus, O come in glo-ry.

Melody

Lord Je-sus, come in glo-ry.

Text: ©1973, I.C.E.L., Inc.
Music: *Heritage Mass;* Owen Alstott, b. 1947 ©1988, OCP Publications.

Memorial Acclamation C

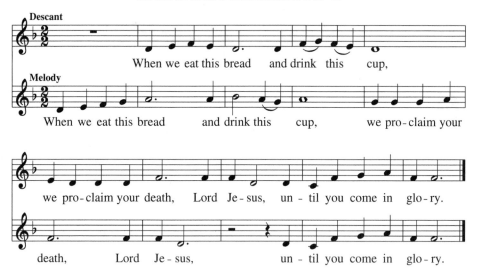

Descant: When we eat this bread and drink this cup,

Melody: When we eat this bread and drink this cup, we pro-claim your

we pro-claim your death, Lord Je - sus, un - til you come in glo - ry.

death, Lord Je - sus, un - til you come in glo - ry.

Memorial Acclamation D

unison: Lord, by your cross and res - ur - rec - tion you have set us

Descant: free. You are the Sav - ior of the world.

Melody: free. You are the Sav - ior of the world.

Amen

Descant

Melody: A - men, a - men, a - men.

Lamb of God

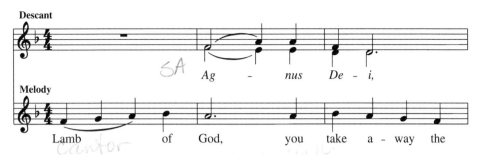

Descant

Ag - nus De - i,

Melody

Lamb of God, you take a - way the

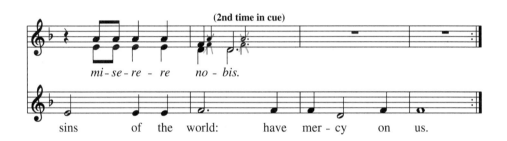

(2nd time in cue)

mi - se - re - re no - bis.

sins of the world: have mer - cy on us.

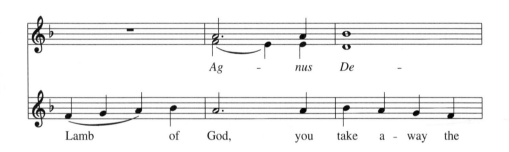

Ag - nus De -

Lamb of God, you take a - way the

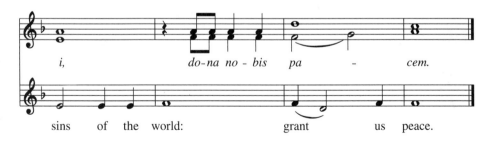

i, do - na no - bis pa - cem.

sins of the world: grant us peace.

Music: *Heritage Mass*; Owen Alstott, b. 1947 ©1978, 1987, 1988, OCP Publications.

Glory to God

*REFRAIN: *Exuberantly* (♩ = 176) 1st time Cantor/Choir; all repeat; thereafter: All

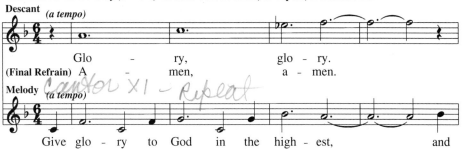

Descant (a tempo)

Glo — ry, glo — ry.

(Final Refrain) A — men, a — men.

Melody (a tempo) *Cantor XI – Repeat*

Give glo - ry to God in the high - est, and

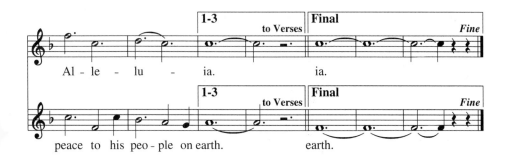

1-3 to Verses | **Final** Fine

Al - le - lu - ia. ia.

1-3 to Verses | **Final** Fine

peace to his peo - ple on earth. earth.

VERSES 1, 2: Cantor (or Men)

Men
1. Lord God, heav - en - ly King, al - might - y God __
2. Lord __ Je - sus Christ, on - ly Son

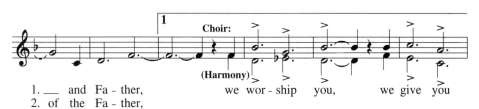

1 Choir:

(Harmony)

1. __ and Fa - ther, we wor - ship you, we give you
2. of the Fa - ther,

rit. D.C.

1. thanks, we praise you for your glo - ry.

*Final Refrain sung twice.

Music: *St. Louis Jesuits*; John Foley, SJ, b. 1939 ©1978, John Foley, SJ and New Dawn Music.

VERSE 3:   *Calmly (♩ = 160)*

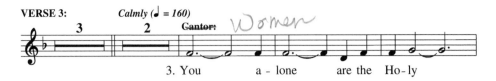

3. You   a - lone   are the Ho- ly

3. One,   you   a - lone   are the Lord,

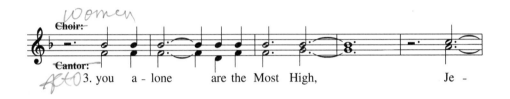

3. you   a - lone   are the Most High,   Je -

First tempo (♩ = 176)

3.   sus   Christ,   with the Ho - ly   Spir- it,   in the

rit.   D.C. al fine

3. glo - ry   of   God   the   Fa - ther.

Holy

Music: *St. Louis Jesuits*; Bob Dufford, SJ, b. 1943 and Dan Schutte, b. 1947 ©1973, Robert J. Dufford, SJ and Daniel L. Schutte.
Administered by New Dawn Music.

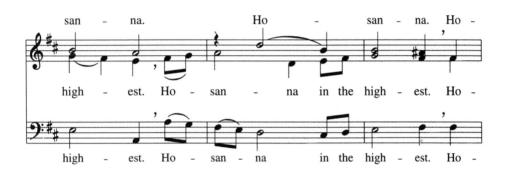

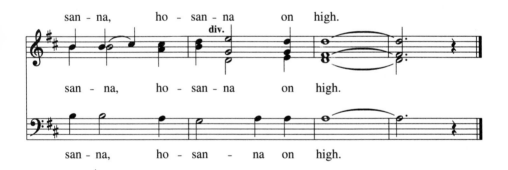

Memorial Acclamation C

Reverently (♩ = 76)

Presider:
There-fore we pro-claim the mys-ter-y of faith:

All:
When we eat this bread of life, when we drink of this ho-ly cup,

Soprano
Alto
we pro-claim your death, O Lord, till you come a-gain.

Tenor
Bass

When we eat this bread of life, when we drink of this ho-ly cup,

we pro-claim your death, O Lord, till you come a-gain!

Text: ©1973, I.C.E.L., Inc.
Music: *St. Louis Jesuits*; Bob Dufford, SJ, b. 1943 and Dan Schutte, b. 1947 ©1977, 1979, 1991, Robert J. Dufford, SJ and
    Daniel L. Schutte. Administered by New Dawn Music.

Doxology

Through him, with him, and in him, in the u - ni - ty
of the Ho - ly Spir - it, all glo - ry and hon - or is yours,
al - might - y Fa-ther, for - ev - er and ev - er.

Amen

Music: *St. Louis Jesuits*; Bob Dufford, SJ, b. 1943 ©1973, 1979, Robert J. Dufford, SJ. Administered by New Dawn Music.

Penitential Litany

INTRO: *Moderately (♩ = ca. 40)*   **VERSES:** Cantor

1. Lord Je - sus,   you are might - y
2. Christ Je - sus,   you are Son of
3. Lord Je - sus,   you are Word made

1. God   and   Prince ___ of ___ peace: ___
2. God   and   Son ___ of ___ Mar - y:
3. flesh   and   splen-dor of the Fa - ther:

REFRAIN:

Cantor or Unison Choir

1. Lord,   have mer - cy.
2. Christ,   have mer - cy.
3. Lord,   have mer - cy.

Soprano/All   **D.S.**
                         Fine

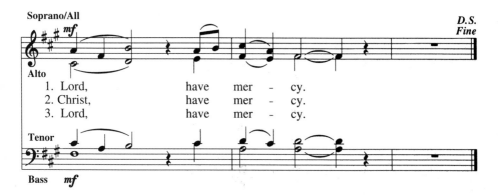

Alto

1. Lord,   have mer - cy.
2. Christ,   have mer - cy.
3. Lord,   have mer - cy.

Tenor

Bass   *mf*

Glory to God

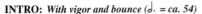

INTRO: *With vigor and bounce (♩. = ca. 54)*

REFRAIN: 1st time: Choir/All repeat; thereafter: All (no repeat)

Glo - ry to you, Lord our God,

Glo - ry to you, Lord our

now and un - til the end of time.

God, now 'til the end of time.

VERSE 1: Choir or Cantor

1. Glo - ry to God in the high - est and

D.S.

1. peace to all peo - ple on earth.

VERSE 2: Choir or Cantor

2. Lord God, heav - en - ly King, al - might - y

Music: *God Here Among Us*; Christopher Willcock, b. 1947 ©1991, Christopher Willcock, SJ. Published by OCP Publications.

2. God and Fa - ther, we wor - ship you, we
2. give you thanks, we praise you for your glo - ry.

VERSE 3: Choir or Cantor
a little slower; warmly (♩. = ca. 48)

3. Lord Je - sus Christ, on - ly Son of the
3. Fa - ther, Lord God, Lamb of God, you take a -
3. way the sin of the world: have mer - cy on us.

VERSE 4: Choir or Cantor
a little slower; warmly (♩. = ca. 48)

4. Lord Je - sus Christ, you are
4. seat - ed at the right hand of the
4. Fa - ther: re - ceive our prayer.

VERSE 5: Choir or Cantor

5. For you a - lone are the Ho - ly One,

5. you a - lone are the Lord,

5. you a - lone are the Most High,

5. Je - sus Christ, with the Ho - ly

5. Spir - it, in the glo - ry of God the

5. Fa - ther, in the glo - ry of God the

5. Fa - ther. A - men, a - men.

to Final Refrain

5. A - men, a - men.

FINAL REFRAIN: All

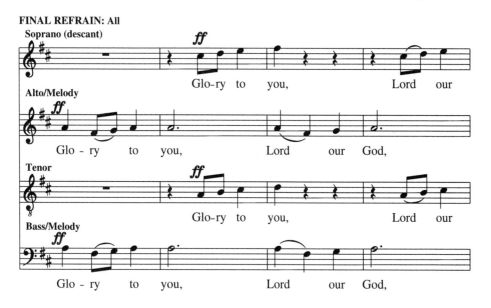

Soprano (descant)
ff
Glo-ry to you, Lord our

Alto/Melody
ff
Glo - ry to you, Lord our God,

Tenor
ff
Glo-ry to you, Lord our

Bass/Melody
ff
Glo - ry to you, Lord our God,

God, 'til the end of time.

now and un - til the end of time.

God, 'til the end of time.

now and un - til the end of time.

CODA:

Eucharistic Acclamations: Holy

*OSTINATO: *At a steady tempo (= ca. 60)*

Choir repeat *ad lib;* Each time thereafter: Assembly

ad lib.

Ho-san-na, ho-san-na, ho-san-na on high.

1

Soprano

Alto

Ho-ly, ho-ly, ho-ly Lord, God of pow'r and

2

might, heav'n and earth, heav'n and earth are full of your

3

Soprano

Alto glo-ry.

Tenor

Bass

Ho-san-na, ho-san-na, ho-san-na on

4

Ho-san-na, ho-san-na, ho-san-na on

high.

*The 4-bar Ostinato is repeated several times by the Choir while the Assembly takes it up;
Choir then starts singing the Verses.

Music: *God Here Among Us;* Christopher Willcock, SJ, b. 1947 ©1991,Christopher Willcock, SJ. Published by OCP Publications.

5

high. *well-sustained*

Blessed is he who comes in the name of the

6

Blessed is he who comes in the name of the

Lord. *f*

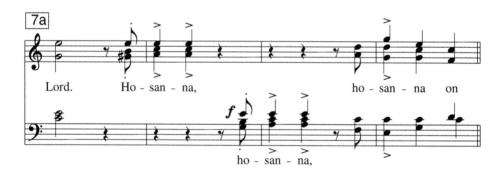

7a

Lord. Ho - san - na, ho - san - na on

ho - san - na,

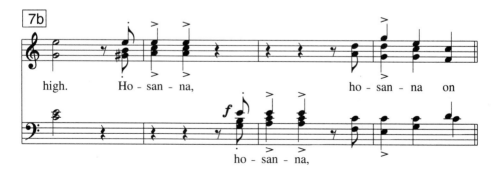

7b

high. Ho - san - na, ho - san - na on

ho - san - na,

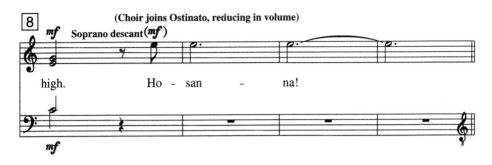

8 (Choir joins Ostinato, reducing in volume)

Soprano descant (*mf*)

high. Ho - san - na!

9

Ho - san - na!

Tenor descant

Eucharistic Acclamations:
Memorial Acclamation B

With strong rhythm (♪ = ca. 186)

Priest: *unaccompanied*

All:

Let us pro-claim the mys-t'ry of faith.   1. Dy - ing you de -
                                           2. Lord_____ Je - sus,

(Fine)

1. stroyed   our death,___   ris - ing you re - stored   our life,
2. come   in glo - ry,   Lord_____ Je - sus, come   in pow'r.

Text: © 1973, I.C.E.L., Inc.
Music: *God Here Among Us;* Christopher Willcock, b. 1947 © 1991, Christopher Willcock, SJ. Published by OCP Publications.

Eucharistic Acclamations:
Doxology and Great Amen

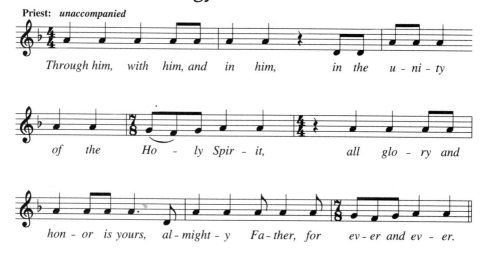

Priest: *unaccompanied*

Through him, with him, and in him, in the u - ni - ty

of the Ho - ly Spir - it, all glo - ry and

hon - or is yours, al - might - y Fa - ther, for ev - er and ev - er.

1st time Choir or Cantor; All repeat *With strong rhythm* ($\quad$ = ca. 182)

Soprano/All

Alto

A - men, a - men, a - men, a - men.

Tenor

Bass

Text: ©1973, I.C.E.L., Inc.
Music: *God Here Among Us*; Christopher Willcock, b. 1947 ©1991, Christopher Willcock, SJ. Published by OCP Publications.

Lamb of God

Text: *Agnus Dei;* alt. by Christopher Willcock, b. 1947.
Music: *God Here Among Us;* Christopher Willcock.
Text and music ©1991, Christopher Willcock, SJ. Published by OCP Publications.

Holy

INTRO: (♩. = 46-52)

Ho - ly, ho - ly, ho - ly Lord,

God of pow - er, God of might, heav - en and earth are

full of your glo - ry. Ho - san - na in the high - est.

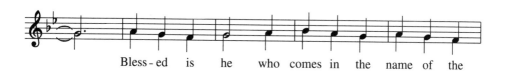

Bless - ed is he who comes in the name of the

Lord. Ho - san - na in the high - est.

ho - san - na in the high - est.

Music: *Mass of Creation*; Marty Haugen, b. 1950 ©1984, G.I.A. Publications, Inc.

Memorial Acclamation A

Text: ©1973, I.C.E.L., Inc.
Music: *Mass of Creation*; Mary Haugen, b. 1950 ©1984, G.I.A. Publications, Inc.

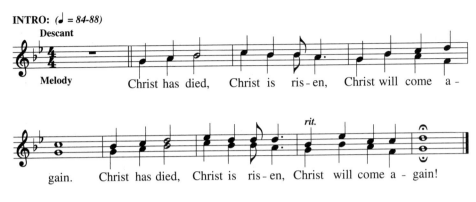

INTRO: (♩ = 84-88)

Descant

Melody

Christ has died, Christ is ris-en, Christ will come a-gain. Christ has died, Christ is ris-en, Christ will come a-gain!

Amen

INTRO: *Strong* (♩ = 84-88)

Descant

Melody

A - men, a - men, a - men! A - men, a - men, a - men!

Music: *Mass of Creation*; Marty Haugen, b. 1950 ©1984, G.I.A. Publications, Inc.

Jesus, Lamb of God

Gently, with some rubato (♩ = 63-69)

Cantor/Choir:

Je - sus, Lamb of God;
Je - sus, Bread of Life;
Je - sus, Prince of Peace;

you take a - way the

sins of the world: have mer - cy on us.

FINAL TIME:

Cantor/Choir:

Je - sus, Lamb of God; you

take a - way the sins of the world:

grant us your peace.

Additional Invocations:

Jesus, Word of God. . .	Jesus, King of Kings. . .
Jesus, Tree of Life. . .	Jesus, Cup of Life. . .
Jesus, Ancient Cup. . .	Jesus, Fire of Love. . .
Jesus, Lord of Lords. . .	Jesus, Bread of Peace. . .
Jesus, Hope for all. . .	

Music: *Mass of Creation*; Marty Haugen, b. 1950 ©1984, G.I.A. Publications, Inc.

SERVICE MUSIC

Water of Life

Text: Stephen Dean.
Music: Stephen Dean.
Text and music ©1981, 1983, Stephen Dean. Published by OCP Publications.

Glory to God

REFRAIN: *Sturdily* Choir (Women or Men in Unison), All repeat; Thereafter: All

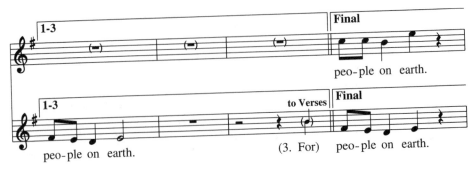

Music: James Biery ©1993, James Biery. Published by OCP Publications.

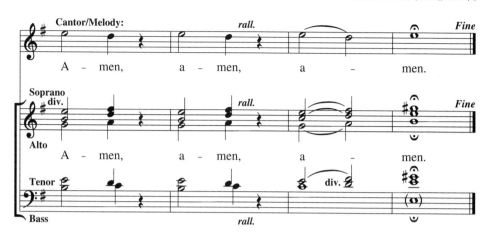

A - men, a - men, a - men.

A - men, a - men, a - men.

VERSE 1: Choir

1. Lord God, heav - en - ly King, al - might - y

1. God and Fa - ther, we wor - ship you, we

1. give you thanks, we praise you for your glo - ry.

VERSE 2: Cantor/Choir

2. Lord Je - sus Christ, on - ly Son of the Fa - ther,

2. Lord God, Lamb of God, you take a - way the sin of the

2. world: have mer - cy, have mer - cy, have

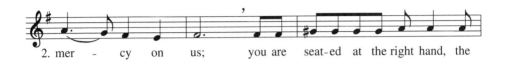

2. mer - cy on us; you are seat-ed at the right hand, the

D.C.

2. right hand of the Fa-ther: re - ceive our prayer.

VERSE 3: Cantor/Choir

3. you a - lone are the Ho - ly One, you a - lone are the

3. Lord, you a - lone are the Most High, Je - sus Christ,

3. with the Ho - ly Spir - it, in the glo - ry of God, the

D.C. al fine

3. glo - ry of God, the glo - ry of God the Fa - ther.

A Christmas Gloria

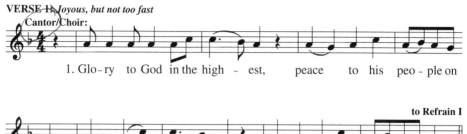

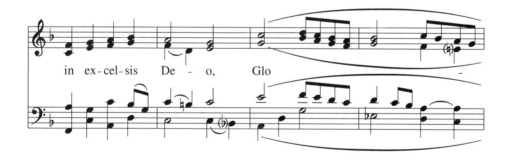

Music: From the Trad. French Carol; arr. by Paul Gibson, b. 1952 ©1988, Paul Gibson. Published by OCP Publications.

VERSE 2: Cantor/Choir

2. We wor - ship you, we give you thanks, we praise you

2. for your glo - ry. Lord Je - sus Christ, on - ly

D. C. to Refrain I

2. Son of the Fa - ther, Lord God, Lamb of God,

VERSE 3: Cantor/Choir

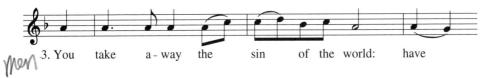

3. You take a - way the sin of the world: have

3. mer - cy on us; you are seat - ed at the

D. C. to Refrain I

3. Fa - ther's right hand: re - ceive our prayer.

VERSE 4: Cantor/Choir

4. For you a - lone are the Ho - ly One,

FINAL REFRAIN:

Glory to God

Music: Peter Jones ©1981, 1982, Peter Jones. Published by OCP Publications.

VERSE 1: Cantor/Choir

1. *Lord God,   heav - en-ly King, al-might-y   God and   Fa - ther.*

S

A

1. *Lord God,   heav - en-ly King, al-might-y   God and   Fa - ther.*

T

B

REFRAIN: All   unison

Glo - ry   to God,   glo - ry in the high - est. Peace to his peo - ple,

VERSE 2:
Cantor/Choir: **All:**

peace on earth. 2.We wor - ship you,   glo-ry in the high - est.

Cantor/Choir: **All:**   **Cantor/Choir:**

2. *Give you thanks, glo - ry in the high - est. Praise you for your   glo - ry.*

REFRAIN: All

Glo - ry to God, glo - ry in the high - est. Peace to his

VERSE 3:
Cantor/Choir: *woman*

peo - ple, peace on earth. 3. *Lord Je-sus Christ, on-ly Son of the Fa-ther,*

3. *Lord God, Lamb of God,* *you take a-way the sin of the world: have*

All: **Cantor/Choir:**

3. *mer - cy on us;* have *mer - cy on us; you are seat-ed at the right hand of the*

All: **2 D.C.**

3. *Fa-ther: re - ceive our prayer,* re - *ceive our prayer.*

Refrain ✗ 2

VERSE 4: Cantor/Choir

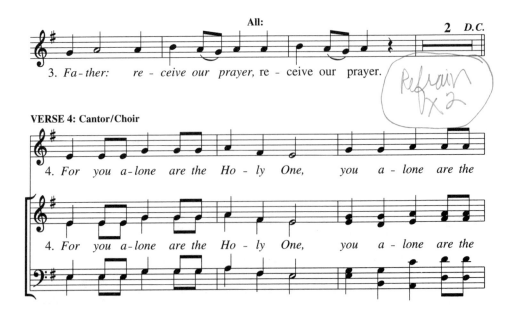

4. *For you a-lone are the Ho - ly One,* *you a - lone are the*

4. *For you a-lone are the Ho - ly One,* *you a - lone are the*

4. Lord, you a - lone are the Most High, Je - sus Christ,

4. Lord, you a - lone are the Most High, Je - sus Christ,

4. with the Ho - ly Spir - it, in the glo - ry of

4. with the Ho - ly Spir - it, in the glo - ry of

D.C. al fine

4. God, the glo - ry of God the Fa - ther.

D.C. al fine

4. God, the glo - ry of God the Fa - ther.

Glory to God

REFRAIN: All *with energy (♩. = ca. 90)*

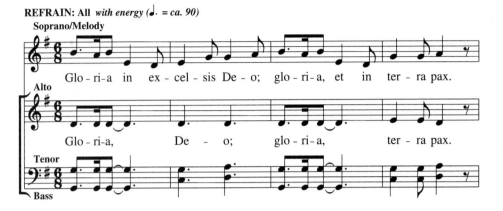

Glo - ri-a in ex - cel - sis De - o; glo - ri-a, et in ter - ra pax.

Glo - ri-a in ex - cel - sis De - o; glo - ri-a, et in ter - ra pax.

VERSE 1: Cantor/Choir

1. Lord God, heav-en-ly King, al - might - y God and Fa - ther,

1. we wor-ship you, we give you thanks, we praise you for your glo - ry.

Music: Scott Soper ©1991, Scott Soper. Published by OCP Publications.

VERSE 2: Cantor/Choir

2. Lord Je - sus Christ, on - ly Son of the Fa - ther,

2. Lord God, Lamb of God, you take a - way the sin of the

2. world: have mer - cy on us; you are seat - ed at the

D.C.

2. right hand of the Fa - ther: re - ceive our prayer.

VERSE 3: Cantor/Choir

3. For you a - lone are the Ho - ly One, you a - lone

3. are the Lord, you a - lone are the Most High, Je - sus

3. Christ, with the Ho - ly Spir - it, in the

D.C. al fine

3. glo - ry of God the Fa - ther. A - men.

Advent/Christmas Gospel Acclamation

ANTIPHON: First time: Cantor
Each time thereafter: All (♩ = ca. 100)

Melody

(last time rit.)   (⌢) Fine

Al-le - lu - ia, al-le-lu - ia, al- le - lu - ia, al-le-lu - ia.

Harmony

(last time rit.)   (◡)

VERSE 1: (Advent)
Cantor:

1. You are the joy of ev - 'ry hu - man heart,

1. king of all the na - tions.   Lord Je - sus come!   D.C.

VERSES 2-4: (Advent) / VERSE 5: (Christmas)
VERSE 6: (Epiphany) / VERSE 7: (Baptism of the Lord)
Cantor:

2. You are Lord,   our jus - tice and our mer - cy.
3. E - ter - nal light,   and sun ___ of ___ jus - tice,
4. Em-man - u - el,   the joy of all ___ na - tions,
5. Born to - day,   our jus - tice and our mer - cy,
6. You are light   that shines ___ in the dark - ness,
7. You are born   of wa - ter and the Spir - it,

All: D.C.
(Harmony)

2. Show us how to live:
3. shine in all our dark-ness:
4. come to us and save us: 2-4. Lord Je - sus come!
5. God in flesh a - mong us: 5-7. Lord, Je - sus Christ!
6. star to guide the na - tions:
7. foun - tain of our dreams:

Text: David Haas, b. 1957.
Music: David Haas.
Text and music ©1986, David Haas. Published by OCP Publications.

674

Praise to You, Lord Jesus Christ
(Lenten Gospel Acclamation)

REFRAIN: *Broadly* (♩ = 78) **1st time: Cantor** *(a cappella)*, **All repeat** *(with acc.)*; **thereafter: All**

Praise to you, Lord Je - sus Christ,

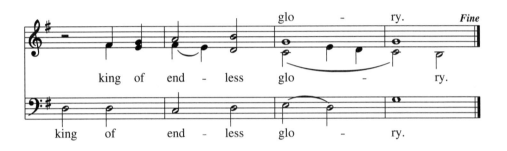

glo - ry. *Fine*

king of end - less glo - ry.

king of end - less glo - ry.

VERSES: *Gently*

1. Our hearts can-not live on bread a - lone, but by
2. I hope in the Lord, I trust the Word; with the
3. O turn to the Lord with all your heart; come to

D.C.

1. ev - 'ry word that comes from God's own mouth.
2. Lord, our God, is mer - cy ev - er - more.
3. know the Lord whose ways are truth and love.

Danish Amen

A - men,   a - men,   a - men.

ACKNOWLEDGMENTS

OCP Publications sincerely thanks the authors, composers and owners or holders of copyright who have so kindly granted permission to use their material. Every effort has been made to determine and acknowledge all credits. The publisher regrets any oversight that may have occurred and will gladly make proper acknowledgment in future editions after written notice has been received.

The English translation of the psalm responses and the Lenten gospel acclamation from the *Lectionary for Mass* ©1969, 1981, International Committee on English in the Liturgy, Inc. (ICEL); the English translation of the Litany of the Saints from the *Rite of Holy Week* ©1972, ICEL; the English translation of the memorial acclamations and other texts from the Order of Mass from *The Roman Missal* ©1973, ICEL. All rights reserved.

"Gift of Finest Wheat" used with permission of the Archdiocese of Philadelphia, 220 N 17th St., Philadelphia, PA 19103.

Selections copyrighted by Augsburg Fortress are used with permission of Augsburg Fortress, 426 S. 5th St., Minneapolis, MN 55440.

"Soon and Very Soon" ©1976, Bud John Songs, Inc./Crouch Music. Admin. by EMI Christian Music Publishing. All rights reserved. Used with permission.

Selections copyrighted by Burns & Oates, Ltd., England used with permission of Burns & Oates, Ltd., Wellwood, North Farm Rd, Turnbridge Wells, Kent, TN2 3DR, England.

Scripture texts from *The New American Bible* ©1970 by the Confraternity of Christian Doctrine are used herein by license of said copyright owner. All rights reserved.

Selections copyrighted by Damean Music used with permission of the Dameans.

Selections by Dan Feiten used by permission of Ekklesia Music, PO Box 22967, Denver, CO 80222.

Selections copyrighted by Birdwing Music/BMG Songs, Inc. are administered by EMI Christian Music Publishing, Inc., Brentwood, TN. All rights reserved. Used with permission.

Selections copyrighted and/or administered by G.I.A. Publications, Inc. are used with permission of G.I.A. Publications, Inc., 7404 So. Mason Avenue, Chicago, IL 60638.

Texts from The Grail (England) used with permission of G.I.A. Publications, Inc., agent.

Selections copyrighted by Eleanor Farjeon reprinted by permission of Harold Ober Assoc., 425 Madison Ave., New York, NY 10017.

Music from "Festival Canticle: Worthy Is Christ" ©1975, 1988, Richard Hillert. All rights reserved. Used with permission.

Selections copyrighted by Hope Publishing Co. are used with permission of Hope Publishing Co., Carol Stream, IL 60188. All rights reserved. Used with permission.

"Let There Be Peace on Earth" used with permission of Jan-Lee Music, PO Box 1517, Honokaa, HI 96727.

Selections copyrighted by F.E.L. Publications, Ltd., and assigned to the Lorenz Corporation have been reprinted with permission of the Lorenz Corporation, 501 E. 3rd St., Dayton, OH 45401.

"How Great Thou Art" used with permission of Manna Music, Inc., 35255 Brooten Road, Pacific City, OR 97135.

Selections copyrighted by WORD OF GOD MUSIC and MARANATHA! MUSIC are administered by THE COPYRIGHT COMPANY, Nashville, TN. All rights reserved. International copyright secured. Used by permission.

"To Jesus Christ, Our Sovereign King" ©1978, assigned to Mrs. Irene C. Mueller, 1441 Hillcrest #1, Cincinnati, OH 45224. Used with permission.

Selections copyrighted by Oxford University Press are used with permission of Oxford University Press, London, England.

"Sing of Mary" © Estate of Roland F. Palmer, c/o Rev. Canon Peter D. Wilkinson, 25 Government Unit 209, Victoria, British Columbia, Canada V8V 2K4.

Text of "All Creatures of Our God and King" copyrighted by J.Curwen & Sons (London) and controlled by G. Schirmer, Inc., 257 Park Ave. South, New York, NY 10010. International copyright secured. All rights reserved. Reprinted by permission.

Text for "A Mighty Fortress" (Schuller text) © Arvella Schuller. All rights reserved. Used with permission.

Texts copyrighted by James D. Quinn are reprinted by permission of Selah Publishing Company, PO Box 3037, Kingston, NY 12401.

Translation of the text of "Panis Angelicus" ©1986, Jerome Siwek. Used with permission.

Text of "Song of Farewell" ©1981 Dennis C. Smolarski, SJ. All rights reserved. Used with permission.

The English translation of the "Phos Hilaron" is copyrighted by William G. Storey. All rights reserved. Used with permission.

"Prayer of St. Francis" by Sebastian Temple is dedicated to Mrs. Frances Tracy. The selection is ©1967, OCP Publications. All rights reserved.

Selections by the Monks of Weston Priory are reprinted with permission of Weston Priory Productions, Weston, VT 05161.

"Precious Lord, Take My Hand" ©1938 by Unichappell Music Inc. Copyright renewed. International copyright secured. All rights reserved.

"We Are the Light of the World" is used with permission of Vernacular Hymns Publishing Co., 6426 Matilija Ave., Van Nuys, CA 91401.

Music from WORD, Inc. reprinted with permission of WORD, Inc. and distributed by OCP Publications.

Text of "Go, Tell It on the Mountain" © Mrs. John W. Work, III. Used with permission.

Selections copyrighted by Cooperative Ministries, Inc. are administered by OCP Publications: exclusive agent.

Selections copyrighted by Ediciones Musical Pax are administered in the United States by OCP Publications: sole US agent.

Selections copyrighted and/or administered by New Dawn Music are used with all rights reserved.

Selections copyrighted by Willard Jabusch are administered by OCP Publications. All rights reserved.

All selections in the copyright of North American Liturgy Resources are now owned and administered by OCP Publications. All rights reserved.

LITURGICAL INDEX

PROPER OF SEASONS

ADVENT SEASON

A Voice Cries Out
Advent/Christmas Gospel Acclamation
Advent Intercessions (Walker: Celtic)
All Hail the Power of Jesus' Name
All That Is Hidden
Alleluia! Give the Glory
Bread of Life (Farrell)
Canticle of Zachary (Joncas)
Center of My Life
City of God
Come Now, Almighty King
Come, Thou Long-Expected Jesus
Every Valley
Flow River Flow
Gather Your People
God, Beyond All Names
God Has Chosen Me
Hold Me in Life
I Will Lift Up My Eyes
In the Breaking of the Bread
Jesu, Joy of Our Desiring
Jesus, Come to Us
Let All Mortal Flesh Keep Silence
Let the King of Glory Come
Let the Valleys Be Raised
Lift Up Your Heads, Ye Mighty Gates
Like a Shepherd
Lo, How a Rose E'er Blooming
Lord of Glory
Love Divine, All Loves Excelling
Mary's Song (Joncas)
Mary's Song (Rieth)
My Soul Rejoices
O Come, Divine Messiah
O Come, O Come, Emmanuel
O God, Hear Us
O Holy Mary
On Jordan's Bank
One Bread, One Body
Our Blessing Cup (Hurd)
Out of Darkness
Pan de Vida
Patience, People
Peace Is Flowing Like a River
People, Look East
Praise to You, Lord Jesus Christ
Ready the Way
Rejoice, the Lord Is King
Save Us, O Lord
Servant Song
Sing a New Song (Schutte)
Sing of Mary
Sing Out, Earth and Skies
Somos el Cuerpo de Cristo
Soon and Very Soon
Taste and See (Dean)
Taste and See (Hurd)

The Advent of Our King
The Coming of Our God
The Cry of the Poor
The King Shall Come When Morning
    Dawns
The Lord Is Near
There Is a Longing
Those Who See Light
Those Who Sow in Tears
To You, O God, I Lift Up My Soul
To You, O Lord (Alstott)
To You, O Lord (Soper)
Turn to Me
Wade in the Water
Water of Life
We Shall Draw Water

CHRISTMAS SEASON
CHRISTMAS (DAYS OF)

A Child Is Born
A Christmas Gloria
Advent/Christmas Gospel Acclamation
All the Ends of the Earth
    (Haas/Haugen)
All the Ends of the Earth (Hurd)
Angels from the Realms of Glory
Angels We Have Heard on High
Away in a Manger
Bread of Life (Cooney)
Bread of Life (Farrell)
Children, Run Joyfully
City of God
Evening Hymn: Phos Hilaron
Every Valley
God Rest You Merry, Gentlemen
Good Christians, All, Rejoice
Hark! The Herald Angels Sing
I Am the Living Bread
It Came upon the Midnight Clear
Joy to the World
Let All Mortal Flesh Keep Silence
Let Heaven Rejoice
Lift Up Your Heads, Ye Mighty Gates
Lo, How a Rose E'er Blooming
My Soul Rejoices
O Come, All Ye Faithful
O Come, Little Children
O Little Town of Bethlehem
Of the Father's Love Begotten
See amid the Winter's Snow
Silent Night, Holy Night
Sing of the Lord's Goodness
Somos el Cuerpo de Cristo
Taste and See (Dean)
The First Noel
The Light of Christ
The Snow Lay on the Ground
There Is Nothing Told
Wake from Your Sleep
We Three Kings of Orient Are

What Child Is This
What Star Is This
While Shepherds Watched Their
    Flocks

HOLY FAMILY

City of God
For the Beauty of the Earth
Lift Up Your Heads, Ye Mighty Gates
Lord of All Hopefulness
Mary, Full of Grace
O Come, Little Children
Of the Father's Love Begotten
Sing of Mary
The Snow Lay on the Ground
There Is Nothing Told
What Child Is This
Where There Is Love

MARY, MOTHER OF GOD

God Rest You Merry, Gentlemen
Hail Mary: Gentle Woman
Hail, Holy Queen
Hark! The Herald Angels Sing
Holy Is His Name
Immaculate Mary
Lo, How a Rose E'er Blooming
Mary, Full of Grace
Mary's Song (Joncas)
Mary's Song (Rieth)
My Soul Rejoices
O Holy Mary
Of the Father's Love Begotten
On This Day, the First of Days
Servant Song
Sing a New Song (Brown)
Sing a New Song (Schutte)
Sing of Mary
The Snow Lay on the Ground
There Is Nothing Told
This Is the Day (Joncas)

EPIPHANY

Advent/Christmas Gospel Acclamation
All Good Gifts
All the Ends of the Earth
    (Haas/Haugen)
Angels from the Realms of Glory
As with Gladness Men of Old
Bread of Life (Farrell)
Center of My Life
Evening Hymn: Phos Hilaron
Songs of Thankfulness and Praise
The First Noel
Though the Mountains May Fall
We Three Kings of Orient Are
What Child Is This
What Star Is This

BAPTISM OF THE LORD

Advent/Christmas Gospel Acclamation
Joy to the World
Lift Up Your Heads, Ye Mighty Gates
On Jordan's Bank
Songs of Thankfulness and Praise
Wade in the Water

LENTEN SEASON
ASH WEDNESDAY

Create in Me
Forty Days and Forty Nights
From the Depths We Cry to Thee
Hosea
Humbly, Lord, We Worship You
I Am the Light of the World
Lift High the Cross
Lord, Who throughout These Forty
    Days
O God, You Search Me
Parce Domine
Prayer of St. Francis
Take Up Your Cross
The Glory of These Forty Days
There's a Wideness in God's Mercy
Turn to Me
What Is This Place

LENT (DAYS OF)

All Glory, Laud and Honor
All That Is Hidden
Amazing Grace
Anthem
At the Cross Her Station Keeping
Be Not Afraid
Be with Me, Lord
Blest Are They
Blest Be the Lord
Bread of Life (Cooney)
Bread of Life (Farrell)
Canticle of Zachary (FOREST GREEN)
Center of My Life
Christ Be beside Me
Come to Me
Come to the Water
Companions on the Journey
Crown Him with Many Crowns
Earthen Vessels
Eat This Bread
Eye Has Not Seen
Fill My Cup, Lord
Flow River Flow
For You Are My God
Forty Days and Forty Nights
From the Depths We Cry to Thee
Gather Us In
Gather Your People
Gift of Finest Wheat
Give Me Jesus
Here I Am, Lord
Holy God, We Praise Thy Name

Hosea
Humbly, Lord, We Worship You
I Am the Bread of Life
I Heard the Voice of Jesus
I Lift Up My Soul
I Will Not Die
Jesus, Come to Us
Lead Me, Lord
Lift High the Cross
Like a Shepherd
Lord of All Hopefulness
Lord, Who throughout These Forty
    Days
Loving and Forgiving
O Bless the Lord
O God, Hear Us
O God, You Search Me
O Sacred Head Surrounded
On Eagle's Wings
Out of Darkness
Pan de Vida
Parce Domine
Praise, My Soul, the King of Heaven
Praise to the Lord
Praise to You, Lord Jesus Christ
Precious Lord, Take My Hand
Psalm 42 (As the Deer Longs)
Remember Your Love
Save Us, O Lord
See Us, Lord, about Your Altar
Servant Song
Shepherd of Souls
Somos el Cuerpo de Cristo
Soul of My Savior
Take Up Your Cross
Taste and See (Dean)
The Glory of These Forty Days
The King of Love My Shepherd Is
The Lord Is Near
The Supper of the Lord
There Is a Longing
There's a Wideness in God's Mercy
This Day God Gives Me
Those Who See Light
Those Who Seek Your Face
Those Who Sow in Tears
To You, O Lord (Alstott)
Turn to Me
Unless a Grain of Wheat (Farrell)
Unless a Grain of Wheat (Hurd)
We Have Been Told
We Praise You
We Remember
We Walk by Faith
We Will Rise Again
What Is This Place
What Wondrous Love Is This
When We Eat This Bread
You Are Mine
You Are Near

PASSION (PALM) SUNDAY

All Glory, Laud and Honor
All That Is Hidden
At the Cross Her Station Keeping
At the Name of Jesus
Behold the Lamb of God
Father, I Put My Life in Your Hands
    (Talbot)
Give Thanks to the Lord
I Will Not Die
Jesus, Remember Me
Lift High the Cross
Lift Up Your Heads, Ye Mighty Gates
Lord of the Dance
O Sacred Head, Surrounded
Pan de Vida
Sing, My Tongue, the Savior's Glory
    (Passion Sunday, Good Friday)
Soul of My Savior
Take Up Your Cross
The King of Glory
We Praise You
Were You There
What Wondrous Love Is This
When I Survey the Wondrous Cross

CHRISM MASS
(HOLY THURSDAY)

Lord, You Give the Great Commission

EASTER TRIDUUM
EVENING MASS OF THE
LORD'S SUPPER
(HOLY THURSDAY)

All That Is Hidden
At the Name of Jesus
Bless the Feast
Blessed by Your Sacrifice
Bread of Life (Farrell)
Center of My Life
Christians, Let Us Love One Another
Eat This Bread
For the Beauty of the Earth
Gather Us In
Gather Your People
I Am the Bread of Life
I, the Lord
In Perfect Charity
In the Breaking of the Bread
Jesus, Remember Me
Let Us Break Bread Together
Lift High the Cross
Lord, Who at Thy First Eucharist
Love Divine, All Loves Excelling
Love One Another
Our Blessing Cup (Hurd)
Our Blessing Cup (Joncas)
Out of Darkness
Pan de Vida
Pange Lingua Gloriosi (ST. THOMAS)

679

Remember Your Love
See Us, Lord, about Your Altar
Shepherd of Souls
Sing, My Tongue, the Savior's Glory
  (Passion Sunday, Good Friday)
Song of the Body of Christ
The Cup We Bless
The Lord Jesus
The Supper of the Lord
There's a Wideness in God's Mercy
This Body
Ubi Caritas
Water of Life
We Have Been Told
We Remember
Were You There
What Is This Place
You Are Our Living Bread

CELEBRATION OF THE LORD'S PASSION (GOOD FRIDAY)

At the Cross Her Station Keeping
At the Name of Jesus
Behold the Lamb of God
Behold the Wood
Come to Me
Father, I Put My Life in Your Hands
  (Talbot)
Jesus, Remember Me
Jesus the Lord
Lift High the Cross
O Sacred Head, Surrounded
Pan de Vida
Remember Your Love
Sing, My Tongue, the Savior's Glory
  (Passion Sunday, Good Friday)
Soul of My Savior
Take Up Your Cross
Unless a Grain of Wheat (Hurd)
Were You There
What Wondrous Love Is This
When I Survey the Wondrous Cross
Wood of the Cross

EASTER VIGIL

Alleluia! Alleluia!
Alleluia! Give the Glory
At the Lamb's High Feast
Be Joyful, Mary
Behold the Lamb of God
Celtic Alleluia (Easter)
Christ, the Lord, Is Risen Today (II)
Come, Holy Ghost
Come to the Water
Creator Spirit, by Whose Aid
For All the Saints
For You Are My God
From East and West
Holy Darkness
I Am the Light of the World

I Know That My Redeemer Lives
  (DUKE STREET)
I Know That My Redeemer Lives
  (Soper)
Jesus Christ Is Risen Today
Litany of the Saints (Becker)
Lord, You Have the Words
Out of Darkness
Resucitó
River of Glory
Send Out Your Spirit
Somos el Cuerpo de Cristo
The Strife Is O'er
This Is the Day (Joncas)
Water of Life
We Shall Draw Water
Ye Sons and Daughters

EASTER SEASON
EASTER (DAYS OF)

All Creatures of Our God and King
All the Ends of the Earth
  (Haas/Haugen)
All the Ends of the Earth (Hurd)
Alleluia! Alleluia!
Alleluia! Alleluia! Let the Holy Anthem
  Rise
Alleluia! Give the Glory
Alleluia No. 1
Anthem
As We Celebrate
At the Lamb's High Feast
At the Name of Jesus
Be Joyful, Mary
Behold the Lamb
Bless the Feast
Canticle of the Sun
Celtic Alleluia
Center of My Life
Christ, Be Our Light
Christ, the Lord, Is Risen Again
Christ, the Lord, Is Risen Today (I)
Christ, the Lord, Is Risen Today (II)
City of God
Crown Him with Many Crowns
Eat This Bread
Eye Has Not Seen
Festival Canticle: Worthy Is Christ
Flow River Flow
For You Are My God
Gather Your People
Give Me Jesus
Give Thanks to the Lord
God, Beyond All Names
Gospel Canticle (Great Is the Lord)
He Is the Lord
Hold Me in Life
How Can I Keep from Singing
I Am the Light of the World
I Am the Living Bread

I Know That My Redeemer Lives
  (DUKE STREET)
I Know That My Redeemer Lives
  (Soper)
I Will Not Die
In Perfect Charity
In the Breaking of the Bread
Jesus Christ Is Risen Today
Jesus Is Risen
Jesus the Lord
Join in the Dance
Lead Me, Lord
Lift High the Cross
Lift Up Your Hearts
Lord of the Dance
Mary's Song (Joncas)
Mary's Song (Rieth)
May We Praise You
Morning Has Broken
Now the Green Blade Rises
Now We Remain
O God, Hear Us
On This Day, the First of Days
One Spirit, One Church
Only a Shadow
Our Blessing Cup (Hurd)
Our Blessing Cup (Joncas)
Out of Darkness
Pan de Vida
Panis Angelicus
Peace
Rejoice, the Lord Is King
Resucitó
River of Glory
Seek Ye First
Shelter Me, O God
Shepherd Me, O God
Shepherd of Souls
Sing a Joyful Song
Sing a New Song (Brown)
Sing Alleluia, Sing
Sing of the Lord's Goodness
Somos el Cuerpo de Cristo
Table of Plenty
Taste and See (Dean)
The Goodness of the Lord
The King of Glory
The King of Love My Shepherd Is
The Light of Christ
The Lord Is Near
The Strife Is O'er
This Alone
This Day Was Made by the Lord
This Is the Day (Joncas)
Those Who See Light
Ubi Caritas
Unless a Grain of Wheat (Hurd)
Water of Life
We Believe (Farrell)
We Shall Draw Water
We Walk by Faith

Ye Sons and Daughters
Ye Watchers and Ye Holy Ones

ASCENSION

All Hail the Power of Jesus' Name
All the Ends of the Earth
　(Haas/Haugen)
Alleluia! Alleluia! Let the Holy Anthem
　Rise
Alleluia! Sing to Jesus
Christ, the Lord, Is Risen Again
Christ, the Lord, Is Risen Today (II)
Come, Christians, Join to Sing
Crown Him with Many Crowns
Hail the Day That Sees Him Rise
Hail, Redeemer, King Divine
He Is the Lord
I Have Loved You
Jesus Is Risen
Lord, You Give the Great Commission
Now Thank We All Our God
Now the Green Blade Rises
Now We Remain
Prayer of St. Francis
Rejoice, the Lord Is King
Send Us Your Spirit (Schutte)
Sing a Joyful Song
Sing of the Lord's Goodness
Spirit, Come
Taste and See (Dean)
The King of Kings, Christ Jesus Reigns
The Strife Is O'er
Those Who See Light
To Jesus Christ, Our Sovereign King
We Walk by Faith
Ye Watchers and Ye Holy Ones

PENTECOST

All the Ends of the Earth
　(Haas/Haugen)
All the Ends of the Earth (Hurd)
Alleluia! Give the Glory
As We Celebrate
Blessed by Your Sacrifice
Canticle of the Sun
Center of My Life
Come to the Water
Come, Holy Ghost
Creator Spirit, by Whose Aid
Eye Has Not Seen
Gather Us Together
Gather Your People
God, Beyond All Names
God Has Chosen Me
God of Day and God of Darkness
Hold Me in Life
In Christ There Is No East or West
Jesus, Come to Us
Lift Up Your Hearts
Lord, You Give the Great Commission
O God, Hear Us
One Spirit, One Church

Pan de Vida
Send Out Your Spirit
Send Us Your Spirit (Haas)
Send Us Your Spirit (Schutte)
Servant Song
Sing of the Lord's Goodness
Spirit, Come
Take Christ to the World
Taste and See (Dean)
Taste and See (Hurd)
The Spirit Is A-Movin'
There Is Nothing Told
Unless a Grain of Wheat (Farrell)
Water of Life
We Believe (Farrell)
We Have Been Told

ORDINARY TIME
(DAYS OF: SEE TOPICAL
INDEX)

SOLEMNITIES
AND FEASTS

IMMACULATE CONCEPTION
(DECEMBER 8)

All That Is Hidden
Blest Are They
Canticle of Zachary (Joncas)
Hail Mary: Gentle Woman
Hail, Holy Queen
Holy Is His Name
Immaculate Mary
Mary, Full of Grace
Mary's Song (Joncas)
Mary's Song (Rieth)
My Soul Rejoices
O Holy Mary
Pan de Vida
Ready the Way
Servant Song
Sing of Mary
The Cry of the Poor
There Is Nothing Told
We Shall Draw Water

PRESENTATION OF THE LORD
(FEBRUARY 2)

All That Is Hidden
Christ Be Our Light
Evening Hymn: Phos Hilaron
I Will Not Die
Jesus, Come to Us
Lift Up Your Heads, Ye Mighty Gates
Mary, Full of Grace
My Soul Rejoices
O God, Our Help in Ages Past
O Holy Mary
Sing a Joyful Song
Sing of Mary

There Is Nothing Told
Those Who See Light

ANNUNCIATION (MARCH 25)

Hail, Holy Queen
Hail Mary: Gentle Woman
Immaculate Mary
Mary, Full of Grace
Of the Father's Love Begotten
Sing of Mary
There Is Nothing Told

TRINITY SUNDAY

All Creatures of Our God and King
All Hail, Adored Trinity
All People That on Earth Do Dwell
All Praise and Glad Thanksgiving
All the Ends of the Earth
　(Haas/Haugen)
Alleluia! Sing to Jesus
Canticle of the Sun
Come Now, Almighty King
Come, Holy Ghost
Creator Spirit, by Whose Aid
Eye Has Not Seen
Glory and Praise to Our God
God, Beyond All Names
Holy God, We Praise Thy Name
Holy, Holy, Holy
I Sing the Mighty Power of God
Lord, Who at Thy First Eucharist
Now Thank We All Our God
On This Day, the First of Days
Praise God from Whom All Blessings
　Flow
This Day God Gives Me
We Believe (Farrell)

BODY AND BLOOD OF CHRIST

Alleluia! Sing to Jesus
Beautiful Savior
Behold the Lamb
Bless the Feast
Christians, Let Us Love One Another
Eat This Bread
Gift of Finest Wheat
I Am the Bread of Life
I Am the Living Bread
I Know That My Redeemer Lives
　(Soper)
In the Breaking of the Bread
Let All Mortal Flesh Keep Silence
Look Beyond
Lord, Who at Thy First Eucharist
Lord, You Give the Great Commission
Now We Remain
Pan de Vida
Pange Lingua Gloriosi (ST. THOMAS)
Praise to the Lord
See Us, Lord, about Your Altar
Shepherd of Souls
Song of the Body of Christ

Soul of My Savior
Take Christ to the World
The Supper of the Lord
We Are Many Parts
We Remember
When We Eat This Bread

SACRED HEART

Christians, Let Us Love One Another
I Heard the Voice of Jesus
In Christ There Is No East or West
Jesu, Joy of Our Desiring
Lord, You Give the Great Commission
Love Divine, All Loves Excelling
The King of Love My Shepherd Is
There's a Wideness in God's Mercy
What Wondrous Love Is This
When I Survey the Wondrous Cross

BIRTH OF JOHN THE BAPTIST (JUNE 24)

Canticle of Zachary (FOREST GREEN)
Canticle of Zachary (Joncas)
Wade in the Water

TRANSFIGURATION (AUGUST 6)

Evening Hymn: Phos Hilaron
Jesu, Joy of Our Desiring
Love Divine, All Loves Excelling
Rejoice, the Lord Is King
Songs of Thankfulness and Praise

ASSUMPTION (AUGUST 15)

For the Fruits of This Creation
Glory and Praise to Our God
God Beyond All Names
Gospel Canticle (Great Is the Lord)
Hail Mary: Gentle Woman
Hail, Holy Queen
Immaculate Mary
Mary's Song (Joncas)
Mary's Song (Rieth)
Mary, Full of Grace
My Soul Rejoices
O Holy Mary
Servant Song
Sing of Mary
Sing of the Lord's Goodness
There Is Nothing Told

TRIUMPH OF THE CROSS (SEPTEMBER 14)

Alleluia! Alleluia!
At the Lamb's High Feast
Behold the Lamb of God
Lift High the Cross
Sing, My Tongue, the Savior's Glory
   (Passion Sunday, Good Friday)
Take Christ to the World
Take Up Your Cross
The King of Love My Shepherd Is
What Wondrous Love Is This

When I Survey the Wondrous Cross

ALL SAINTS (NOVEMBER 1)

All Hail the Power of Jesus' Name
Beatitudes
Blest Are They
Christians, Let Us Love One Another
Eye Has Not Seen
For All the Saints
For the Beauty of the Earth
God Has Chosen Me
Jerusalem, My Happy Home
Lift High the Cross
Litany of the Saints (Becker)
Lord, Who at Thy First Eucharist
Praise the Lord, Ye Heavens
Praise, My Soul, the King of Heaven
Prayer of St. Francis
The Church's One Foundation
Unless a Grain of Wheat (Farrell)
We Walk by Faith
Ye Watchers and Ye Holy Ones

ALL SOULS (NOVEMBER 2)

Come, Ye Thankful People, Come
For the Beauty of the Earth
Jerusalem, My Happy Home
Lord, Who at Thy First Eucharist
Praise the Lord, Ye Heavens
The Church's One Foundation
Ye Watchers and Ye Holy Ones

CHRIST THE KING

All Glory, Laud and Honor
All Hail the Power of Jesus' Name
All the Ends of the Earth
   (Haas/Haugen)
All the Ends of the Earth (Hurd)
Alleluia No. 1
Alleluia! Alleluia!
Alleluia! Alleluia! Let the Holy Anthem
   Rise
Alleluia! Sing to Jesus
At the Lamb's High Feast
At the Name of Jesus
Beatitudes
Beautiful Savior
Behold the Lamb of God
Blessed by Your Sacrifice
Center of My Life
Come Now, Almighty King
Come, Christians, Join to Sing
Crown Him with Many Crowns
Festival Canticle: Worthy Is Christ
For All the Saints
Glory and Praise to Our God
Hail, Redeemer, King Divine
Hail the Day That Sees Him Rise
He Is the Lord
I Know That My Redeemer Lives
   (Soper)
Jesu, Joy of Our Desiring

Jesus Is Risen
Jesus the Lord
Join in the Dance
Let All Mortal Flesh Keep Silence
Let the King of Glory Come
Lift High the Cross
Lift Up Your Heads, Ye Mighty Gates
Lord of Glory
Now Thank We All Our God
O Bless the Lord
Praise, My Soul, the King of Heaven
Praise the Lord, Ye Heavens
Praise to the Lord
Rejoice, the Lord Is King
Servant Song
Sing a Joyful Song
Sing Alleluia, Sing
Sing of the Lord's Goodness
Soon and Very Soon
Take Christ to the World
Taste and See (Dean)
The King of Glory
The King of Kings, Christ Jesus Reigns
The King of Love My Shepherd Is
The King Shall Come When Morning
   Dawns
To Jesus Christ, Our Sovereign King
Water of Life

RITES

CHRISTIAN INITIATION

ACCEPTANCE

All the Ends of the Earth (Hurd)
Amazing Grace
Beatitudes
Blest Are They
Bread of Life (Farrell)
Center of My Life
Flow River Flow
God Has Chosen Me
I Heard the Voice of Jesus
I Know That My Redeemer Lives
   (Soper)
Jesu, Joy of Our Desiring
Lift High the Cross
Lift Up Your Heads, Ye Mighty Gates
Pan de Vida
River of Glory
Take Up Your Cross
Taste and See (Hurd)
Water of Life
We Believe (Farrell)
We Believe (Walker: Celtic)
We Will Rise Again
When I Survey the Wondrous Cross

SENDING

Christ, Be Our Light
Dismissal of the Catechumens
   (Walker: Celtic)

God Has Chosen Me
Let Heaven Rejoice
May God Bless and Keep You

ELECTION

All That Is Hidden
Christ, Be Our Light
Faith of Our Fathers
For the Fruits of This Creation
Give Me Jesus
God Has Chosen Me
I Heard the Voice of Jesus
In Christ There Is No East or West
Lift High the Cross
Lord, You Give the Great Commission
Lord, You Have the Words
Now We Remain
Out of Darkness
This Day God Gives Me
This Day Was Made by the Lord
Those Who Seek Your Face
You Are Mine

SCRUTINIES

Flow River Flow
O God, You Search Me
Those Who Seek Your Face
You Are Near

BAPTISM

All That Is Hidden
All the Ends of the Earth
    (Haas/Haugen)
All the Ends of the Earth (Hurd)
Alleluia! Give the Glory
As We Celebrate
At the Lamb's High Feast
Beatitudes
Blest Are They
Bread of Life (Farrell)
Center of My Life
Come to the Water
Create in Me
Flow River Flow
From the Depths We Cry to Thee
Gather Your People
Give Me Jesus
Here I Am, Lord
How Lovely Is Your Dwelling Place
    (DeBruyn)
I Am the Living Bread
I Heard the Voice of Jesus
Jesu, Joy of Our Desiring
Lift Up Your Heads, Ye Mighty Gates
Litany of the Saints (Becker)
Lord, You Have the Words
Love Divine, All Loves Excelling
May God Bless and Keep You
Now We Remain
On Jordan's Bank
Out of Darkness
Pan de Vida

Parce Domine
River of Glory
Shelter Me, O God
Shepherd of Souls
Sing a New Church
Sing of the Lord's Goodness
Somos el Cuerpo de Cristo
Soul of My Savior
Take Christ to the World
Taste and See (Dean)
Taste and See (Hurd)
The Goodness of the Lord
The King of Love My Shepherd Is
The Light of Christ
This Day Was Made by the Lord
Wade in the Water
Water of Life
We Are Many Parts
We Believe (Farrell)
We Believe (Walker: Celtic)
We Shall Draw Water
We Walk by Faith
You Are Mine

CONFIRMATION

All the Ends of the Earth
    (Haas/Haugen)
All the Ends of the Earth (Hurd)
Alleluia! Give the Glory
Beatitudes
Blest Are They
Center of My Life
Christ, Be Our Light
Come, Holy Ghost
Come to the Water
Create in Me
Creator Spirit, by Whose Aid
Flow River Flow
Gather Your People
God Has Chosen Me
Here I Am, Lord
I Am the Living Bread
Lift Up Your Heads, Ye Mighty Gates
Lift Up Your Hearts
Litany of the Saints (Becker)
Lord, You Give the Great Commission
May God Bless and Keep You
O God, Hear Us
One Spirit, One Church
Out of Darkness
Prayer of St. Francis
River of Glory
Send Out Your Spirit
Send Us Your Spirit (Haas)
Send Us Your Spirit (Schutte)
Servant Song
Somos el Cuerpo de Cristo
Take Christ to the World
Take Up Your Cross
The Lord Is Near
The Spirit Is A-Movin'

This Day Was Made by the Lord
We Believe (Farrell)
We Believe (Walker: Celtic)
We Shall Draw Water
We Walk by Faith
Where There Is Love
You Are Mine

EUCHARIST
(SEE THE ORDER OF
MASS: COMMUNION)

MARRIAGE

All Creatures of Our God and King
All Good Gifts
All People That on Earth Do Dwell
Amazing Grace
Bless the Feast
Blest Are They
Christians, Let Us Love One Another
City of God
Eye Has Not Seen
For the Beauty of the Earth
For the Fruits of This Creation
For You Are My God
Gather Your People
Glory and Praise to Our God
He Is the Lord
Hear Us Now, Our God and Father
How Great Thou Art
I Have Loved You
In Perfect Charity
Joyful, Joyful, We Adore Thee
Lift Up Your Hearts
Lord of All Hopefulness
Love Divine, All Loves Excelling
Love One Another
Loving and Forgiving
May God Bless and Keep You
May God Bless You
Morning Has Broken
My Soul Rejoices
Our Blessing Cup (Hurd)
Our Blessing Cup (Joncas)
Pan de Vida
Praise God from Whom All Blessings
    Flow
Praise the Lord, Ye Heavens
Praise to the Lord
Sing a New Song (Schutte)
Somos el Cuerpo de Cristo
Songs of Thankfulness and Praise
This Day God Gives Me
This Day Was Made by the Lord
This Is the Day (Joncas)
Ubi Caritas
We Praise You
When We Eat This Bread
Where There Is Love

HOLY ORDERS

All That Is Hidden
Anthem
Center of My Life
Come to the Water
Companions on the Journey
Faith of Our Fathers
Flow River Flow
For the Fruits of This Creation
Gather Your People
God Has Chosen Me
Gospel Canticle (Great Is the Lord)
Here I am, Lord
In Christ There Is No East or West
Jesu, Joy of Our Desiring
Lift High the Cross
Lift Up Your Heads, Ye Mighty Gates
Lord, You Give the Great Commission
Love One Another
May God Bless and Keep You
My Soul Rejoices
Our Blessing Cup (Joncas)
Out of Darkness
Peace Is Flowing Like a River
Servant Song
Sing a New Church
Somos el Cuerpo de Cristo
Take Christ to the World
Taste and See (Dean)
The Spirit Is A-Movin'
To You, O God, I Lift Up My Soul
Unless a Grain of Wheat (Farrell)
We Shall Draw Water

PENANCE (RECONCILIATION)

Amazing Grace
Be with Me, Lord
Beatitudes
Blest Are They
Bread of Life (Farrell)
Come to Me
Eye Has Not Seen
From the Depths We Cry to Thee
Gather Your People
Hosea
Humbly, Lord, We Worship You
I Have Loved You
I Heard the Voice of Jesus
Jesus, Remember Me
Joyful, Joyful, We Adore Thee
Now We Remain
O Bless the Lord
O Bless the Lord, My Soul
One Spirit, One Church
Out of Darkness
Parce Domine
Praise, My Soul, the King of Heaven
Save Us, O Lord
Seek the Lord
Send Us Your Spirit (Haas)

Shepherd Me, O God
Sing a New Church
Song of the Body of Christ
The King of Love My Shepherd Is
There Is a Longing
There's a Wideness in God's Mercy
We Are Many Parts
We Have Been Told
We Remember
What Wondrous Love Is This
Without You

ANOINTING OF THE SICK

Amazing Grace
Be with Me, Lord
Because the Lord Is My Shepherd
Come, Holy Ghost
Come to Me
Come to the Water
Every Valley
Fill My Cup, Lord
Flow River Flow
Holy Darkness
I Heard the Voice of Jesus
Like a Shepherd
Lord of All Hopefulness
Loving and Forgiving
May God Bless and Keep You
May God Bless You
Now We Remain
O Bless the Lord
O Bless the Lord, My Soul
Peace Is Flowing Like a River
Save Us, O Lord
Shelter Me, O God
Take Up Your Cross
There Is a Balm in Gilead
There Is a Longing
There's a Wideness in God's Mercy
Those Who Sow in Tears
You Are Mine

CHRISTIAN FUNERALS
FUNERAL MASS FOR ADULTS

A Mighty Fortress
All My Days
All That Is Hidden
Alleluia! Alleluia!
Alleluia! Alleluia! Let the Holy Anthem
    Rise
Alleluia! Give the Glory
Alleluia! Sing to Jesus
Amazing Grace
At the Lamb's High Feast
At the Name of Jesus
Be Not Afraid
Be with Me, Lord
Because the Lord Is My Shepherd
Blest Are They
Center of My Life
Christ Be beside Me

Come to Me
Crown Him with Many Crowns
Eat This Bread
Eye Has Not Seen
For All the Saints
Gentle Shepherd
Gift of Finest Wheat
Give Me Jesus
Glory and Praise to Our God
Grant Them Eternal Rest
Gospel Canticle (Great Is the Lord)
Hail Mary: Gentle Woman
Hail, Holy Queen
Here I Am, Lord
Holy Darkness
Holy God, We Praise Thy Name
Hosea
How Can I Keep from Singing
How Great Thou Art
I Am the Bread of Life
I Am the Living Bread
I Heard the Voice of Jesus
I Know That My Redeemer Lives
    (DUKE STREET)
I Know That My Redeemer Lives
    (Soper)
I, the Lord
I Will Not Die
Jerusalem, My Happy Home
Jesu, Joy of Our Desiring
Jesus Christ Is Risen Today
Jesus, Remember Me
Jesus the Lord
Joyful, Joyful, We Adore Thee
Lead Me, Lord
Lord of All Hopefulness
Lord, You Have Come
Lord, You Have the Words
Love Divine, All Loves Excelling
Loving and Forgiving
Mary's Song (Rieth)
May God Bless and Keep You
My Soul Rejoices
Now Thank We All Our God
O God, Our Help in Ages Past
On Eagle's Wings
Out of Darkness
Praise the Lord, Ye Heavens
Praise to You, Lord Jesus Christ
Praise, My Soul, the King of Heaven
Prayer of St. Francis
Precious Lord, Take My Hand
Rejoice, the Lord Is King
Shepherd of Souls
Song of Farewell (Sands)
Song of Farewell (Smolarski)
Soon and Very Soon
Take Up Your Cross
Taste and See (Dean)
The Advent of Our King
The Church's One Foundation

The Coming of Our God
The Goodness of the Lord
The King of Kings, Christ Jesus Reigns
The King of Love My Shepherd Is
The Lord Is Near
The Strife Is O'er
The Supper of the Lord
There Is a Balm in Gilead
There Is a Longing
There's a Wideness in God's Mercy
This Alone
Those Who Sow in Tears
To Jesus Christ, Our Sovereign King
To You, O God, I Lift Up My Soul
Unless a Grain of Wheat (Farrell)
Unless a Grain of Wheat (Hurd)
Water of Life
We Believe (Farrell)
We Will Rise Again
What Wondrous Love Is This
Whatsoever You Do
When I Survey the Wondrous Cross
Ye Sons and Daughters
Ye Watchers and Ye Holy Ones

Funeral Mass For Children

Christ Be beside Me
Like a Shepherd
O God, You Search Me
On Eagle's Wings
Prayer of St. Francis
The King of Love My Shepherd Is
You Are Near

Dedication of a Church

All People That on Earth Do Dwell
Christ, Be Our Light
He Is the Lord
How Lovely Is Your Dwelling Place
  (DeBruyn)
How Lovely Is Your Dwelling Place
  (Walker)
Lord, Who at Thy First Eucharist
The Church's One Foundation
We Gather Together
What Is This Place

Eucharistic Exposition and Blessing (Benediction)

Holy God, We Praise Thy Name
May God Bless and Keep You
May God Bless You
O God, Hear Us
Tantum Ergo (ST. THOMAS)

The Order of Mass

Entrance Song: Gathering/ Processional

A Mighty Fortress (Original Text)
A Mighty Fortress (Schuller Text)
A Voice Cries Out
All Creatures of Our God and King
All Glory, Laud and Honor
All Hail the Power of Jesus' Name
All Hail, Adored Trinity
All People That on Earth Do Dwell
All Praise and Glad Thanksgiving
All That Is Hidden
All the Ends of the Earth
  (Haas/Haugen)
All the Ends of the Earth (Hurd)
Alleluia! Give the Glory
Angels from the Realms of Glory
As We Celebrate
Bless the Feast
Canticle of the Sun
Christ, Be Our Light
Christ, the Lord, Is Risen Again
City of God
Come, Christians, Join to Sing
Come, Holy Ghost
Come Now, Almighty King
Come, Thou Long-Expected Jesus
Come, Ye Thankful People, Come
Companions on the Journey
Crown Him with Many Crowns
Every Valley
Eye Has Not Seen
Festival Canticle: Worthy Is Christ
For the Beauty of the Earth
For the Fruits of This Creation
For You Are My God
From All That Dwell below the Skies
From East and West
Gather Us In
Gather Us Together
Gather Your People
Give Thanks to the Lord
Glory and Praise to Our God
God of Day and God of Darkness
Hail, Redeemer, King Divine
He Is the Lord
Hold Me in Life
Holy God, We Praise Thy Name
Holy, Holy, Holy
How Great Thou Art
I Will Lift Up My Eyes
I Will Not Die
Join in the Dance
Joyful, Joyful, We Adore Thee
Let Heaven Rejoice
Let the King of Glory Come

Let the Valleys Be Raised
Lift High the Cross
Lift Up Your Heads, Ye Mighty Gates
Lord of Glory
Morning Has Broken
O Bless the Lord
O Bless the Lord, My Soul
O Come, All Ye Faithful
O God, Our Help in Ages Past
On This Day, the First of Days
One Spirit, One Church
Out of Darkness
Pan de Vida
Praise the Lord, Ye Heavens
Praise to the Lord
Ready the Way
Save Us, O Lord
Send Us Your Spirit (Haas)
Sing a Joyful Song
Sing a New Song (Brown)
Sing a New Song (Schutte)
Sing of the Lord's Goodness
Song of the Body of Christ
Spirit, Come
Table of Plenty
Taste and See (Hurd)
Thanks Be to God
The Glory of These Forty Days
The King of Glory
There's a Wideness in God's Mercy
This Day Was Made by the Lord
This Is the Day (Joncas)
We Gather Together
We Have Been Told
We Remember
We Shall Draw Water
We Walk by Faith
What Is This Place
You Are Mine

Sprinkling Rite

River of Glory
Sprinkling Rite (Walker: Celtic)
Water of Life
We Shall Draw Water

Penitential Rite

Kyrie (Walker: Celtic)
Litany of Praise (Walker: Celtic)
Lord, Have Mercy (Alstott: Heritage)
Lord, Have Mercy (Walker: Celtic)
Penitential Litany (Willcock: God Here
  Among Us)
Penitential Rite B (Walker: Celtic)

Glory to God

A Christmas Gloria (Gibson)
Glory to God (Alstott: Heritage)
Glory to God (Biery)
Glory to God (Foley: St. Louis Jesuits)
Glory to God (Jones)
Glory to God (Soper)

Glory to God (Walker: Celtic)

Glory to God (Willcock: God Here Among Us)

RESPONSORIAL PSALM

16	Center of My Life
	For You Are My God
	Shelter Me, O God
19	Lord, You Have the Words
23	Because the Lord Is My Shepherd
	Shepherd Me, O God
25	Hold Me in Life
	I Lift Up My Soul
	To You, O God, I Lift Up My Soul
	To You, O Lord
27	The Lord Is Near
	This Alone
31	Father, I Put My Life in Your Hands
34	Taste and See
	The Cry of the Poor
42	Psalm 42 (As the Deer Longs)
51	Create in Me
62	Only in God
63	I Will Lift Up My Eyes
81	Shelter Me, O God
84	How Lovely Is Your Dwelling Place
91	Be with Me, Lord
	On Eagle's Wings
96	Let the Heavens Be Glad
98	All the Ends of the Earth
104	Send Out Your Spirit
116	Our Blessing Cup
118	This Day Was Made by the Lord
	This Is the Day (Joncas)
126	Those Who Sow in Tears
139	You Are Near
145	Sing a Joyful Song
148	O Bless the Lord

GOSPEL ACCLAMATION

Advent/Christmas Gospel Acclamation

Alleluia! Give the Glory

Celtic Alleluia

Lenten Gospel Acclamations (Walker: Celtic)

Praise His Name

Praise to You, Lord Jesus Christ

PROFESSION OF FAITH

We Believe (Farrell)

We Believe (Walker: Celtic)

PRAYER OF THE FAITHFUL

Advent Intercessions (Walker: Celtic)

General Intercessions (Hansen)

General Intercessions (Walker: Celtic)

O God, Hear Us

PREPARATION OF THE GIFTS

All That Is Hidden

Beatitudes

Because the Lord Is My Shepherd

Bless the Feast

Blest Are They

Bread of Life (Farrell)

Center of My Life

Come to Me

Eye Has Not Seen

Flow River Flow

For the Beauty of the Earth

God, Beyond All Names

Humbly, Lord, We Worship You

I Know That My Redeemer Lives (Soper)

Jesus, Come to Us

Praise God from Whom All Blessings Flow

Prayer of St. Francis

See Us, Lord, about Your Altar

Somos el Cuerpo de Cristo

Table of Plenty

That There May Be Bread

Unless a Grain of Wheat (Farrell)

We Are Many Parts

We Have Been Told

We Remember

We Walk by Faith

You Are Mine

EUCHARISTIC ACCLAMATIONS

Preface (Walker: Celtic)

Preface Dialogue (Walker: Celtic)

HOLY

Holy (Alstott: Heritage)

Holy (Farrell: Mass of Hope)

Holy (Haugen: Mass of Creation)

Holy (Hurd/Canedo: Mass of Glory)

Holy (St. Louis Jesuits)

Holy (Walker: Celtic)

Holy (Willock: God Here Among Us)

MEMORIAL ACCLAMATION

Memorial Acclamation A (Alstott: Heritage)

Memorial Acclamation A (Farrell: Mass of Hope)

Memorial Acclamation A (Haugen: Mass of Creation)

Memorial Acclamation A (Hurd/Canedo: Mass of Glory)

Memorial Acclamation A (Walker: Celtic)

Memorial Acclamation B (Alstott: Heritage)

Memorial Acclamation B (Farrell: Mass of Hope)

Memorial Acclamation B (Walker: Celtic)

Memorial Acclamation B (Willcock: God Here Among Us)

Memorial Acclamation C (Alstott: Heritage)

Memorial Acclamation C (Farrell: Mass of Hope)

Memorial Acclamation C (St. Louis Jesuits)

Memorial Acclamation C (Walker: Celtic)

Memorial Acclamation D (Alstott: Heritage)

Memorial Acclamation D (Walker: Celtic)

Eucharistic Prayer II: Post Narrative 2 (Hurd/Canedo: Mass of Glory)

DOXOLOGY

Doxology (St. Louis Jesuits)

Doxology/Amen (Walker: Celtic)

Doxology and Great Amen (Willcock: God Here Among Us)

AMEN

Amen (Alstott: Heritage)

Amen (Danish)

Amen (Haugen: Mass of Creation)

Amen (St. Louis Jesuits)

Amen For Use with Acclamation A (Farrell: Mass of Hope)

Amen with Spoken Doxology (Farrell: Mass of Hope)

Eucharistic Prayer: Amen 2 (Hurd/Canedo: Mass of Glory)

Great Amen (Willcock: God Here Among Us)

THE LORD'S PRAYER

The Lord's Prayer (Walker: Celtic)

PEACE PRAYER

Peace Prayer (Walker: Celtic)

LAMB OF GOD

Jesus, Lamb of God (Farrell: Mass of Hope)

Jesus, Lamb of God (Haugen: Mass of Creation)

Jesus, Lamb of God Litany (Walker: Celtic)

Lamb of God (Alstott: Heritage)

Lamb of God (Hurd/Canedo: Mass Of Glory)

Lamb of God (Walker: Celtic)

Lamb of God (Willcock: God Here Among Us)

COMMUNION

A Voice Cries Out
All My Days
All That Is Hidden
Alleluia! Sing to Jesus
At the Lamb's High Feast
Behold the Lamb
Behold the Lamb of God
Bless the Feast
Bread of Life (Cooney)
Bread of Life (Farrell)
Bread That Was Sown
Center of My Life
Christians, Let Us Love One Another
City of God
Eat This Bread
Fill My Cup, Lord
Gentle Shepherd
Gift of Finest Wheat
Give Thanks to the Lord
Here I Am, Lord
Hold Me in Life
I Am the Bread of Life
I Am the Living Bread
I Heard the Voice of Jesus
In the Breaking of the Bread
Jesus, Remember Me
Jesus, the Bread of Life
Jesus the Lord
Let Us Break Bread Together
Look Beyond
Lord, Who at Thy First Eucharist
May We Praise You
Now We Remain
One Bread, One Body
Our Blessing Cup (Hurd)
Our Blessing Cup (Joncas)
Pan de Vida
Panis Angelicus
See Us, Lord, about Your Altar
Seed, Scattered and Sown
Send Us Your Spirit (Schutte)
Shepherd Me, O God
Shepherd of Souls
Somos el Cuerpo de Cristo
Soul of My Savior
Table of Plenty
Taste and See (Dean)
Taste and See (Hurd)
Taste and See (Talbot)
The Cup We Bless
The King of Love My Shepherd Is
This Alone
This Body
To Be Your Bread
Unless a Grain of Wheat (Farrell)
Unless a Grain of Wheat (Hurd)
We Are Many Parts
We Have Been Told
We Remember
We Walk by Faith

We Will Rise Again
When We Eat This Bread
Without You
You Are Our Living Bread

MEDITATION

All That Is Hidden
Because the Lord Is My Shepherd
Behold the Wood
Bread of Life (Farrell)
Center of My Life
Christians, Let Us Love One Another
Come to Me
Flow River Flow
Gift of Finest Wheat
God, Beyond All Names
God Has Chosen Me
How Lovely Is Your Dwelling Place
    (Walker)
I Have Loved You
I Know That My Redeemer Lives
    (Soper)
I Will Lift Up My Eyes
Jesus, Come to Us
Lord, You Have the Words
May God Bless You
On Eagle's Wings
One Spirit, One Church
Our Blessing Cup (Hurd)
Pan de Vida
Servant Song
Taste and See (Dean)
There Is a Longing
There Is Nothing Told
Water of Life
We Will Rise Again
Where There Is Love
Yes I Shall Arise

DISMISSAL

Blessing and Dismissal (Walker: Celtic)
Dismissal of the Catechumens
    (Walker: Celtic)
Easter Blessing and Dismissal
    (Walker: Celtic)
May God Bless and Keep You
May God Bless You

SENDING FORTH/
RECESSIONAL

A Mighty Fortress (Original/Schuller)
A Voice Cries Out
All Creatures of Our God and King
All Glory, Laud and Honor
All Hail the Power of Jesus' Name
All Hail, Adored Trinity
All My Days
All People That on Earth Do Dwell
All Praise and Glad Thanksgiving
All That Is Hidden
All the Ends of the Earth
    (Haas/Haugen)

All the Ends of the Earth (Hurd)
Alleluia! Sing to Jesus
Anthem
As We Celebrate
At the Name of Jesus
Beatitudes
Blessed by Your Sacrifice
Blest Are They
Canticle of the Sun
Canticle of Zachary (FOREST GREEN)
Canticle of Zachary (Joncas)
Christ, Be Our Light
Christ, the Lord, Is Risen Today (I)
City of God
Companions on the Journey
Every Valley
Faith of Our Fathers
Flow River Flow
For All the Saints
For the Fruits of This Creation
From East and West
Give Me Jesus
Go, Tell It on the Mountain
God Has Chosen Me
God of Day and God of Darkness
Hail, Redeemer, King Divine
He Is the Lord
Hold Me in Life
How Can I Keep from Singing
How Great Thou Art
I Am the Light of the World
I Heard the Voice of Jesus
I Will Lift Up My Eyes
I Will Not Die
In Christ There Is No East or West
Let Heaven Rejoice
Let the Heavens Be Glad
Let the King of Glory Come
Let the Valleys Be Raised
Let There Be Peace on Earth
Lift High the Cross
Lift Up Your Hearts
Lord of Glory
Lord, You Give the Great Commission
Love Divine, All Loves Excelling
May God Bless You
May We Praise You
Now Thank We All Our God
O Bless the Lord
O Bless the Lord, My Soul
O God, Our Help in Ages Past
One Spirit, One Church
Out of Darkness
Praise the Lord, Ye Heavens
Prayer of St. Francis
Save Us, O Lord
Send Us Your Spirit (Schutte)
Sing a Joyful Song
Sing of the Lord's Goodness
Somos el Cuerpo de Cristo
Take Christ to the World

Thanks Be to God
This Day God Gives Me
This Is the Day (Joncas)
We Have Been Told
We Walk by Faith

LITURGY OF THE HOURS

MORNING PRAYER

All Creatures of Our God and King
Beatitudes
Beautiful Savior
Blest Are They
Canticle of the Sun
Canticle of Zachary (FOREST GREEN)
Canticle of Zachary (Joncas)
Create in Me
Eye Has Not Seen
For the Beauty of the Earth
Gather Us In
Holy, Holy, Holy
I Am the Light of the World
I Heard the Voice of Jesus
I Sing the Mighty Power of God
Joyful, Joyful, We Adore Thee

Lord of All Hopefulness
Morning Has Broken
Morning Hymn: Psalm 95
On This Day, the First of Days
Opening Dialogue
Seek the Lord
Send Us Your Spirit (Haas)
Sing a Joyful Song
Sing of the Lord's Goodness
Taste and See (Hurd)
That There May Be Bread
The Church's One Foundation
The King of Glory
The King Shall Come When Morning
    Dawns
There's a Wideness in God's Mercy
This Day God Gives Me
This Is the Day (Joncas)
We Praise You
We Shall Draw Water
Ye Watchers and Ye Holy Ones

EVENING PRAYER

All Creatures of Our God and King
Beautiful Savior
Day Is Done

Evening Hymn: Phos Hilaron
Eye Has Not Seen
For All the Saints
For the Beauty of the Earth
God of Day and God of Darkness
Gospel Canticle (Great Is the Lord)
Hold Me in Life
How Can I Keep from Singing
I Sing the Mighty Power of God
Jesus, Remember Me
Lord of All Hopefulness
My Soul Rejoices
O God, Our Help in Ages Past
Proclamation of Light
We Walk by Faith
You Are Mine

NIGHT PRAYER

Be with Me, Lord
Blest Be the Lord
On Eagle's Wings

DEVOTIONS
STATIONS OF THE CROSS

At the Cross Her Station Keeping

TOPICAL INDEX

ADORATION, PRAISE, WORSHIP

A Mighty Fortress (Original Text)
A Mighty Fortress (Schuller Text)
Abba! Father
All Creatures of Our God and King
All Hail the Power of Jesus' Name
All Hail, Adored Trinity
All My Days
All People That on Earth Do Dwell
All Praise and Glad Thanksgiving
All the Ends of the Earth
    (Haas/Haugen)
All the Ends of the Earth (Hurd)
Alleluia! Alleluia!
Alleluia! Give the Glory
Alleluia No. 1
Alleluia! Sing to Jesus
At the Lamb's High Feast
At the Name of Jesus
Beatitudes
Beautiful Savior
Blessed by Your Sacrifice
Blest Be the Lord
Bread of Life (Farrell)
Canticle of the Sun
Canticle of Zachary (Joncas)
Center of My Life
Come, Christians, Join to Sing

Come, Ye Thankful People, Come
Creator Spirit, by Whose Aid
Crown Him with Many Crowns
Evening Hymn: Phos Hilaron
Festival Canticle: Worthy Is Christ
For the Beauty of the Earth
For the Fruits of This Creation
From All That Dwell below the Skies
Give Thanks to the Lord
Glory and Praise to Our God
God, Beyond All Names
Great Is the Lord
He Is the Lord
Holy God, We Praise Thy Name
Holy, Holy, Holy
Holy Is His Name
How Can I Keep from Singing
How Great Thou Art
How Lovely Is Your Dwelling Place
    (Walker)
Humbly, Lord, We Worship You
I Sing the Mighty Power of God
Jesus Christ Is Risen Today
Jesus, Come to Us
Jesus the Lord
Joyful, Joyful, We Adore Thee
Let the Heavens Be Glad
Lift High the Cross
Lift Up Your Hearts
Love Divine, All Loves Excelling

Loving and Forgiving
May We Praise You
O Bless the Lord
O Bless the Lord, My Soul
O God, Our Help in Ages Past
On This Day, the First of Days
Pange Lingua Gloriosi (ST. THOMAS)
Praise God from Whom All Blessings
    Flow
Praise His Name
Praise, My Soul, the King of Heaven
Praise to the Lord
Servant Song
Sing a Joyful Song
Sing a New Church
Sing a New Song (Schutte)
Sing, My Tongue, the Savior's Glory
Sing of the Lord's Goodness
Songs of Thankfulness and Praise
Taste and See (Hurd)
The Cry of the Poor
The Glory of These Forty Days
This Day Was Made by the Lord
This Is the Day (Joncas)
Though the Mountains May Fall
We Gather Together
We Praise You
We Shall Draw Water
When I Survey the Wondrous Cross

SCRIPTURAL INDEX

HYMN TUNE INDEX

METRICAL INDEX

INDEX OF COMMON TITLES

INDEX OF COMMON TITLES